THE MENNINGER STORY

The Menninger Story

By WALKER WINSLOW

Doubleday & Company, Inc., Garden City, N.Y., 1956

FOR MRS. SHIRLEY FISHER

of McIntosh & Otis, Inc.

. . . an agent with a genius for diplomacy and patience.

ACKNOWLEDGMENTS

IT IS MY HOPE that this book will in some measure live up to the efforts of all who have helped in its making, for it is, like all works of its kind, a sort of mass collaboration. But there are many people to whom I owe a special expression of gratitude. I am especially indebted to Don Lawder, Director of Information Services for the Menninger Foundation, whose patience I must have sorely tried, and to his assistants Helen Morrison and Marilyn Hesse, now Mrs. Donald Durrel of Kansas City. Irving Sheffel and Lester Roach of the administrative staff of the Menninger Foundation were always my champions at court and opened up channels of information that would otherwise have been closed to me. All of the medical staff of the Foundation were helpful to me and gave freely of their time and wisdom whenever I called upon them for information. Doctors Robert R. Holt and Lester Luborsky, of the psychological staff, unselfishly gave me material they were collecting for a book of their own on the selection of psychiatric residents for the School of Psychiatry, and Dr. Bert Booth, director of education at Winter V. A. Hospital, loaned me the historical files of the School of Psychiatry. Dr. Harry Levinson, of Topeka State Hospital, was equally generous with material from the files of that institution.

Graduates of the Menninger Foundation School of Psychiatry were generous with their time wherever I found them and whenever I called upon them for help. Outstanding among them were James M. Mott, Jr., M.D., Beverly Hills, California; Arthur Marshall, M.D., Sherman Oaks, California; Walter Poznanski, M.D., and Jean Chambers, M.D. (Mrs. Poznanski), formerly of Los Angeles; Russell Williams, M.D., Monterey, California; and Dorothy Dimont, M.A., of Los Angeles. These people, in effect, brought Topeka, and the spirit of Topeka, to the West Coast, where I was living. Robert P. Knight, M.D., formerly of Menningers' and now medical director of Austen Riggs Foundation, gave me much valuable advice and information.

Whenever I have called on members of the medical profession for advice, historical data, or moral support I have found them to be generous and selfless, and I wish to extend them my gratitude. Some of these men are Douglas Forde, M.D., Pacific Palisades, California; Warren Jones, M.D., Metropolitan State Hospital, Norwalk, California; George Creswell Burns, M.D., Compton, California; Max Seymon, M.D., Los Angeles; Charles McGoey, M.D., Santa Fe, New Mexico; and my good friends Earle M. Marsh, M.D., and James G. Terry, M.D., of San Francisco, California.

Part of this book was written while I was on a fellowship at Huntington Hartford Foundation in Pacific Palisades, California, and I want to thank Mr. Hartford and the director of the Foundation, Dr. John Vincent, for their kindness. Two fellows at the Foundation, Professor Richard Hagopian, of the University of California at Berkeley, and Dr. C. Wright Mills, of Columbia University, read parts of the manuscript and made valuable suggestions. My most consistent help, in the form of suggestions and moral reinforcement, came from Elaine and David Duncan of Los Angeles.

There is no way in which I can properly thank the Menninger family for allowing me to write this book and for giving me such assistance as medical ethics would permit. Material that was especially favorable to Doctors Karl and Will was in all cases obtained without their aid and knowledge and from reliable sources which they could not disclose to me in the name of either ethics or modesty. I myself have sorted the facts and been the judge of their role in modern psychiatry and have found many enlightened physicians who concur with me. They trusted me, and I can only hope that I have been worthy of that trust. Since Dr. C. F. Menninger was an extremely reticent and modest man he literally had to be prodded into talking about himself. Mrs. C. F. Menninger applied the prod in the gentlest and most subtle manner, and thus made my interviews with the doctor much more fruitful than they would otherwise have been. She could not prevent the doctor from giving me a course in conchology and mineralogy during the interviews, but I am the gainer for that. Edwin Menninger, who is also writing a book about his father, was far more generous than I had any right to expect him to be; I can only hope that he will not be too critical of my effort.

The editorial support and help of Karen Rye Seldes and Francis K. Price, of Doubleday, have been of the order that authors usually find in fantasy rather than reality. This is their book as much as mine.

Los Angeles,
September 7, 1955

THE MENNINGER STORY

i

IN THE SUMMER of 1908 Dr. Charles Frederick Menninger, a prominent physician from Topeka, Kansas, went to Rochester, Minnesota, to attend a medical convention. In his quest for learning he had attended every important medical convention he could get to; most of them had been held in large metropolitan centers. Now he found, to his surprise, that the one he had most looked forward to had brought him to a town which, with a population of 6000, was scarcely a fifth of the size of his own city. It was the achievements of the Doctors Mayo, a father and two sons, that had impelled him to visit Rochester; in this setting their achievements seemed more impressive than ever.

Most of the doctors who attended the convention had come because of their interest in surgery, for which the Doctors Mayo were becoming world famous; Dr. Menninger, on the other hand, was interested in the art and science of diagnosis, which he believed to be a key to the Mayos' surgical success. Although he listened to most of the papers that were read at the convention, Dr. Menninger was seldom in the amphitheater when operations were being performed; instead he was in the unpretentious offices the Mayos had on the ground floor of the Masonic Building. There he had found laboratories working steadily as a stream of patients was examined by the Mayos' associates. With these examining doctors, Dr. Charles Menninger was at home; much of the work they were doing was of a piece with the work he did in his own practice. Perhaps the Mayo associates were astonished by Dr. Menninger's grasp of the many new techniques they were using; when the convention was over he was invited to stay on. Since the invitation came from the Mayo Brothers, who had not seen him in the surgery, it must have been his eagerness to learn more about diagnosis that attracted them.

Tall, handsome, scholarly, and serious to a fault, Dr. Menninger was, at the age of forty-six, slightly the junior of the brothers Mayo and just a little older than most of their assisting staff. No reputation had preceded him, and he was the sort of man who made an impression on the basis of his merit as a doctor or not at all. Unlike others who came and stayed on, he was not interested in joining the Mayos; his one desire was to take more knowledge back to his home city. This, too, must have impressed the doctors he observed and worked with during his short stay in Rochester, although they may have been surprised by his intense interest in the workings of the Mayo partnership and its beginnings.

Dr. Menninger was curious about the Mayos because he wondered why what he had seen in Rochester could not be made to work in Topeka. The thing that had impressed him most was that, under the Mayos, physicians working in many separate areas of medicine were contributing to the whole of a partnership practice. In his work with patients and in his research, each of these doctors could restrict himself to his special field. As a solitary general practitioner, Dr. Menninger was attempting to keep up in all the fields these men pursued separately. If he had a right to be proud that he had kept up so well, he also had a right to be discouraged as he viewed the ever widening field of medicine.

As he watched doctors working closely together and sharing their total knowledge, Dr. Menninger was sharply aware of the isolation of the individual general practitioner. Only recently children had suffocated from diphtheria because the one or two physicians who knew about intubation had chosen to keep this lifesaving technique as a practice builder. He was to read of this innovation in a foreign medical journal, one of the dozens he subscribed to, before he discovered, through an enlightened physician, that it was being used at home. And so it had been in his obstetrical practice; some men who could have helped him with unusual complications were often willing to let another man's failure serve as an indication that they should have been called in the first place. Dr. Menninger also knew that his own special knowledge in the field of metabolic diseases, even though he shared it eagerly and willingly, was not made use of in consultations.

The Mayos and their associates were men who had nothing to hide and who, indeed, were willing to give of their time to make their knowledge the property of any physician who sought it. And yet Dr. Menninger remembered that some of his colleagues bitterly accused the Mayos of unethical advertising and self-aggrandizement. Odd charges, in the light of the experience he was now having. Actually what the Mayos had done was so simple that it could lead only to success wherever their method was followed. As the surgical practice had demanded more and more of the Mayos' time, they had sought out the best local physicians to take over other phases of their practice. Significantly, all their early associates were found in the Rochester area. As they joined the Mayos they were allowed to follow their particular inclinations and were sent on trips to other medical centers where they could add to their knowledge. The firm, if the Mayos and their associates could be called that—it was not yet a clinic—was loosely organized. All the income from the joint practice went into a common fund and was then divided. No man, not even the Mayos, father and sons, owned more than his own personal property and the current year's income from practice. St. Mary's Hospital, where all Mayo patients went for surgery and other treatment, belonged to the Sisters of St. Francis. The Mayos' greatest asset had been a desire to give their townspeople the best that medical science had to offer, and that best had turned out to be good enough for the world at large.

As he went back to Topeka, Dr. Menninger wanted mightily to give his own town something of the sort he had seen in Rochester, but, recalling his failures in attempting to organize clinical study groups in Topeka, he knew that he was not a strong enough rallying point for the organization of such a project. Nevertheless he felt that there must be a way.

The doctor got home just in time for breakfast with his wife, Flo, and with their three sons, Karl, Edwin, and Will. Karl, the eldest boy, was barely in his teens, but as Dr. Menninger looked at his sons before bowing his head for the morning prayer he saw something that gave his prayer a new meaning.

The hungry boys thought that their father was spending an

unusual time in silent prayer and might even have fallen asleep
after his long train trip. At last, however, he raised his head,
looked at each boy in turn, and said, "I have been to the Mayos
and I have seen a great thing. You boys are going to be doctors
and we are going to have a clinic like that right here in Topeka."

There was no element of command in the father's voice; he
spoke simply as a man who is announcing a foreseeable fact.
There was no further discussion of the clinic or of the boys' careers
at breakfast that day, or for many years to come.

ii

By 1953, the last year of Dr. Charles F. Menninger's life,
the prayer and prophecy made at the breakfast table in 1908
seemed to have been fulfilled. The name of the Menninger Foundation was, if anything, as well known as the name of Mayos'.
But something seemingly strange had come to pass: a doctor
whose one desire was to improve the practice of general medicine
had established one of the greatest psychiatric clinics in the world.
To physicians in search of the best in psychiatric training, and
for the mentally ill seeking the most modern psychiatric treatment, Topeka had become a Mecca.

Anyone trying to imagine the type of clinic that could have
been founded by the general practitioner who visited Mayos' in
1908 would probably arrive at something quite like the Menninger Clinic of 1953. Because it treated mental patients, the
clinic would have to be on the outskirts of town. Since the most
likely setting would be an old farm with a large residence, that
is precisely what the nucleus of the Menninger Clinic was. The
Menninger Clinic, or the Foundation that has its center at the
clinic, was just about what one would expect of a small-city mental sanitarium that serves a fairly large region; its plant and its
initial ambitions could be duplicated throughout America. By
1953 native resourcefulness had turned farm buildings into recreation centers, libraries, offices, and workshops, and when small
hospital buildings were added in order to bring the capacity of
the clinic up to sixty-five patients, the new structures were more
residential than institutional in architecture. There was nothing

especially remarkable about the Menninger Clinic's physical structure; over a dozen private sanitariums in America were larger and on most counts more modern.

Since Dr. Menninger was a horticulturist of local renown, and responsible for many of the fine plantings in Topeka's parks, it was to be expected that the grounds would be lovingly landscaped, and they were. As a man who took the practice of medicine seriously, it was also to be expected that effective treatment and not luxurious living would dictate the housing and facilities for the patients; no one was likely to mistake Menningers' as a resort for the idle. As of 1953 the pharmacy and the laboratories were crammed into the basement of the old residence that was the administration building, a setting that in no way detracted from the effectiveness of their functioning.

The physical aspects of the Menninger Clinic of Dr. Menninger's last years would make for an American success story, but not an unusual one, for any hard-working physician with two loyal physician sons could have built such an institution without attracting much attention. At best, such a sanitarium could have trained two young doctors each year and treated a few hundred in- and out-patients. With an instinctive learner and teacher as its head, it would have held "institutes" and "clinics" for the benefit of local doctors.

A stranger looking at the Menninger Clinic in 1953 might have exclaimed, "Why, we do better than this in my home town." Of course, the same person could say, and with just as much relevance, that the local high school teacher and Dr. Albert Einstein were the same size. There was something within the fairly commonplace setting that turned the ordinary into the extraordinary. Dr. Charles Frederick Menninger's clinic had become the center of a medical empire. And anyone who examines closely the history of modern medicine will not find it strange that psychiatry dominates the whole of the Menninger enterprises.

iii

Long before Dr. Charles Menninger visited Mayos', he was aware that there was a vast area of human illness and suffering that lay beyond his art as a healer and his scope as a scientist. Far too often he saw desperate people insist on dangerous and painful surgery even when there was nothing organically wrong that could be objectively demonstrated. At times he was aware that his patients were communicating their suffering to him through what seemed to be imaginary aches and pains. But were they imaginary, and could people possibly simulate the agony he frequently saw? When he let such patients pour out their troubles to him he saw that they were often as relieved as they might have been had he lanced a painful abscess, and yet the doctor's medical training had in no way prepared him for such cases, nor did he find much help in his medical reading.

He was not alone in his dilemma; early case notes at the Mayos' show that they were encountering the same situation and were equally baffled by it. "Feels weak, pain no particular place, some water trouble, constipated. Full of witchcraft nonsense," is one cryptic case note made by a Mayo physician. There is mention of another sufferer who complained of night terror, crying and screaming and, noted the doctor, "Gave me a sample of her scream." As time passed the Mayos could not number the patients who could be classified as "neurasthenic and neurotic." They were forced to refer them back to the doctor who had sent them or to the local asylum. There were no psychiatrists available outside mental institutions and these men rarely contributed to the whole of medical practice.

The Association of Medical Superintendents of American Institutions for the Insane—the parent body of the American Psychiatric Association—is one of the oldest of American medical associations, having been founded in 1844. In the latter half of the nineteenth century its publications and conventions were chiefly concerned with the management of institutions. Neurology, which developed as a medical specialty after the Civil War, took over what little private practice of psychiatry was being done. Since the neurologists were research-minded, and felt that there was much to be discovered by studying the patients confined to state institutions, they became quite impatient with what they considered the sloth of the Medical Superintendents of American Institutions for the Insane. Among these neurologists was Dr. S. Weir Mitchell, who had developed the famous "rest cure"; he seems to have stated the situation quite clearly when he told a group of hospital superintendents:

"You were the first of the specialists and you have never come back into line. It is easy to see how this came about. You soon began to live apart, and you still do so. Your hospitals are not our hospitals; your ways are not our ways. You live out of range of critical shot; you are not preceded or followed in your ward work by clever rivals, or watched by able residents fresh with the learning of the school. . . . There are too many signs of contented calm born of isolation from the active, living struggle for intellectual light and air . . ."

This was the situation that prevailed during Dr. Menninger's medical-school days and his early years of practice. When in 1890 he wished to prepare a paper on *The Insanity of Hamlet,* he sought out a medical superintendent and found that he could learn little from him even though he was an enlightened man for his day. The research that was taking place was mainly physiological and performed on the autopsy table, where pathological data was sought without any special reference to the signs and symptoms of the mental illness it may have caused. This in spite of the fact that as early as 1843 Dr. Amariah Brigham, of Utica State Asylum, had reported that "with Pinel, Esquirol and Georget [the French psychiatrists], we believe that moral causes are far more operative than physical." No research into the "moral causes" of mental illness was undertaken, however, and pathological research continued.

Although in 1886 the French physician, Charcot, had demonstrated that hysteria could produce the symptoms of most known physical disorders, and that hysteria, in turn, could be induced and alleviated by suggestion or hypnosis, America paid scant attention to this pioneer work in psychosomatic medicine. Dr. Menninger eagerly read everything he could find about the work of Charcot but had neither the time nor the opportunity to follow through.

Dr. Sigmund Freud did, however, find time to study with Charcot and in less than ten years was able to report on a new method of treatment for a case of hysteria that had been accompanied by severe physical symptoms. Americans had written of hypochondriasis and neurasthenia but ascribed these disorders to brain inflamation. The psychological school of medicine that was slowly emerging in Europe was unpopular in America.

One thing that hampered research in psychiatry was the lack of any descriptive system; mental diseases were not divided into diagnostic categories in the way physical illnesses were. Thus when the German psychiatrist, Dr. Emil Kraepelin, established a system of classifying mental disorders his work was at once embraced by most American psychiatrists. The separation of mental illnesses made prognosis possible, too, for it soon became evident that there was a higher recovery rate in some categories than in others. Aside from the continued work in neuropathology, diagnosis and prognosis became the end and aim of practice. Therapy, as such, was just where it had been before—non-existent. More time was spent studying the patients but only to a diagnostic and prognostic end. This was the practice of what became known as descriptive psychiatry and it was to predominate until World War II.

In the beginning of the twentieth century, psychological medicine began to penetrate America in a small way. A young New York physician, Dr. A. A. Brill, having despaired of neuropathology and descriptive psychiatry, went abroad to study at Burghölzli Institute, in Zurich—one of the first psychoanalytic centers. Returning to America convinced of the validity of Freud's dynamic concept of the personality structure, he was the first American physician to enter practice as a psychoanalyst. Later he was to translate most of Freud's writings and spread the new theory among his English-speaking colleagues. Dr. Adolph Meyer was another neuroanatomist who branched out into a wider field of psychological medicine; he soon proclaimed that mental disorder could be a maladjustment of the total personality instead of a localized disease of the brain. Interesting himself in the environment from which his patients had come, he did a good deal of social work. Although he did not totally accept Freud's theory, he insisted that his students at Manhattan State Hospital, and later at Johns Hopkins, familiarize themselves with its concepts. He called himself a psychobiologist, and he was to have a great influence on psychiatry and psychiatric education.

Freud visited America in 1909 and delivered five lectures at Clark University in Worcester, Massachusetts, and although he won few outright converts, the Freudian dynamic began to inch its way into American psychiatric thinking. Dr. William Alanson White, of St. Elizabeth's Hospital in Washington, D.C.—an institution in which one of Dr. Menninger's sons was to get some of his training—became an articulate champion of Freud, as did Dr. Smith Ely Jelliffe, who was to become a close friend of Dr. Charles F. Menninger.

However, in their earlier phases, the Freudian and psycho-biological movements were not likely to reach into the life of a general practitioner in Topeka, Kansas, and indeed they reached few of the state hospital directors. Although there were always to be small and notable exceptions, descriptive and what could be called managerial psychiatry continued to dominate American institutions. The only innovations in therapy were mechanical and chemical—electric shock, insulin coma, narco-rest, and the like. In the main, the institutional psychiatrists—and they constituted 80 per cent of all the psychiatrists in the nation—were to remain just about as isolated as they had been in Dr. Mitchell's time. Dr. Menninger was always able to familiarize himself quickly with what was going on in the newer medical specialties, but his instruction in psychiatry had to wait until his eldest son came home. As will be seen, Dr. C. F. Menninger was always keenly aware of that area of medical practice that was to become known as psychosomatic medicine. When Banting discovered insulin and freed Dr. Menninger from the treatment of diabetics, which had become his special preoccupation, it was inevitable that he turn to psychiatry. It was his view that the practice of psychiatry had to come out of isolation, make its contributions in sight of all who wished to witness, and then merge itself into the general practice of medicine so that it would be available to all patients. Although his sons were to be his spokesmen, the man who prayed for a clinic on that morning in 1908 was the originator of all that the name Menninger has come to imply.

iv

What Dr. C.F., as Dr. Charles F. Menninger was called in Topeka, had in mind when he told his boys, "We will have

our own clinic right here in Topeka," was not a hospital or even
a sanitarium. The Mayos did not have a hospital of their own;
they were merely an integrated medical group in which all the
specialties of medicine collaborated closely in diagnosis and treatment, and their treatment—mainly surgery—took place in hospitals owned and managed by other organizations. When Dr. Karl
A. Menninger, or Dr. Karl, as he was to become known, returned
from Harvard Medical School and psychiatric training in Boston
in 1919, the Menninger Diagnostic Clinic, which was then
founded, was organized along the same lines as the Mayo Clinic.
Two young Topeka physicians were taken into the family practice and complete diagnostic laboratories were set up in the office
of the group.

When patients needed hospitalization they were sent to hospitals where the Menningers were staff members. Dr. C.F. had
his own setup for treating diabetics in Christ's Hospital—that is,
he had his own dietician and specially trained nurses. Although
Christ's Hospital had at one time built a small psychiatric section,
the people in the neighborhood were afraid of mental patients
and obtained an injunction forbidding its use. Nevertheless, Dr.
Karl, who specialized in psychiatry and neurology from the beginning, did of necessity use this section for a time. Aside from
these semi-illegal facilities there was no place where mentally ill
people could go other than the state hospital. Quite soon it
became imperative that the Menningers establish a sanitarium
where they could treat the mentally ill under more favorable circumstances.

The Menninger Sanitarium was launched by selling stock to
interested Topekans and then acquiring a large farm house, several outbuildings, and some land on the outskirts of Topeka. The
sanitarium was considered an adjunct of the clinic, which practiced from its downtown offices. Southard School, a treatment
center for mentally ill children, which was established in the same
year, 1925, was another adjunct. When Dr. William C. Menninger
—Dr. Will—came home from Cornell and an internship at Bellevue Hospital, in New York, he became the director of the sanitarium. As the fame of the sanitarium spread, it had to be
enlarged, and in order to avoid duplication of equipment the
Menninger Clinic was moved to the sanitarium. Many times there

would have been a deficit had it not been for Dr. C.F.'s large general practice. There is little doubt that the merging of the sanitarium and the clinic contributed greatly to the general excellence of treatment that was available to sanitarium patients, for something that could be called total medicine emerged. Within fifteen years of its founding, the Menninger Sanitarium was rated among the first five of American sanitariums, and had initiated and was financing education and research out of the earnings of private practice.

The idea of the Menninger Clinic as Dr. C.F. had conceived it on his visit to Mayos' was never to disappear. Just as the older Dr. W. W. Mayo's general practice was to be dominated by the specialty of surgery, so psychiatry became the leading specialty at Menningers'. If anything, the Menninger practice seems to be proof, as many physicians have contended, that 60 per cent of all patients the average doctor sees have illnesses in which there is some degree of emotional involvement.

By 1941 the Menningers were beginning to realize that their private funds could no longer finance the great amount of research and psychiatric education that was needed. They set up a non-profit Foundation through which funds could be raised. This early Foundation did not encompass the Menninger Sanitarium, which represented the total wealth and life savings of the Menningers. By 1945, however, Dr. C.F. and his sons saw that nothing but an all-out effort would enable them to fulfill the responsibilities they felt toward psychiatry, especially in the training of more psychiatrists. In that year they and the stockholders of the sanitarium corporation gave their holdings to the Menninger Foundation. The Menninger Sanitarium had become a non-profit institution; thus the Menninger Foundation was able to finance the largest school of psychiatry in the world. Menninger physicians treat patients, teach new doctors, and do research in several institutions, notably Winter Veterans Administration Hospital, Topeka State Hospital, the Menninger Sanitarium, and the Foundation out-patient department, not to mention a variety of other state institutions.

As of today, the Menninger Foundation operates more nearly on the Mayo plan than ever before. Dr. C.F. lived to see his earlier ideal reach fulfillment. He had begun his adult life as an educator, and it is as an educational center that Menningers' seems likely to win its most enduring fame. Dr. C.F.'s principles were quite simple, and early in his career he had said, "Man's first responsibility is to God; this responsibility can best be demonstrated by a reverence for life that should make each of God's creatures a humble seeker and learner. Where knowledge is gained it should be shared."

v

In 1952, on his ninetieth birthday, Dr. C.F. was asked to lay the cornerstone of a new hospital that was to bear his name. Outstanding citizens of Topeka and the nation were present, as were physicians from many parts of the world. When the time came for Dr. C.F. to speak, the tall, stately gentleman who seemed far younger than his years looked into the faces of those around him knowing, as he later said, that they expected to hear his medical credo and the secret of what they supposed to be his success. Actually, he had prepared some such statement, but when the time came to address the group he could speak only from his heart. These were his words:

"From the very beginning, God's hand has been guiding this, and it is fitting to invoke His blessing on what we are going to do. We believe that He put it into our hearts to build this hospital for the art of healing men."

After a moment of silence he bowed his head and prayed, "Almighty God, Father of Mercies and God of all comfort, look upon us with favor as we dedicate this building to that end. Bless all who come here sick and troubled. And bless, we pray, all who labor here to relieve affliction. Direct us, we beseech Thee with thankful hearts, in Thy way of righteousness and peace, and to Thee be glory and praise, now and forevermore. Amen."

When, in May of 1954, the new hospital was opened, it was called The Charles Frederick Menninger Memorial Hospital, for he had passed on. By ordinary standards it was not a large hospital; coupled as it was with the older lodge buildings of the sanitarium it had a capacity of only 113 patients. Costing $1,500,000, it represented the contributions of more than 3000 people who wished to share in the ideals which the old doctor had represented. Some of this money had been contributed by doctors who had worked at the Foundation, using converted hot-dog stands and garages as offices. Dr. C.F. had said that with the proper spirit and training a physician could cure patients in a barn; during the growing days of the Foundation many doctors had the opportunity to test this thesis. Among other things, the new hospital meant that for the first time all the Foundation physicians would have adequate office space. Between 1945 and 1955 the staff of the Foundation had increased tenfold.

The size of the 113-bed hospital is very deceptive, for the Foundation, which has its headquarters on the hospital grounds, has over 400 employees, 175 of whom are in psychiatry or allied specialties, and who make up the faculty of the Menninger School of Psychiatry which enrolls 10 per cent of all the young physicians in psychiatric training in America. This school of psychiatry reaches into Winter V. A. Hospital, the Veterans Administration pilot hospital for psychiatric treatment and training; Topeka State Hospital; Southard School for children; and the Kansas Industrial School for Boys, as well as into many other hospitals in the Kansas institutional system. In these hospitals and schools between four and five thousand patients are under treatment and over 100 young physicians, psychologists, marriage counselors, social workers, and adjunctive therapists are getting training. There are even interneships for chaplains, and an annual institute of religion and psychiatry. Since Dr. Karl has recently been appointed to a commission to study Kansas' penal institutions it is to be expected that Menninger doctors will soon enter that field. Dr. Will Menninger's interest in the field of industrial and preventive psychiatry will lead to more opportunities for study in that area.

Already nearly 400 psychiatrists have received training under the Menninger auspices and are teaching and practicing in most of the states and in several foreign countries. There would appear to be a high degree of dedication among this group; the majority have shunned remunerative private practice in order to work and teach in those institutions where they are most needed. One medical journal said, "It's interesting to speculate why this is so—why a specialist who could earn as much as $35,000 (a year) on his own prefers to accept an appointment at as little as $9000." In any case, these young doctors work throughout America with ever increasing influence and each year there are more applications for training at Menningers'.

The Menninger influence is felt in other ways. In 1954 there were sixty-nine separate publications of learned and popular articles by Menninger staff members; fifty-six staff members were guest lecturers during the year, frequently over radio and television networks; fifty staff members either hold offices or serve on committees of the organizations of their various specialties; and in 1954 the Foundation had over 1000 professional visitors, many of them from abroad. Few modern physicians have been interviewed and quoted with as great frequency as Doctors Karl and Will Menninger.

No one has any way of knowing the extent of the medical services that Dr. C. F. Menninger foresaw in 1908, but, in 1954, 2197 patients received psychiatric and neurological diagnosis or treatment at what had been the clinic. Twenty-seven per cent of the adult patients and 41 per cent of the children received medical services for less than cost. Foundation psychiatrists gave 22,264 hours of psychotherapy, and the neurological and neurosurgical service saw 1006 patients. Of the 142 hospitalized psychiatric patients, 78 had been discharged in from one to sixty days and only 14 patients remained during the entire year. Seven hundred and ninety-eight people were seen as out-patients at the clinic offices; most of them came from other states and stayed in hotels and boarding homes during treatment. There is a day hospital for out-patients; they go home at night, but during their waking hours they are subject to the same hospital routine as the regular hospital patients. This is a low-cost service that makes the Menninger type of treatment available to more people.

An idea of just what medical care at the Menninger Foundation is like can be suggested by comparing the staff per patient with that of the median state hospital.

	Menningers'	State Hospital
Patients per psychiatrist	6	225
Patients per attendant	1½	9
Patients per R.N.	3	150
Patients per social worker	10	600
Patients per psychologist	62	1500

With such a staff and in such a setting it is inevitable the research should flourish, and it does. There are sixteen major research projects under way, some in areas that have scarcely been touched upon, but even these are curtailed by the limited funds that are available. In 1954 the Foundation had a deficit of over $700,000. At the last meeting of the Foundation trustees at which Dr. C.F. presided, a long-range plan was presented in which $17,000,000 would be raised to finance a ten-year plan of research and development. Under such a plan both research and education would have a more stable base.

When such figures as these are considered, anyone who knew Dr. C.F. cannot help thinking of the days when the purchase of a bicycle on which to make his house calls constituted a major bit of financing. These figures indicate a success story, but a success story with a difference—the story of a man who wanted nothing for himself and who bequeathed to his sons a burden of responsibility that would crush most men.

vi

The story of Dr. C.F. cannot be entirely separated from the story of his sons, or the story of his wife. Certainly his wife was an outstanding and strongly dedicated woman, and it could be said that he was fortunate also in his sons, although his sons would be the first to tell you that they were extremely fortunate in having the father they had. Edwin, who could not go into medicine, is a newspaper publisher in Florida and an outstanding authority on flowering trees—in this latter pursuit following one of his father's special interests.

Dr. C.F.'s physician sons, Doctors Karl and Will, went into medicine because of the powerful example their father set for them, both as a man and as a physician. Their careers were to a large degree shaped by the influence of this modest, religious, and ardently scholarly man. It was not in him to direct that the boys do this or that; he merely set the example and then let them follow their own course. It could be truly said that he governed best by governing least.

Dr. Karl A. Menninger, after graduation *cum laude* from Har-

vard Medical School, served an interneship in Kansas City and
then returned to Boston to study psychiatry and neurology under
Dr. E. E. Southard. Even while in training he was an instructor
in neuropathology. Returning to Topeka in 1919, he joined his
father in practice and restricted himself to psychiatry and neurology. He published dozens of papers in these fields during his
first years of practice, becoming one of the most prolific medical
writers in the Middle West. During the 1920s he became interested in the theories of Freud and in 1930 published his best seller
The Human Mind, a book that gave the psychopathology of everyday life, and the mechanisms of the mind, a new meaning to
many Americans. The popularity of this book made him something of a spokesman for psychiatry, and he carried the message
of psychiatry to the public with a missionary's zeal, even though
his writing was tempered with a scientist's caution. In the same
year that the book was published he received his psychoanalytic
training from Dr. Franz Alexander and was awarded Certificate
No. 1 of the Chicago Institute for Psychoanalysis. His books, *Man
against Himself* and *Love against Hate* dealt with the conflict
between destruction and creation and reached both a popular
and scientific audience. Dr. Karl is also the author of *A Manual
for Psychiatric Case Study*, and co-author of *The Healthy Minded
Child* and *A Guide to Psychiatric Books*. He has been an active
committee member in all of the organizations of his profession and
is a past president of the American Psychoanalytic Association.
A list of the organizations to which he has belonged or been a
consultant, and the positions he has held, take up most of a column in Who's Who. He is chairman of the Board of Trustees of
the Menninger Foundation as well as chief of staff, and director
of the Department of Education. His son, Dr. Robert Menninger,
has just completed training at the Menninger Foundation School
of Psychiatry.

Dr. William C. Menninger, Dr. C.F.'s youngest son, graduated
from Cornell Medical School, interned at Bellevue, did a psychiatric residency at St. Elizabeth's, and later took his training analysis at the Chicago Institute for Psychoanalysis, devoting some
time to study in England and Germany as well. His production
of learned papers for the professional journals was almost equal

to that of Dr. Karl and in recent years has surpassed Dr. Karl's. He is a leader in the Boy Scout movement, a member of the National Executive Board on Scouting, the author of a handbook for seascout leaders. His books in the field of medicine and psychiatry are: *Juvenile Paresis, You and Psychiatry, Psychiatry: Its Evolution and Present Status,* and *Psychiatry in a Troubled World.* During World War II, Dr. Will was chief consultant on psychiatry to the Surgeon General, attained the rank of brigadier general, and was awarded the Distinguished Service Medal for his work in organizing the psychiatric services of the Army. He is a past president of the American Psychiatric Association, the American Psychoanalytic Association, the Central Neuropsychiatric Association and a former chairman of the Group for the Advancement of Psychiatry. He has also been given the Lasker Award for outstanding contributions in the field of mental health. Dr. Will is so much in demand as a speaker and consultant, especially in the field of broader social applications of psychiatry, that during crucial periods he is away from Topeka 70 per cent of the time. He is general secretary of the Menninger Foundation and in that role must conduct most of the fund-raising campaigns. Two of Dr. Will's sons have gone into medicine. William Walter, the youngest, is still in medical school, and Roy, the eldest, has been graduated from Cornell and is now completing psychiatric training.

The public honors and offices that were given to Dr. C.F. were few, but that is the way he would have had it. Praise embarrassed him, and the time spent in organizing functions in his honor he considered wasted unless some larger purpose could be served. As a man who broke the ground and prepared the way, he never felt neglected; so long as there was something to learn and something to teach his life was full. Even after his ninetieth year he was teaching three classes a week at the Foundation and was treating a patient or two. These patients were men who were having problems with the aging process; who better than Dr. C.F. could have helped them?

To the end he remained an ageless figure. In him always was the eagerness of a child, the maturity of a sage, and the concern of a father. So steady were these qualities that he seemed a rather impossible figure; somehow too good to be true. But in Dr. C.F. goodness was something more than the absence of evil. It was a force worth studying; within the man there may be found a message or a method that is much needed in our time.

CHAPTER ONE

i

CHARLES FREDERICK MENNINGER was born into a community that was orderly and peaceful, in a country that was racked by a civil war. The Swiss and Germans who had founded Tell City, Indiana, in midcentury were too busy building a new life in a new land to become involved in the issue of the war. While men fought each other elsewhere, the men of Tell City helped each other. The fine timber along the Ohio River had attracted a little group of skilled workers with wood, and soon, through joint effort and community financing, their guilds and unions had set up furniture factories and cabinet shops. As the fame of their products spread, more workers were imported from the old country, and building and loan societies financed homes for them. German was the language of the town; not a half dozen of its 1500 citizens knew English. Even news of the Civil War had to cross a language barrier.

Tell City was only one of many such Germanic islands in the center of America. But it was more fortunate than most of these communities in that it could turn a natural resource into a finished product with a minimum of friction. As homesteaders cleared their land they could partly finance themselves by selling the trees to the sawmills. German orderliness had altered the usual wastefulness of the frontier. The great stands of trees that stood between the land and the plow became chairs, tables, beds, wheel spokes, ax handles, and pews and pulpits. Moreover, as the farmers cleared their land they had a market ready and waiting. Tell City was a town that could have instilled optimism in any nature.

August V. Menninger, Charles's father, owned and operated

one of the town's sawmills. Since he had left Germany at the age of seventeen to get away from conscription, he had traveled in America, looking for a place to settle and raise his family. In Tell City he had found just what he wanted: independence in the midst of order. Although he sold his product to the guilds and unions, his mill was a private enterprise. While he spoke English and could have worked or gone into business elsewhere, he understandably preferred to live in a German community. Another thing had drawn him into the lumber business: it not only offered him a chance to know the homesteaders and the rivermen, but his buying trips allowed him to follow the study of nature that had always fascinated him. James Fenimore Cooper had had almost as much to do with bringing him to America as had conscription.

While he liked living in a German community, the freedom from certain of the old-country traditions meant a great deal to August Menninger. He was a Catholic and he had married a Lutheran girl, Katherine Schmidberger. Although members of their families had objected to the marriage because of this difference in religion, he had no objection to the christening of his nine living children in the Lutheran Church. He believed that their religious upbringing was up to their mother. His family had a tolerance such as is found in few families. There was no discussion of the concept of one God; it was accepted.

Although he lived in a German community within America, August Menninger was not sentimental or patriotic so far as Germany herself was concerned. He wanted to bring all the members of his family out of that land and then break all ties with it. His children either met their aunts, uncles, and grandparents in America or else heard nothing more about them. Few of the children knew the cities from which he and his wife had come; certainly none knew that a Menninger had been knighted by Maria Theresa and that Menninger von Lerchenthal was a more common name than Menninger. Though he, himself, had wanted a classic German education, he would not send his children to Germany for such schooling. They would get the best that the new land had to offer.

August Menninger was not rich, but he was moderately secure. His home was solid and commodious, in no way lavish. There was no frugality, nor was there any waste, for Katherine Menninger was a good manager and a hard worker, and with Mother Schmidberger to help her she could can and preserve the products of the garden and the orchard. For that matter, she had plenty of helpers, since seven of her children were daughters. The only time help was ever hired was when she was having a child, or when the animals were being butchered and meat had to be put up before it was spoiled. As the boys grew, the father found ways of making them useful. The household was always busy, but pleasantly so. Theirs was not a struggle for survival; each simply made his or her contribution to a well-ordered life, and abundance meant that more should be given to others.

Father Menninger was a father to more than his own flock; he was foster father to most of the town's orphans. When a child was left homeless he would appear in court and have himself appointed guardian. Until he found good homes for these children his home was theirs. His own children accepted this naturally, as did their mother.

Although he had none of the skill or learning of most of the imported craftsmen of the town, August Menninger was probably the most respected citizen of Tell City. No one, including his own family, had ever seen him angry, but then no one had ever pushed him beyond the point where his voice sounded the firm tones of warning that he had better be obeyed—a rare occasion. It was for his gentleness that he was remembered.

ii

Charles, born on July 11, 1862, was the sixth child of the Menninger family, and the first to be born in Tell City, where his family were to live for the rest of their lives. He had four elder sisters and an elder brother, Gus; three sisters were born after him and a brother who died in infancy. His childhood might be called idyllic. He was not lost in a large family; being the youngest boy, he had the undivided attention of his older sisters. There was no rivalry between him and his older brother Gus. Gus was mechanically inclined and attracted to the mill. Charles was a born student; he acquired a reading knowledge of

German before he went to school. August Menninger was delighted with his son's curiosity and especially with his interest in the specimens of plants and minerals which he brought back from field trips.

Charles's first contact with the English language and things American came when he entered school, where English was taught and used for half of the school day. The town itself remained solidly German, officially and culturally; German was the tongue of the pulpit and the press, and all civil records were kept in that language. It was through their children that the elders of the town ventured into America, and their ventures were cautious. Both the Catholic and Lutheran churches taught the catechism in German and made sure that the children spent increasing hours at these studies as they grew older and were more exposed to American life.

From the first grade onward, Charles was at the top of his class. Before he was in the third grade the family had taken it for granted that he would be a scholar. His father was pleased; he already had a son who was eager to join him in business, and he had always wished for more education for himself. Charles was not pampered, however. He kept up his share of work in the house and garden, and when he was old enough worked at the mill in the summertime. Here the father made the son his clerk and proudly exhibited Charles's neat figures for tally against those of the man who would be selling the logs and was keeping track of the measurements as they were called out. Charles liked this work because it took him out onto the log rafts in the river and brought him into contact with men upon whom he could try his English. He was interested in the trees, too, and by the time he was eleven or twelve he could estimate their ages by their rings and read the story of droughts or floods that had taken place long before his own birth. When his father taught him such things, they were very close.

Somehow Charles seemed to have no instinct for games. He liked to swim and fish, but even when out swimming and fishing he would be collecting specimens of minerals, or birds' nests and rare plants. Each year he carefully watched the migrations of birds. He learned to read the world about him as he read his books.

Because most of the sons of the town's craftsmen went into apprenticeships directly from grade school, the town had no equivalent of a high school. Children who aspired to higher education were usually sent to relatives in the larger cities, and for a while it was assumed that Charles would go to an aunt and uncle in Cincinnati. But that was before John Patrick successfully courted Charles's oldest sister, Margaret.

John Patrick, a native-born American of Irish stock, was an agent for the furniture-makers' guild of Tell City, which meant that his job was to act as an English-speaking go-between for that guild and the world outside. He had come to the town as a schoolteacher and had been popular in that capacity. His popularity had increased when he entered the business world, and lately he had become active in politics and was running for the office of county clerk. He had always wanted to be a lawyer, and when he found that Tell City needed a representative at the county seat of Cannelton, it seemed to him that work of this kind would be the next best thing. John Patrick liked Charles and thought he saw in him a future lawyer. Even before he was elected to the post, he had committed himself to taking Charles to Cannelton where he would find a suitable tutor to prepare him for college.

After Patrick's election Margaret died of a burst appendix. Patrick, however, had grown too close to the Menninger family to leave it. He married Margaret's next youngest sister, Annie.

iii

It was in 1875, when Charles was thirteen, that he went to Cannelton to live with the Patricks. In Tell City Charles had been only halfway into America; he had learned the language and history of the country, but he had had no direct contact with a real American community. Cannelton was a coal-mining town, and fairly rough, but Charles's life there was carefully planned. Arrangements had been made for him to work as a clerk in the court in exchange for his board, room, and tuition. As he grew more adept at the work, money would be put away for his expenses at college.

Charles's teacher was the Reverend Richard Tuton, an Episcopalian minister. In the years between 1875 and 1879 this man taught Charles much more than he could have learned in the high schools of that time. The boy studied algebra, geometry, trigonometry, general science, and Greek and Latin, going as far as the *Anabasis* and Caesar. Since the school was held in the rectory and its hours were only from nine in the morning until one in the afternoon, there was much homework to be done.

At thirteen Charles was almost six feet tall and weighed little more than 100 pounds, but he seemed healthy and energetic. His workday started at six-thirty in the morning when he would go to the county clerk's office, air the rooms, start the fires, and do general cleaning. Immediately after school in the afternoon Charles was back in the office again, working as an assistant to his brother-in-law. As rapidly as he could learn legal procedures and forms, his responsibilities widened until the only part of John Patrick's job he could not do was to swear in witnesses. By the time he was fourteen, Charles was issuing licenses of all sorts; at fifteen he was able to give clients of the court simple legal advice. But what he liked best was keeping the records of the courts. Here he came into contact with judges and lawyers who were learned and eloquent men. The way some of these men handled the human problems that came before the court gave the boy a new insight into human responsibility. Like his father and John Patrick, they became heroes whom he worshiped. Things that he was learning from the Reverend Tuton took on a new meaning as he saw learned men in action.

There was little time for play during these four years, but weekends at home were pleasant interludes. During the long walk between Tell City and Cannelton, Charles could ponder on his experiences of the week. In the outside world he had seen weakness, disorder, and crime that were unknown in Tell City. There was poverty too, and some injustice. To Charles it seemed that men's minds worked in strange ways, and he watched their workings with all the objectivity of a child from another planet. Slowly this objectivity grew into a sort of compassion for the world at large: he became noticeably more considerate and more concerned with people he met, and he came to understand how it was that his father took in the world's waifs.

Those years at Cannelton would fit perfectly into the biography of a Supreme Court justice. John Patrick was now reading law, and, in the hope that Charles would one day become his partner, he wanted the boy to be given a background in the field. Charles's apparent passivity was attributed to his youth. Only those who watched the boy describe to his parents and sisters what he had learned during each week could have seen the slightest hint of vocation. There an instinctive teacher was at work.

When Charles chose to go to college at Central Normal College in Danville, Indiana, it was generally understood that he was still preparing for law, perhaps with a few interim years of teaching until he could finance himself. The boy said neither yea nor nay. No one suggested that he become a physician.

iv

In 1879, Central Normal College was a well-established co-educational school that Charles remembers as having an enrollment of as many as 2000 students. Most of these students were schoolteachers who had not as yet finished their undergraduate studies. They came for only a few months out of the year, and as a rule attended special "institutes." The regular student body was probably less than 500. The faculty was large and it was adequate, if not spectacularly good. To Charles, at that point, Central Normal was the greatest of schools.

In the first months at college Charles roomed with a boy from Tell City who shared none of his scholarly interests. Though Charles might understand games and enjoy one glass of beer in a German beer garden, he was suspicious of any activity or association that did not contribute to his education. He was not pompous, but the past four years of his life, when fourteen hours a day of work and study had been the rule, had given him a fear of idleness. When he left his roommate it was to move into the house where G. Dallas Lind, his favorite professor, roomed.

G. Dallas Lind had won Charles's devotion because of his teaching methods. He was professor of sciences and as such spent much more time in investigation and demonstration than he did in lecturing. Though Charles had only two classes under this man, he at once arranged his time so that he could attend almost all of

Professor Lind's classes, especially when there were field trips. His attachment to two women teachers was almost equally strong. These women, Dora Lewellyn and Kate Huron, who taught English and Latin, claimed most of the remaining hours.

Dora Lewellyn had organized a reading club of which Charles was a member during his entire four years at college. Indianapolis had a fine legitimate theater that booked most of the great players of the time. As soon as Miss Lewellyn knew that a play was coming, her club would read it, discuss it, and then go to Indianapolis to see it performed. In this way Charles read and saw most of Shakespeare's plays. Kate Huron had a Latin club in which she let her students declaim to their hearts' content, taking the part of whatever noble Roman they chose.

Both these teachers were spinsters and narrowly religious, but somehow their intolerance and their need to convert almost everything into a religious text did not disturb Charles's own tolerance. He admired zeal, and these women had plenty of that. He was sure that they represented the highest type of American womanhood and his association with them made all his female classmates fall short of his ideals. Though he sang in the choir, he made no attachments to the girls in it.

Before he was halfway through college he knew that he was going to become a college teacher, but he kept this knowledge from his family. The faculty, however, were aware of his plan and ready to help him. If anything troubled Charles it was that he appeared to have a much easier time than his classmates and the other people he saw. He was always at the head of his class; he had no economic worries, for Patrick, true to his word, paid his way. Nor did he seem to experience the emotional conflicts that disturbed so many young people around him. It would have been easy to be self-righteous, but Charles's upbringing had destroyed any tendency of that sort. He had been fortunate and he knew it and at times this may have given him a feeling of guilt.

When Charles received his degree in 1882, his twentieth year, he was valedictorian. The theme of his speech, "The Young Men's Record," was that "in every soul there are the germs of possible excellence," which are difficult to nourish when the parents of the scholar have failed to provide a stimulus to exertion. He saw his own good fortune; he did not blame others because they lacked it.

There would undoubtedly have been positions waiting for Charles at any number of established colleges in the more settled parts of the Middle West, but he chose to go to a new college in what seemed to his advisers and family the remotest wilderness —Kansas. Perhaps his decision was provoked by a feeling of guilt about his own good fortune. Or perhaps he was more of an adventurer than he thought of himself as being. At any rate, he told worried relatives that he could outrun the Indians, and that he was too skinny to be affected by cyclones, and, in spite of their protests, accepted a position on the faculty of Campbell College in Holton, Kansas. John Patrick was bitterly disappointed, and the rest of the family were saddened, but as Charles stepped on the train for Kansas his father said, "I'm always with you. If you ever need help of any kind just ask for it."

v

Campbell College was not merely an institution of higher learning; it was an institution at which higher learning in the accepted sense could be had, but which also adapted itself to the general educational needs of Kansas. Primary-school teachers, few of them high school graduates, stopped in for three- and four-month courses in "Education"; boys who wanted to become telegraphers learned that science at Campbell. Life in Kansas was such that few could spare time from the struggle for existence in order to complete four years of college. The school had to be everything to everyone, and it was. It was sacrificing its future to the demands of the present, and rendering a service that had a permanent effect on the state of Kansas.

The young professor was entranced with both the school and its setting. The Great Plains fascinated him; they were virgin territory for the natural scientist. The migrations of the birds were well defined here; there were no hills or trees to shield their flight. On the Plains storms were violent, and in order to study them further Charles became an amateur meteorologist and then a state weather observer. Keeping one jump ahead of his natural-science classes, he became a student of the Kansas earth and all that grew from it or swept over it. He wrote excited letters to Professor

Lind, but there was an element of homesickness in his comparison of Kansas with Indiana.

Ordinarily, there was not much time for homesickness, for Charles taught German, geology, botany, mineralogy, physics, and whatever other science courses he was prepared for. While he taught these subjects he prepared himself to teach telegraphy, and graduated himself only when he could stand outside the railroad station and take messages as fast as they came over the wires. He taught himself engineering, too, and surveyed the town of Holton for practice—practice that Holton took seriously and paid him for. In spite of the variety of his undertakings he had adopted the motto, "Not how much, but how well." Wherever possible he taught by example, experiment, and demonstration. He was popular with his students; girls went out of their way to gain his attention.

Professor Charles Menninger was attractive, if scrawny. He stood well over six feet tall and at his best and dressed in his best he rarely tipped the scales at over 125 pounds. He ate well enough, but from dawn until bedtime he never rested. All his energies went into everything that he did; he put sheer physical force into teaching the backward students; he gave out with full voice in the church choir. Even as he strolled around the town square with a girl, he would be learning from her, finding out what her way of life had been and what she believed. He didn't know that he was thinking of marriage, but he knew that he was thinking of girls, and that there was more to know than Dora Lewellyn, Kate Huron, and his own sisters and mother had taught him. For reasons that were not quite clear to him he had pasted many clippings on feminism and women's suffrage into his scrapbook. Somehow he identified his own cause, whatever it might be, with the cause of women.

Among his male friends in Holton, Dr. George R. Dean, a homeopathic physician, was the man Charles most admired. Dr. Dean, a cultivated person, enjoyed having young people in for evenings of music and talk. He was a fine violinist and a finished reciter of poetry who introduced Charles to Pope's "Essay on Man" and moved him profoundly when he declaimed Burns's *A Man's a Man for a' That*. Since Dr. Dean was the most learned man in town, he took it for granted that his medical education had been a major contributing factor.

The salary for the first year's teaching at Holton was $365, an adequate amount in a time when the best board and room could be had for two dollars a week. Charles did not save, for even a minimum of plenty meant that he should give the surplus to his family and friends. He assumed that if you did everything you could with your day the future would take care of itself. He had never in his life known economic anxiety.

When students came to Campbell College in search of a special course the question of whether the course was in the catalogue or not never arose. If anyone had the time or the knowledge, it would be given. Thus, when three young men came to the college in search of a pre-medical course, something no one at the school had heard of before, Charles, as a science teacher, acquired them as students. He knew nothing about medical education, but, by consulting Dr. Dean and Dr. Adamson, the school doctor, and by doing some research, he was able to construct a course that would meet the new requirements of medical schools. Until this time most medical schools had required no pre-medical education and their courses had included the basic sciences.

Charles was learning just one jump ahead of his students, and he was thoroughly enjoying himself. Biology, physiology, and chemistry all engrossed him, as did other sciences. Although only three were officially students, there were actually four students in that class. The three pre-medical students all became successful physicians, one of them an outstanding surgeon.

vi

Among the students in Charles's classes was a twenty-year-old girl, more plainly dressed than the others, who seemed to be hurrying every course along out of some personal urgency. She was not only bright, which of course pleased Charles, but there was a sort of burning desperation about her that attracted him. This girl, Charles could tell, was carrying a heavy load and carrying it valiantly, and she made his security and comfort uncomfortable. Although he did not know her, she made him feel that he was not doing enough and that he was, in fact, almost frivolous. He was surprised by the intensity of his response to her presence.

When he wrote her a note and asked her if she would accompany him on a buggy ride, he was sure that she would consider such an excursion frivolous. But Flo Knisely did accept, and what was to have been a Saturday-afternoon ride into the country became an exploration into a past that was beyond Charles's imaginings. Not only had this girl taught school from the time she was fifteen, and in a region where she had to ride horseback and fight off prairie wolves, but she had been the only person who could provide money for a widowed mother and four younger brothers and a sister. Flo, who was comparatively frail, had plowed, milked, built fences, and dug storm cellars. Since she was eight years old she had taken care of the younger children, and when her father had died in Mechanicsburg, Pennsylvania, when she was ten, she had had to live with grandparents who were afraid that her mother and the children would become an impossible burden. Because of this situation, her mother had come to Kansas to farm, and was fighting valiantly, if unequally, with drought, insects, poor land, and fluctuating prices. She had started with less than $300 in capital. In the midst of this battle Flo was educating herself for better teaching jobs and trying to arrange her life so that she could become responsible for the education of her younger brothers and sisters.

Charles listened with awe. This girl showed no self-pity, she complained of nothing but her own inadequacies. She was not embittered, but sure that she would accomplish anything that she set out to do. Moreover, her Christian principles were all that Dora Lewellyn or Kate Huron could have expected. Hardship had not damaged her virtues or her ideals; if anything they had become more firm. She was a member of the River Brethren, a sect that considered the ordinary fundamentalist Baptists of the period to be decadent hell-raisers. This feeling was no affectation in Flo Knisely; none of the things her church was against, such as card playing, smoking, drinking, dancing, and idleness, had any place in her life. If she did what she had to do and got to where she was going, there would be no time for these things or for people who had truck with them.

Before Charles took Flo home to her boardinghouse, he knew that he was in love, and that he loved the girl's suffering and struggle because they were part of her as a person. Before he could think of marriage to such a woman he would have to become worthy of her. From now on he would be accomplishing things *for someone.* Straightway, he resigned from teaching for the next year, resolving to work toward a master's degree—a project that would at least put him, along with his beloved, on a financial tightrope.

vii

Charles's attentions to Flo became a school scandal. Fortunately Flo's brother, Elmer, had joined her at school and was sharing quarters with her, but in spite of his presence as chaperone, it soon became clear that a marriage was not only desirable but wise. Charles went to see Manda Knisely, to ask for her daughter's hand. "Come, thou Heavenly Muse," he wrote in his journal, "and sing of Charley's trials—that will never do—it is too lofty a strain with which to begin the record of the 'trials and tribulations' experience by (one of the latter day saints) Charley. It must be more soft and melodramatic so that the words will be fully suited to the thought—the act of experience; nor must the pen be given such freedom that the real grandeur of the truth is obscured. Oh! If it were only the ability of a Hamlet that gives these stage directions; they would be rich and flow out in copious language, possibly in meter and rhyme, though clothed in a sable shroud of solemn truth and sight of how Charley won the hand of Flo and the consent of her mother to take her as wife. I only wish that I may be worthy of her love and affections. I pray that I will be . . . God bless her always."

The young man who could get drunk enough on love to write a passage like that couldn't be expected to wait long.

The wedding took place at the home of Campbell's president, J. H. Miller, at seven o'clock on the evening of January 15, 1885. The bride wore her woolen school dress, trimmed for the occasion with a bit of lace at the neck, and the groom had a new necktie. The local Baptist minister officiated, after Elmer had frozen his

ears going to fetch him. A yellow glass pitcher and two glasses
were the wedding present from the faculty; Charley almost broke
them as he fell into an abandoned well on the way home. One
moment he was walking on clouds; the next he was fumbling
blindly at dank walls. When he pulled himself out of the well his
feet were on earth again, and were to be for some time to come.

viii

The couple moved into the quarters that Flo had shared
with Elmer, and Elmer stayed on. Flo, being practical, decided
that they should not have children until they were comfortably
situated and out of debt. And debts were piled high. Things at
the ranch had gone from bad to worse; Charley was still paying
on the board bill he had run up while taking his master's degree.
The forty dollars a month that Charles earned, though it was
adequate to the couple's immediate needs, was indicative of the
lack of future in teaching. Flo thought her husband to be capable
of success in any kind of profession, and where John Patrick had
been unable to persuade Charles toward law, Flo and Elmer did
persuade him. Elmer was attracted to the law, and it was possible
that they might become partners.

Under a young attorney who had recently been graduated from
Columbia Law School, Charley and Elmer began to read law.
Charles, with his experience in Cannelton, and his aptitude for
learning, could probably have passed the state bar examination
by the time the next term was out. But for some reason he was
reluctant to do so and decided to wait until Elmer had completed
college, then take the examinations with him so that they could
go into practice together. It seems probable that the studying in
itself was more important to Charles than law was. He felt a need
to drive himself as he never had before.

If Charles had hitherto been spared the struggles of life, he
was plunged into them now. Spring and summer brought disaster
to the Knisely family. Manda Knisely had borrowed money to
invest in cattle, and cattle prices dropped. Grasshoppers, chinch
bugs, and drought hit the crops; the banks became impatient.
When the banks were paid off she had only the small home place

left, and her boys wanted to be out on their own. Flo, of course, went to her mother's assistance. Since she and Elmer would be in college for the next two years, she decided to set her mother up in a boardinghouse in Holton so that she could be near her. Mrs. Knisely was not pleased with the idea, and Flo and Charles had to live with her to help her in her distress. Soon they were doing most of the work.

The one big hope of the summer lay in Elmer. He had found a job on a railroad-surveying gang which paid five dollars a day, an extraordinary amount for those times. Before he was well started on the job, however, he and most of his party became ill. Back in Holton the disease was diagnosed as typhoid fever, and the medicine of that time could not save him. With the death of his future partner, Charles dismissed from his mind all idea of going into law.

When Charles found a job teaching at a summer institute that was close to Indiana, he took Flo with him and at the end of the summer took her to meet his parents. The Menningers wanted to meet their boy's bride, and they sent a check to cover the expenses of the trip.

To the Menningers Flo was a new sort of woman. They were glad that she was German on her mother's side and had the language, but in all other ways she was strange to them. They could not understand her background nor the Western freedom that allowed her to go fishing and boating with Charles and allowed her to dominate every facet of his life. Still they welcomed her, and believed that she was good for their son. On a Sunday evening, wishing to celebrate the acceptance of a new member into their family, Father Menninger went down to the cellar and brought up a bottle of his finest and oldest wine. As he poured a glass for everyone, Flo moved to Charles's side and gripped his hand.

There had been no intemperance in the Menninger family and very little in Tell City. Wine was a symbol of a festive evening, when Father Menninger would have a glass or two, and Charles, with the other children, would have a taste of it. When Charles, with his bride clutching his arm, not only refused the wine but made a temperance speech, August Menninger was deeply

shocked and hurt. As he stalked out of the room he was as angry as anyone had ever seen him.

Flo was proud of Charles; he had shown his mettle. They were glad to leave Tell City, and Charles was tired, very tired, from the summer.

But there was to be no rest. Mrs. Knisely was sent back to the farm and Charles and Flo took over the boardinghouse. While Charles taught music, telegraphy, penmanship, German, and sciences, he also made the boardinghouse beds and on Saturday helped with the laundry. Flo cooked, and both washed dishes. To get more money out of the available rooms, the couple moved into the basement where they were never quite warm and Charles developed a cough and lost weight. Dr. Adamson, the school doctor, warned the now cadaverous young professor that he would have to take care of himself, but he didn't say how. Somehow Charles kept going throughout the school year.

ix

As spring came Dr. Adamson told Charles that, if he wished to live, he would have to rest and be free from worry for a while. When Flo found a place where both she and Charles could work and let the boardinghouse go, Adamson said no to that, too.

Charles, who had always been interested in the manifestations of nature around him, began to pay some attention to its manifestations within him. Quite suddenly the study of medicine appealed to him. School had always been restful; if he could get into a medical school he could rest and learn a profession. He wondered now if he had not been stifling this desire to study medicine ever since he had taught the pre-medical class. Even then he had tried to explore the field. He had, for instance, written to Dr. Oliver Wendell Holmes about a problem in physiology and received a short, humorous reply, referring him to such "rare works" as Gray's *Anatomy*. Also, he had studiously clipped newspaper stories about the great writing physicians of the day, and while he was teaching anatomy he had made a special effort to study the functions of the nerves.

When Charles confided to Flo that he was thinking of taking up medicine, he found her enthusiastic. Physicians had stable incomes; as a rule they were Christian gentlemen. The problem of getting Charles through medical school seemed no problem at all to Flo since her life had been a long series of problems. She could teach and pay his way. Charles saw gratefully that there could be no turning back.

August Menninger would gladly have paid for Charles's medical education, but, having accepted Flo's way of life, Charles never thought of that.

Although it was Dr. Adamson, an allopathic physician, who had guided Charles into his decision to become a physician, he went to Dr. Dean for advice as to the school he should go to. Cornell had been his choice, but the cost placed it out of the question. Dr. Dean recommended his own homeopathic school, Hahnemann Medical College, in Chicago, and at once got Charles accepted for the next year. The decision was made swiftly and desperately. There was no time to be critical.

During the summer Flo and Charles attended a teachers' conference in Topeka. While they were there, Flo looked for a job for the next year and found a good one, which would commence in the fall of 1888, that would enable her to see Charles through school. Since she was going to be in Topeka, Charles looked for a preceptor there and found a Dr. Roby, one of the city's leading homeopaths, willing to accept him. He could come back and work in the doctor's office during the summer vacation. Many years later Dr. C.F. said that even then, as he walked about Topeka's streets and admired the trees, he knew that this town was to be his home.

When Flo put him on the train for Chicago his normal good health was already coming back, but if he could have read the report that Abraham Flexner was to make on his school thirty years later, there might never have been a C. F. Menninger, M.D.

Flexner was to report that students were accepted at Hahnemann on the basis of a high school education or its equivalent, and that "the school occupies a building wretchedly dirty, excepting only a single laboratory, fairly equipped and devoted to pathology and bacteriology. The equipment covers in a meager way also anatomy, physiology, histology, chemistry. In an adjoining hospital there are accommodations in the wards for sixty beds, but there are no ward clinics. The superintendent is a layman who does not believe in admitting students to the wards. There is no way for them to see the common acute diseases, as only amphitheater clinics are held. Hospital interns do all of the obstetrical work; students look on. The school also holds two appointments to the surgical side of Cook County Hospital. There is a fair dispensary."

Hahnemann went on to become an adequate school, but if Charles could have known what he was faced with then and made some comparison with the best schools in the East, he would have rebelled. Flo could not have paid for a better school. For once in Charles's life, ignorance was a blessing.

CHAPTER TWO

i

WHEN CHARLES F. MENNINGER arrived at Hahnemann
Medical College in early September of 1887, Samuel Christian
Friedrich Hahnemann, the founder of homeopathic medicine, had
been dead for forty-four years. Except in England, homeopathy
as such had almost ceased to exist in Europe. Its greatest strong-
hold was in America, where there were ten homeopathic medical
schools. Although the students who were graduated from homeopathic schools were given a medical degree and granted certificates to practice in all the states, homeopathic physicians were
not accepted by their allopathic colleagues. They were, however,
somewhat up the scale from their osteopathic brethren.

Hahnemann had discovered, or adapted from Paracelsus, the
theory of *similia similibus curantur*—"like cures like." Thinking
that he had observed that fever was produced by cinchona bark,
the source of quinine, Hahnemann stated that the fever he believed to be intrinsic in the drug was what cured the fever of the
disease, malaria. Proceeding on this theory, he prescribed hot compresses for burns, sedative drugs for somnolence, stimulants for
excitement, and so on. This therapy was the opposite of that
used by the allopaths who believed in *contraria contrariis*, the
giving of drugs that produced effects that counteracted the symptoms of the disease; i.e., sedatives for excitement, stimulants for
depressions.

In the Europe of Hahnemann's time, and all too frequently in
the America of Charles Menninger's time, the allopaths, or regular
physicians, gave massive doses of drugs, often in the most frightening mixtures. Their attacks on disease were, to say the least, heroic.

Anything that had ever worked on any disease was thrown into the pot, so to speak, and the concoction was then poured into the patient. Specific drugs were rarely given alone. Physician vied with physician for stranger and stronger potions and compounds. The patient's stomach became a veritable alchemist's retort.

Not all physicians prescribed so lavishly, and a few of the more astute and sensitive knew that such dosing was harming the patients and was an assault on nature. In *Medical Essays* Oliver Wendell Holmes had written, as early as 1860, "Throw out opium, which the Creator Himself seems to prescribe, for we often see the scarlet poppy growing in cornfields, as if it were foreseen that wherever there was hunger to be fed there must also be pain to be soothed; throw out the few specifics which our art did not discover; throw out wine, which is food, and the vapors that produce the miracle of anesthesia—and I firmly believe that if the whole *materia medica*, as now used, could be sunk to the bottom of the sea, it would be all the better for mankind—and all the worse for the fishes."

Hahnemann, quite naturally, unaware of what Dr. Holmes was to write, immersed and diluted the *materia medica* in a sea of alcohol or a desert of sugar of milk, as the case might be. Using reasoning that was almost wholly mystical, he came to the conclusion that drugs became more powerful by dilution. Thus he recommended what he called the "thirtieth potency." For drugs in a liquid form, an original agent would be prepared and then two drops would be diluted with ninety-eight drops of alcohol; one drop of this solution would be further diluted with another ninety-eight drops of alcohol until the process had been repeated thirty times. With drugs that were in powder form, the process was carried out by dilution in sugar of milk.

Homeopathy gained in popularity because it worked; patients treated by homeopaths got well where patients treated by the allopaths often did not. Perhaps Hahnemann was an intuitive genius who was cursed with one of the worst systems of rationalization in medical history. Without wishing to be, he was an iconoclast; he destroyed the conventional use of the *materia medica*. In doing this he did mankind a great service. People no longer died of the cure; if they died, they died of the disease.

At the time of the advent of homeopathy, the use of scientific control was almost unknown. Nevertheless, Hahnemann did a little scientific work in the effect of drugs. He gave various agents to well people and observed the symptoms produced. Of course he was in search of symptoms that would match the symptoms of various diseases; still, new knowledge of drugs was acquired. Apparently it never occurred to him to give one hundred patients with similar symptoms his routine therapy and another hundred no treatment at all in order to check group against group.

One of the more eccentric aspects of Hahnemann's theory was the belief that the stars impress the "signatures" of disease on the plants from which drugs that can treat that disease must be obtained. The orchid had a testicle-shaped root, therefore urinary diseases should respond to the extract of the orchid; the nutmeg resembled the brain and therefore would be good for diseases of the brain. Blessedly, Hahnemann's exotic and esoteric reasoning was diluted by an equally mystical element of potency in reverse, and the end results spelled out the simple truth that Nature often did best when left to her own devices. This was a strange return to the precepts of Hippocrates—the use of the health of nature for the health of the body. Baths, sunlight, fresh air, rest, good food, and an absence of violent assaults on the system by the physician—these, sheathed in the mysticism of homeopathy, gave healing a new meaning.

By 1887 homeopathy had adapted somewhat to the changes it had wrought in the practice of medicine. Without the overdosing, bleeding, and purging, the symptoms of diseases became more clearly defined and better understood, and the processes behind the symptoms were examined and attacked. As a bow to progress, Hahnemann Medical College in Chicago had a small laboratory, and a smattering of bacteriology, histology, and pathology was taught, although the emphasis was still on treating symptoms with drugs that could produce like symptoms. Of course, homeopaths were also surgeons and in that field differed not at all from their brother surgeons of the other schools.

ii

Charles Menninger knew nothing of the history of medicine when he entered Hahnemann, and he didn't know one system of medicine from the other, but one thing that he quickly recognized was that he had had better training in the basic sciences than had any of his classmates and most of his professors. The pre-medical course he had devised back in Holton was more thorough than the first-year course at Hahnemann. Indeed, some of the things he was taught were a direct offense against scientific method as he had come to know it.

With Flo running the boardinghouse and teaching school so that he might become a physician, Charles put down his disappointment in his school and resolved to get all that he could out of it. That was not hard to do. Before he was well into the first semester, the faculty informed him that because of his background in the sciences he would be graduated in two years instead of the three that were required at that time. Since his health was returning, this was good news.

To fill in his idle time, Charles helped organize Bible classes for the school, and a school unit of the Y.M.C.A. At the same time he was availing himself of the cultural opportunities of the city. At the McVicker's Theatre he saw Henry Irving and Ellen Terry in *Faust* and Edwin Booth in *Hamlet*.

Twice each week he wrote to Flo and heard from her as often. Although she was working hard and living frugally, she encouraged him to go to the theater. By Christmas time things were looking up; a buyer had been found for the boardinghouse, and he took immediate possession. Having a little surplus time and money, Flo sent for her sister, Leah, so that she might enter school. Flo was determined to educate her family.

At Christmas Charles sent the first of the expensive gifts that were to please and plague Flo for the rest of her life. Money would never have the same meaning to Charles that it had to Flo. Out of the little money she had been sending him he saved ten dollars and invested it in a handsome sealskin cap for her. That cap turned out to be a good investment. As late as 1940, Flo's sister

Leah was still wearing it during the winter on the ranch, and the waste of money on such a "useless" gift was still bothering Flo.

iii

On the surface it would seem that Charles had heard no clear and overpowering voice calling him into the healing arts. He had looked upon the physician as a moral and cultural force in the community rather than as a healer. Though he had been saddened by Elmer's death from typhoid, he seems to have been fatalistic about typhoid deaths. When he discussed with Flo the possibilities of a career as a physician, the questions of income and social standing seemed to be of paramount importance. But Charles did take into medicine his dedication as a scholar and a teacher.

From childhood onward, he had felt compassion for those who suffered, for whatever reason. His anxiety about those who had an unequal struggle was probably responsible for the shaping of his love for Flo. He had married her to help her, although soon it was she who was helping him through medical school. He had become another member of her brood and was, it would seem, being molded by her. Behind her relentless, selfless drive was a burning ambition that conveyed itself to him in every letter, and when she prayed for success, he knew that he had to answer her prayer.

There appears to have been a certain passivity toward women in Charles's make-up. At least he desired to please them by becoming what he thought they wished him to be. For example, he had not questioned his own feelings about his family's custom of serving wine and its relationship to the national prohibition movement but had accepted Flo's dictum that wine was evil, and had gone against his own father in order to please her. At college his women teachers had found no protest in him when they violated classic literature by turning it into a moral text for the narrow religious beliefs of their day. He had obtained his secondary education as a result of the marriage of his elder sisters. At home he was the favorite male simply because he had striven mightily to be the male the women of the family wished him to be. He never questioned the wisdom or judgment of women; he accepted it, uncritically, as fundamentally right.

Up to a point, it could be said that the pleasing of the women in his life had been a substitute for personal morality. Like the "Good Boy" of Carl Sandburg's song, he could say, "I've always done exactly what was expected." In his life with Flo, Charles had certainly done just what was expected, even to turning on his own father. But what had been expected of him had finally broken his health. It seems quite likely that there had been a rebellion of the spirit that husbanded that health, and that that rebellion of the spirit had indirectly launched him on a new career. When Flo took over the sponsorship of this new career, Charles was again in the position of having to do what was expected; he was again the captive of Flo and of his own anxiety to please.

He did what was expected. Functioning within the confines of the moral and religious precepts of his teachers and of Flo, Charles tried to link the Y.M.C.A. and Bible classes to medical education; he attended plays in order to receive "moral enlightenment"; he lived frugally and almost priggishly. Beyond this, he was also a good student in just the way the women would have wished him to be. He learned what was taught. It would seem that he was moving within the same pattern of passivity that had brought him to near disaster. The next step would have been to become what the women would think was an ideal physician.

Charles Menninger appears, however, to have been a man who was more attentive to his inner processes than most. He seemed to know that his success and health lay in an unusual sort of revolt against the passivity that seemed to be his enemy. While he was still in medical school, Charles apparently saw that his salvation lay in doing more than was expected—much more.

Even while he was moving about among the classes of all three years of the medical school, Charles found the time, and had the diligence, to win the clerkships for which all the students competed. Each professor had a student clerk, whose chore it was to stand by the teacher as he examined patients and presented their cases. This clerk recorded findings, wrote prescriptions under the professor's supervision, and was often allowed to assist in examinations. To be a clerk the student had to be at the top of the class. Charles was for a time a clerk in surgery, the specialty in which

he had the least interest. For this reason, he probably got a little
more clinical training than most students did.

In order to win these clerkships, Charles had to be an outstanding student of homeopathy and pass examinations that were offensive to his basic scientific judgment. When he got the clerkships
he discovered that the professors themselves did not always use
the methods that were the basis of homeopathy. This contradiction
did not puzzle him for long. He also did more than was expected
of a homeopathic student; he read whatever he could find about
the art and science of healing. He knew very well that the chemical duplication of the symptoms of a disease was not the essential
of medical practice.

iv

Charles's relationships and experiences in the world of
men had a positive side. His father had initiated him into the
world of nature and taught him to observe. Charles's work in the
courts had taught him that morality, and the responsibility attached to it, was something greater and more personal than the
stringent and fundamentalistic interpretations of scripture. Professor Lind, with his willingness to risk his science in the laboratory
of the fields, had inculcated in Charles the principles of scientific
investigation.

Two contradictory forces were at work in Charles. He effected
a painless reconciliation by behaving as though they were one
force. He could be what the women expected him to be and at the
same time try to become all that he expected himself to be as a
man. If a professor presenting a case said: "Gentlemen, here we
have three distinct symptoms; vomiting, diarrhea, and fever. The
indications are clear. *Similia similibus curantur.* An emetic for the
nausea; a physic for the diarrhea; a pyretic for the fever. The
pains the patient describes are secondary and will disappear when
the primary symptoms have been removed," Charles memorized
the lesson; he could recite it verbatim. In this he had done what
was expected. But when he saw a burst appendix and peritonitis
in a case with the same symptoms he could also see that doing

exactly what was expected, no more, no less, was a formula for murder.

While Charles was able to report to Flo that he was at the top of his class as a medical student, he realized how little that standing had to do with becoming a good physician. A new conscience had taken hold of him and was driving him relentlessly.

v

When Charles came back to Topeka from his first year in medical school, Flo moved all her possessions from Holton and joined him. The couple found a room in a rooming house and lived frugally, for although Charles was working for Dr. Roby, his preceptor, he received only token payment for his services. Flo attended some teachers' institutes that were held during the summer, but she had no salaried job until school opened in the fall. The little money that had been salvaged from the boarding-house debacle had to see them through.

Flo found that Charles had changed a good deal; his health had returned, and he was more quiet and more sure of himself. He could immerse himself in medical texts more deeply than he had in any other study. There was none of the facility and flair with which he had attacked and conquered other subjects. She realized that medical study had put him at one remove from her, that it was something she could not share. Something more than scholarly values was involved now; human lives were at stake. Although Flo didn't know about it, Charles had stood by several deathbeds with Dr. Roby, and for the first time had realized the terrible responsibility of the career he was launched upon. Whenever Charles seemed especially troubled, Flo would ask him to pray with her and this would bring him close to her again.

Since there wasn't enough to occupy Flo all summer she spent some time on the farm helping her mother. Even an hour of idleness could make Flo nervous; two hours could bring on a depression. She had to teach and give of herself in order to live; she was incapable of play and could see only doom in idleness. Although she was only in her early twenties, her family had been dependent on her for years. Before she was ten, she had taught a woman to read and write in exchange for nursing services for her mother. Until she started teaching at fifteen she had had to take care of her sister and brothers so that her mother might be free to work. That her husband had to depend on her for his professional education seemed only natural and right to her; she was unable to imagine a life in which people were not dependent on her.

Charles and Flo Menninger made no close friends during that summer; they did not fit into the conventional society of the town. "We'll have to create our own environment," Charles told Flo, and when he left for Chicago she saw very clearly what he had meant. At first it was a frightening experience to be alone. She had rarely gone out on the streets without Charles, and his tall, professorial dignity had given her some security. She had been proud when people glanced at them; now when they glanced at her she thought it must be because she was odd. There was only one thing to do—get busy.

Flo's first school in Topeka was Branner Primary School, which was near the Santa Fe tracks and not in the most desirable residential district in the city. The other teachers all lived in the better parts of town, but Flo felt more at home in the neighborhood of the school and found a room there. The other teachers thought this was an odd choice. On the one occasion when she was invited to a party with the other teachers, no one bothered to introduce her to anyone. But one woman, Mrs. Ed Whitacker, did notice the strange and lonely girl, and by doing so became her lifelong friend.

Flo was incapable of brooding about social slights; she simply asked herself what she could do with her spare time and began to do it. With permission from the principal, she gave readings after school hours for pupils who wished to attend. That winter she read most of Louisa M. Alcott's works. Making use of her evenings, she called on the family of every child in her class. Most of them were poor, and this was something Flo understood; she helped many a tired mother with her cooking and sewing and washing. With the tithe that she normally set aside for the church, Flo bought stockings for the poorer children, and finally she attended a meeting of the Missionary Society at one of the churches and asked them if they could not give their old clothes to her students and their families. Flo's life was full; it contributed greatly to the lives of others. If anyone had commented on the good she was doing she would have been puzzled. What else, she would ask, could she do?

The teachers who had ostracized Flo were in for a shock. She was so successful as a teacher that the superintendent of schools soon had her giving lessons to the other teachers. While she might be able to teach them classroom techniques, she could not, however, instruct them in the warmth and sympathy that were naturally hers and that drew students to her. As her reputation grew, the editor of the *Kansas State School Journal* asked that she contribute articles on teaching. On Saturdays she had a very popular class in mechanical drawing. Out of her loneliness and insecurity, Flo was fashioning her own environment and the city was getting its first example of the zeal that was to be associated with the name of Menninger.

Whatever fame came to Flo was a startling by-product of the fact that she kept busy and followed her natural bent. The shy girl who came to Topeka in 1888 would have been frightened if anyone had hinted at the success she was to have and the reputation she was to earn. She could not be accused of paving the way for her physician husband; most of the friends Flo made were too poor to pay medical fees.

vi

On his return to Chicago and medical school, Charles was more realistic than before. On his first trip he had had visions of entering a great institution of learning where his mettle as a scholar would be tried; when he went back the second time he knew that he was going on to make the best of the limited opportunities that Hahnemann offered in order to come away with the medical degree and certificate that would entitle him to enter into practice. Only then could he really begin to learn medicine.

Charles no longer had any great illusions about his preceptor, Dr. Roby. Dr. Roby appeared to be a more than adequate physician, but Charles already knew that the doctor would never allow a young man to enter very deeply into his practice or offer him clinical instruction that included any of his "trade secrets." But, aside from the clinical aspects of medicine, Charles felt that there was much to be learned from the doctor. Roby was highly respected in Topeka and had a large practice. He impressed people and knew how to get along with them. At least, Charles felt, the doctor could teach him how to be a professional man.

Back at school, Charles was again immersed in the contradictions of the homeopathic philosophy and was still ignorant of the history of medicine, especially in recent times. Scientific medicine was in the ascendancy now that signs and symptoms of disease were no longer compounded, masked, muddled, and distorted by massive doses of drugs. With bleeding and purging on the wane, the sources of disease could be sought out and studied. Pasteur, who had completed his work on anthrax only seven years before, was active; Lister and Semmelweis had made their contributions since the advent of homeopathy; anesthesia and sterile technique were bringing surgery into a stage where scientific investigation was possible. Hahnemann Medical College had, as has been noted, bowed to scientific medicine by installing a small laboratory and collecting a small library, but so long as the philosophy of treatment continued to be a study of symptoms with the sole purpose of finding an herb, a vegetable, or a mineral that would reproduce those symptoms, a scientific investigation of the causes of the disease would only confuse the homeopathic student.

One thing impressed Charles. Some homeopathic physicians were very successful with their patients and while their teachings were homeopathically orthodox a deep and genuine concern for the ill set them apart from their colleagues. Experience had taught these physicians the pitfalls that lay in following the homeopathic scripture too literally. Homeopathy, however, had taught them to make a more thorough investigation of the patient's symptoms. Clinical experience had given them an intuitive knowledge of disease processes; what appeared to be intuition often led them to initiate unconventional treatment with good results. But these men did not in fact know what they were doing, and they were unable to report scientifically on what they had done. Indeed, most of them were so emotionally bound to the doctrine of homeopathy that they suppressed reports of any experience that went against the doctrine. Experiences were rarely shared on any worthwhile level.

If the medical education that Charles was receiving seems inadequate and pathetic, it must be remembered that it was probably above the average for American physicians of that period. No more than a half dozen medical schools functioned on a level consistent with the new advances in science. Twenty years later the Carnegie Foundation was to report that only 31 of the 155 medical schools deserved to survive. There were many diploma mills that had no clinical services or laboratories. It was only recently that three-year courses had been introduced, and schools that required pre-medical training were rare indeed. A good 75 per cent of the physicians with whom Charles was to compete would be graduated from schools of lesser quality than the one he attended.

If it had not been for the pre-medical course that Charles himself had devised and taught, and his experience with Dr. Lind, the natural scientist, dogma might have won out over science. As it was, Charles was adept at memorizing the dogma while he applied scientific checks against it wherever possible.

He had to bow to economic reality and get into practice as quickly as he could while he depended upon availing himself of the instruction of the best physicians of Topeka. They could at least suggest courses of reading to follow, and perhaps discuss cases and discoveries with him. He felt sure that the majority were not as incommunicative as Dr. Roby.

When Charles saw patients in the school clinic or hospital, he listened to them attentively and prescribed carefully. His natural optimism brought courage to his patients and he was well liked. But he dreaded the day when he would get his first obstetrical case. In the Hahnemann Hospital he had been allowed only to observe, and of the complications of childbirth he knew little or nothing that he had not learned through incidental reading. So it was with many areas of medicine. In his whole time at medical school he never saw one emergency case and in the clinic most of the patients he saw were suffering from chronic diseases.

Still, there was an excitement in being graduated and in being called Doctor for the first time. As he packed his things and prepared to quit his room he knelt and prayed. His prayer was not that he be allowed to become a great physician, merely that he become a responsible man who would be able to guard against vanity and presumptuousness.

vii

Charles Frederick Menninger, M.D., made an inauspicious entrance into the medical life of Topeka. He was in no sense in practice with Dr. Roby, and his name appeared nowhere except in a paid notice (in which Dr. Roby's name was displayed in huge type, and Charles's in small) where it was announced that DR. ROBY had an assistant. Dr. Menninger's pay was forty dollars a month plus the use of two small rooms behind the doctor's offices. He was to be on call twenty-four hours a day.

In these rooms Flo and Charles set up housekeeping with a one-burner oilstove, some apple boxes for tables and cupboards, and a couple of chairs. They were happy, however, and they had some security. As a schoolteacher—and she continued to teach— Flo earned more than her physician husband did. Children were still held in abeyance until such a time as Charles was really established, perhaps in a partnership with Dr. Roby.

One of the first shocks suffered was in finding that homeopathic physicians were not accepted by other physicians, and that he was therefore cut off from the sources of medical instruction he had hoped for. The reading Dr. Roby suggested was out of date, but slowly Charles found the medical texts that would be helpful to him. Wherever possible he let the cases he saw direct his reading. For example, if a patient with tuberculosis appeared, Charles would read all he could find on that subject and check it against his own findings with the patient. There were evenings when he was so immersed in his books that Flo and he said scarcely two words. He had learned that he couldn't discuss medical practice with her, that it contributed nothing useful to her knowledge, and that such discussions taxed him needlessly. Besides, medicine was an island where he was comparatively free from the pressures of Flo's anxieties. She believed wholeheartedly that Dr. Roby would soon see what an asset he had in young Dr. Menninger and invite him into his practice.

Charles began to discover two things at once: the incredible gullibility of patients and the superb showmanship of his preceptor. Dr. Roby looked the great physician, acted the great physician, dressed the part, and conducted himself with a ponderous and spectacular dignity. The role of physician came naturally to him; he was a good doctor or, at least, he had that reputation. His patients had great faith in him and would accept treatment, however bizarre, should he suggest it.

Soon Charles found that he was not only playing the secondary role that he expected to play, but that he was a sort of stage prop as well. It might happen that he would be asked to examine a patient only to have Dr. Roby step in before he was well started and jovially push him aside while he impressed the patient at Charles's expense. When Charles was allowed to complete examination and treatment he knew that the patient was a man or woman of no status or substance. At times it seemed that Roby was demonstrating that where other physicians might have assistants without medical degrees he, Roby, could afford to have a physician do his menial work for him.

In spite of this obstacle, Charles won the confidence of the patients he did see. He was a good listener, a man who could make people feel his concern for them without frightening them. However minor the complaint, he took a complete history, kept records of the treatment prescribed, and where he could, made at least one call on the patient after he was well. The latter practice was not based on a desire for good will alone, but was a means of keeping clinical records complete and checking results. Soon there were patients who asked for Dr. Menninger instead of for the great Dr. Roby.

As Charles's popularity with patients grew, and as he became more effective, he and Flo became certain that a partnership was not far off. They didn't expect much, perhaps 10 to 15 per cent of the income of the office. A sign, "DR. ROBY AND DR. MENNINGER, Physicians and Surgeons," would be meaningful, too. Then, at last, there could be a house, or rooms away from the office, and perhaps children.

A partnership with Dr. Roby meant different things to Charles and Flo. Charles was never very practical about financial affairs or economic security. He felt keenly that he was not being allowed to develop as a physician, and that Dr. Roby, fearing him as a possible future competitor was withholding instruction and clinical opportunities. Dr. Roby had pushed Charles into his first maternity cases without supervision or instruction and without Charles's even being sure that he could get hold of Dr. Roby should he get into trouble. It went against his nature to have to learn at the patient's expense. But that was the only way he could learn, and the patient's faith in him brought out powers that he didn't know he possessed.

With his first maternity cases Charles had to make one of the great decisions of his life. The patient must always come first; medical cults and ambitions could be dealt with on their own level. In a business sense he was morally and ethically bound to his employer, Dr. Roby. Roby, he knew, would not care to have his assistant admit failure and call for help other than his. This would be true, Charles felt, even if the good doctor were not available. Charles knew that he could not do a Caesarean section or cope with other serious complications. Moreover, he had no faith in the ability of the other homeopathic physicians of the town as obstetricians. Since the homeopaths were ostracized by the allopaths, it would be a cardinal sin to call on one of the latter group, even if that was the only source of competent assistance.

Through discreet inquiry, Charles found out who the best allopathic obstetricians were, and who he could get in touch with quickly; then he went about his work with a clear conscience.

Though Charles dropped hints that the money he was bringing into the office warranted a raise from his forty-dollar-a-month salary and perhaps even a partnership, Dr. Roby ignored the hints but made it clear that Charles was bound to continue under his sponsorship and that their working agreement was a contract that could not be broken. Since Dr. Roby had sponsored Charles and introduced him to the community, he had the right of approval of any plans Charles might wish to make. This, according to Roby, was ethical and just. Hadn't he introduced Charles to his patients and mightn't Charles steal them? Such an attitude was something of a shock to Charles, who had thought of patients only as people whose suffering was to be relieved by whatever man or method. Competition in medicine, when conducted on a business level, was always to puzzle him even when he was forced to enter into it.

Flo, with her practical mind, was able to keep track of the earnings Charles brought into the Roby office. Since they lived on the premises and had access to the books, she also knew approximately what percentage of partnership Charles should have. She encouraged him to come right out and ask for it. But Charles had a streak of caution in him that was coupled with his own sort of practicality. He had made friends with some of the young lawyers of the town, and he consulted them on his legal rights in leaving Dr. Roby. He was informed that he could legally leave the doctor and go into practice on his own if he followed certain procedures. Before asking for a partnership, he had the necessary papers prepared. He had decided that unless he won a partnership, or went on his own, he was doomed as a physician.

There was one thing about Dr. Roby that especially irritated Charles. When the doctor went out of town for any reason he would announce in the papers that he was going to visit whatever medical facilities there were in the vicinity of his destination. Thus every trip took on the appearance of a pilgrimage for knowledge even when this might be far from the case. While he was away, Dr. Roby might farm out his more lucrative patients to his competitors in the homeopathic field, rather than leave them to Charles. In justice to Dr. Roby, he may have believed that these cases should have been in the hands of more experienced men. But Charles had a feeling that economic rather than clinical status determined just which patients should be farmed out.

When Dr. Roby returned from his trips, he invariably called a sign painter and had a notice inscribed on the sidewalk in front of his office in large and often colored letters: "DR. ROBY IS BACK FROM . . ." A well-known medical center would be named. Charles *really* wanted to go to these medical centers; perhaps there was some envy in his resentment of Roby's rather blatant advertising.

viii

Before coming to a showdown with Dr. Roby, Charles and Flo had a serious conference. Flo could continue to teach and, with her small savings, help to finance an office. It hardly seemed that Charles could do worse in private practice. The advantage in staying with Dr. Roby was that Charles might eventually inherit his practice, which was one of the best in the city; in the meantime security would be assured. The arrangement appealed to Flo, but only if Roby would grant a partnership. When every eventuality had been discussed and prepared for, the young couple joined in prayer and turned their problem over to God.

For Charles the idea of going into private practice was a frightening but inviting adventure. He knew very well how ill prepared he was as a physician. Others might be equally ignorant, but they were blessed by not knowing that they were; they could move comfortably within the often lethal limits of professional inadequacy. They were the physicians who could comfort themselves by saying at the deathbed of a patient, "I have done all I know how to do." They would never say, as Charles would, "This is happening because I have not learned all that I could learn. When knowledge exists, and I have neglected to acquire it, I have failed my patient." In a measure, Dr. Roby offered Charles an excuse for not improving himself as a physician, but Charles knew he would be better off and happier without that excuse whatever the other penalties might be.

When young Dr. Menninger confronted Dr. Roby with the proposition that he be taken into partnership, the elder physician gave an indignant snort. "There are young men who would *pay* for the chance I've given you," he said. He went on to say that a raise in salary was a possibility, but a partnership, even on the modest terms which Charles proposed, was out of the question.

This conversation left Charles elated rather than rebuked and rejected. There was no reason to be angry; the outcome was just what he had wanted. Fifty years later he would wonder whether or not he had stacked the cards so that the chances of attaining a partnership were small. Perhaps Dr. Roby's intentions were better than those he credited him with at the time, for certainly the freedom he gave Charles was a greater gift than partnership with him would ever have been.

That evening Flo and Charles went office hunting. Though they tried to be sober and businesslike, they were as excited as children.

CHAPTER THREE

i

CHARLES F. MENNINGER, M.D.
PHYSICIAN & SURGEON

THIS SHINGLE appeared at 727 Kansas Avenue on the last day of August 1890. Protruding from a stairway, the sign was illuminated by night so that no one would have trouble finding the doctor in the event of a nocturnal emergency. Dr. Menninger's living quarters adjoined his offices, and he would be available.

Flo and Charles had looked long and hard to find this office and home. Although the rent was only thirty-five dollars a month, this sum represented two thirds of Flo's salary, the only income the couple could be certain of. Most of their savings had gone for equipment and medicine, but Flo knew that they could live on fifteen dollars a month if they had to. Since the place was their own, it seemed almost like a home; if they wished to entertain friends the reception room could become a living room in the evening.

Charles studied more diligently than ever. He knew that, as a new doctor in the town, and as the only physician available on Topeka's main street, he would have to depend on, and would probably get, emergency cases chiefly. As he awaited such calls he prepared for every conceivable type of emergency—poisonings, knifings, gunshot wounds, fractures, fits, and horse bites. He wanted to be able to address himself to any disaster, group or individual, with assurance and dexterity. Flo's reading was often interrupted as the doctor practiced on her with bandages and splints.

Charles was equally studious about his appearance. Even in the heat of August, he wore a frock coat of heavy woolen material, a batwing collar, and a high hat that acted as a sort of a solar heating unit. For added dignity and discomfort there was a full beard. Neither the clothes nor the beard were an affectation; they were the uniform of the day for the practicing physician. A man in cool clothing and without a beard could not have inspired confidence. Only during surgical procedures and deliveries could the doctor of the nineties divest himself of the heavy coat. Often the stethoscope was carried in the hat simply because there was no room for it in the crowded medical bag. It was routine to carry lancets, thermometers, and percussion hammers in the pockets, along with a hefty pocketknife that could be used for carving splints.

The homeopath's medical bag was well filled; while the doses of drugs might be small, the variety was large, and the physician dispensed his own drugs. Along each side of the bag, vials of medicine were caught like cartridges in bandoleers. Almost all medication was given in the form of sugar pills that had been immersed in a solution of alcohol and a tincture of the drug prescribed. This called for an additional supply of empty bottles. In the center of the bag were the liniments, salves, splints, bandages, and instruments. In a day when hospitals were rarely used, the medical bag brought the hospital into the home. It was a rare physician who didn't walk with something of a list, and Charles had reason to walk with a list. Unable to afford a horse and buggy, he made his calls on foot or by horsecar.

As he had anticipated, most of his first calls were emergencies, but few were in the downtown district. On the outskirts of town were the roadhouses where drunken brawls often resulted in fractures. Dr. Menninger was often called on to treat the wounded, and whatever he may have felt about the combatants' morals, he treated these patients as if they had fallen in honorable battle. His nights of study and practice were rewarded; he was dexterous and assured as he applied splints and bandages. Men who have time to drink also have time to talk; his reputation spread. Patients began to come into his office during the day, and soon he found himself with the nucleus of a practice.

In those days the fee for an emergency call might run as high as two dollars, for an office call one dollar, and for an obstetrical case, which might involve as many as a dozen calls in addition to the delivery, fifteen dollars. Even at these rates Charles did better than he had done when he was working for Dr. Roby. But Flo nervously counted calls and felt certain that such immediate good fortune could not last. She was determined to continue teaching until she was sure that the doctor was established.

ii

When he went into practice on his own, Charles knew that he was making a break with homeopathy, even though he would have to rely upon it to some extent until he had mastered better techniques. Although he did not force himself upon the allopaths of the town, he did call them when he needed a consultant. Physicians who had an opportunity to work with him were impressed by his earnestness and knowledge. Doctors who had ignored him on the streets when he was with Dr. Roby now spoke to him pleasantly, and with one of them, a Dr. McGee, he read and studied pathology. A unique young allopath was pleased to be able to teach him the principles of histology and although he could not become a member of the Shawnee County Medical Society, he was soon invited to attend meetings and was appointed to the staff of Storemont Hospital. It is doubtful that any other man with homeopathic training could ever have broken through the barriers of prejudice, but there was about Charles a sort of an innocence that dissolved prejudice. He believed that the art of healing transcended all sects and schools, and that men could not possibly want to quarrel about anything that might bring health to a sick person.

This is not to say that Charles was utterly blind to the malpractice that went on all around him, either through ignorance or design. He knew that there were men who capitalized on the gullibility of patients, but he simply refused to accept such people as physicians. He was sure that the honest physicians of the community—and they were in the majority—would always win out over the dishonest and incompetent physicians and, through sharing their knowledge, would force the ignorant to improve themselves.

One thing young Dr. Menninger never doubted was the sincerity of the patient. Like all young doctors he got his share of undiagnosable cases, part of the group that wanders from physician to physician in search of relief. As he took the histories of these patients, he learned how wise Dr. Oliver Wendell Holmes had been when he had written, "There is nothing men will not do, there is nothing they have not done to recover their health, and save their lives. They have submitted to being half drowned in water, half choked with gases, to be buried up to their chins in earth, to be seared with hot irons like galley slaves, to be crimped with knives like codfish, to have needles thrust into their flesh, and bonfires kindled on their skins, to swallow all sorts of abominations, and to pay for this: as if to be singed and scalded were a costly privilege, as if blisters were a blessing and leeches a luxury. What more can be asked of them to prove their honesty and sincerity?"

As Charles saw patients who had a long history of surgical and other drastic treatment, and who seemed to have nothing organically wrong with them, he got an inkling of the emotional nature of their illness. Homeopathic training had taught him to be persevering in eliciting symptoms; as patients talked to him he recognized that their emotional suffering was real even if their method of communicating this suffering was not realistic or accurate. He saw, too, that it did them good to talk to him and that often his best role was that of a non-committal listener. Just why this was, he did not quite understand, but he wanted to. He was anxious to learn all available methods of dealing with patients who did not respond to the treatments then in use. He had read, for example, of the work in hypnosis that had been done by the French physician, Charcot and others; the method interested him, but he knew that it would be foolhardy for an isolated Midwestern physician to attempt such an innovation in treatment even if he could find a place to learn the technique.

In dealing with another type of patient that inevitably came to a new doctor, Charles found that his skill as a teacher was useful. These patients were the diabetics who, although they could be treated by diet, were usually pronounced hopeless because of their inability to combat even the most minor infection. When other doctors did treat such patients, they invariably communicated their own feeling of hopelessness, and thus created a deadly psychological situation. When Charles saw his first diabetic he began the study of nutrition, metabolic diseases, and the pathology of the pancreas. It was his belief that diabetes did not have to be a progressive disease, and that with careful diet some of the function of the pancreas could be restored. This belief gave Charles an optimism that transmitted itself to the patients. As a teacher, he was able to give the patient an understanding of his disease, and it was good for diabetics to feel that they had some control over their destiny. "The atmosphere of people getting well," something that was to be given meaning by the Menningers, began to develop in the little office on Kansas Avenue. Charles had not been in practice very long before some of Topeka's best physicians were referring patients to him.

The most disheartening part of medical practice at that time was the diseases of children: meningitis, diphtheria, scarlet fever, typhoid, and the like. Too often the doctor was entirely helpless; the best he could do was to soften the blow that was about to fall on the parents. At such times Charles would silently pray, asking God to lead him further into the light of knowledge and proficiency. It was not easy for him to accept the death of a child as God's will. Needless death was taken by Charles to be a sign of man's imperfection and sloth. Charles's God was not one who would let him say, "I have done all that I could do."

Young Dr. Menninger had a special touch with children. He liked them and they liked him. Instinct told him that the friction between the developing individual and his environment was bound to create some physical fever and revolt. Often the sugar pills he gave were not immersed in a solution of medicine, but were given with a human warmth and understanding that gave them a greater potency than existed in any known medicine.

Homeopathy's greatest gift to Charles was that it made him perpetually aware of his lack of adequate training. A lifetime seemed too short a span in which to catch up. Also, by launching him into his medical career as a member of an unacceptable minority group, it put him on his mettle. Many doctors, graduates of the better schools, hung their diplomas on their walls, content with what they had learned. The only medical meetings they ever attended were class reunions. They were established, secure in their ignorance of new developments, satisfied to cultivate clinical proficiency and nothing more. Charles tended to believe that all new knowledge was something he had been denied because of the inadequacy of his training. Even though he may have been the most progressive physician in Topeka he was always sure that he was merely catching up. There was an engaging humbleness in his quest for further learning; and it was a compliment to his colleagues, since he always seemed to assume that they already had most of what he was trying so hard to acquire. While homeopathic training might well have been disastrous to another man, it was a blessing to Charles, and to his patients.

iii

Dr. Charles Menninger was learning something about loneliness, as well. He did not find the companionship he had expected with other physicians, and he knew that he would never be able to talk to anyone about his own troubles and difficulties. When he became a physician he accepted the lonely role of always being the one to whom others appealed for help of every sort. He had learned also that his manner must be reassuring to others and that his own troubles or loneliness must never be evident. If he mentioned to Flo anything that troubled him, she always suggested prayer and he did find some solace in praying with her. She had endured so much that any complaint he might have seemed inconsequential.

Although Flo and Charles were putting their extra money into a brown jug in the hope of eventually getting a house of their own and a place to have children, other things came first. For example, Flo's brother, Dave, had to be put through veterinary college. The couple had great hopes for this boy and wanted the best for him. It was as if a debt to Elmer were being paid through him, and anything they could contribute brought satisfaction.

Often, in the evening, Charles would look up from the book he was studying and gaze at Flo's face. Always he was moved. He loved her and he knew that in her own way she loved him. Even the anxiety she showed over the number of patients he saw and the income for the month was part of what he loved. He wanted to be able to calm her anxiety and would, indeed, feel some guilt until he could. Flo's valiance in the face of many hardships wrung his heart, and he hoped for the day when security and plenty would enable her to share with him a closer emotional relationship.

Flo's constant drive onward and upward had made her into something of a zealot. Although she was kind and generous to people who were in need, she had little patience with ordinary human weaknesses and no time at all for social niceties. Every minute had to be spent productively, and in this he was growing like her; moments of lightness were becoming rare. Even if he looked at Flo too long and too tenderly, he would come to feel that he had given way to a wasteful tendency. If she noticed him looking at her, she would ask whether something was wrong or whether there was anything she could do so that he might be able to get on with his studying.

The gestures of affection that Flo made were small and timid, but each one could sustain him for days. Charles had a great deal of impersonal love to give to people; it went out to all his patients; he was a man with an abundance of kindness, concern, and warmth.

Once Dr. Menninger's ideal physician had been the learned man, the scholar, and to a certain extent this idea still prevailed. In his relationships with people he was usually the teacher; his conversation was never aimless, but was always a teaching or learning opportunity which he skillfully exploited. Those who could not instruct him received instruction from him on whatever subject came to hand. He could laugh as well as the next man at a good story well told, and he could accept friendly banter in good grace, but he could never remember or repeat a story unless it could be used to make a point. The young business- and professional men of the town liked to have him as a luncheon companion because he listened as well as he talked. When there were controversial discussions, he was likely to take the most progressive view. Politically, he was not a party man; he was moved by issues. He came out strongly against the high tariff that was killing international competition and creating monopolies in America. It seemed to him that this tariff was also threatening the exchange of knowledge between nations. He was informed and articulate about this subject, as he was about women's rights. Although Charles was thought by some to be a prude, there was one luncheon where he was the sole defender of Walt Whitman who was at that time accused of being an "obscene monster."

iv

   One of Charles's diversions was the Topeka Saturday Night Club, a group of young professional men who met to read their literary productions and debate current topics. Flo did not object to this organization as she did to fraternal orders, which she would never let Charles join. In her mind, besides being a waste of time and money, secret orders were related to the anti-Christ.

When Charles's turn to read a paper to the club approached, he decided that he would attempt to explore the human mind by doing a literary analysis of some great figure in literature. Although he had seen only one or two psychotic patients, he was becoming aware of the as yet unrecognized borderland of neurosis that existed between the psychosis and normality. While he was in medical school, and even before that, *Hamlet* had had a peculiar fascination for Charles. He had tried earnestly to understand the prince. Now the study of medicine had brought some of his ideas about Hamlet into sharper focus. Before he could do Hamlet justice, however, he needed a mentor with a knowledge of mental illness. With this in mind, he sought out Dr. B. D. Eastman, the superintendent of Topeka State Hospital for the mentally ill.

A doubly fortunate relationship grew out of his meeting with Dr. Eastman. When Charles went to call on the doctor, he found him selecting trees to be planted on the hospital grounds. Eastman was not the naturalist that Charles was, and in the younger doctor he found an eager assistant for his project of landscaping. In every hour Charles could spare from his practice, he was out at the hospital helping Dr. Eastman with his plantings. As the two men worked they would discuss mental illness, while Charles also observed and talked with the patients who were helping them.

When Dr. Charles Menninger began his study of the insanity of Hamlet in 1890, he found an abundance of literary material, but nothing that resembled a psychiatric study. There was, in fact, no medical text that could offer him any guidance in diagnosing the prince's malady. Kraepelin's work, which was to give descriptive psychiatry a base, had not yet been published in English. Dr. D. Hack Tuke's *Dictionary of Psychological Medicine* was not to be published for two years. The neurologists who then dominated American psychiatry held that insanity could be accounted for only by brain lesions, and for this reason most research into mental illness was done on the autopsy table. It is likely that Charles Menninger read of the work of Charcot in the newspapers rather than in medical publications. Although he subscribed to German medical journals very early in his career, it seems impossible that he could have heard of the work of Freud at a time when many of Freud's colleagues in Vienna had not heard of him. Though Dr. Eastman seems to have been a good physician and a man of good will, he made no pretense of understanding the mechanism underlying mental illness.

There was one school of thought, in medicine and out of it, that held that mental illness was inherited. At that time mental deficiency was not, as a rule, separated from other mental disorders. Thus, schizophrenia could often pass for idiocy, especially in a time when no case histories were kept. While Dr. Menninger may have appeared to lean toward the theory that mental illness might be inherited, it was clear from his paper on Hamlet that he meant that it was inherited not so much through physiological characteristics as through the hereditary environment. It is to be remembered that at his valedictory address he had blamed the parents rather than the young for the failure of the young to carry through.

As Charles worked on his paper, *The Insanity of Hamlet*, he seems to have been summing up the random thoughts of many years. Tendencies he had noted in himself and others, happenings in the courts, case histories that led inevitably to the last threshold of the consciousness and then stopped before a labyrinth, and his observation of children—these all contributed to his conjectures about Hamlet. Medical discipline had given him a method. Perhaps he felt, in some idealistic way, that the humanistic physician should interest himself in the curious workings of the human mind.

Certainly he had been offended by the view of many lay critics
who held that Hamlet had been feigning insanity. Charles did not
like the word "feign" to be applied to any disease, mental or
physical. He felt that men did the things they had to do in order
to be able to live at all, and that a man who was in a position
to have to feign was indeed ill, even if his illness had neither
name nor status.

Dr. Menninger read *The Insanity of Hamlet* to his club on Saturday night, October 18, 1890—an event which might be considered in effect to mark the debut of the name of Menninger
in the field of psychiatry. The tall and handsome young physician
probably made more of an impression with his bearing and with
the gentleness of his spirit, however, than he did with his speech.
He himself had no way of knowing the scope of his insight as
he said:

"Life in all of its forms, physical and mental, morbid and
healthy, is a relation; its phenomena result from the reciprocal
action of an individual organism and of external forces; health
is the consequence and the evidence of successful adaptation to
the conditions of existence . . . while disease marks a failure in
organic adaptation to external conditions and leads to disorder,
decay and death. The harmonious relation existing between the
organism and its environment, which is the condition of health,
may be disturbed either (1) by a cause in the organism (2) by a
cause in the environment (3) by a cause or causes in both. . . .
Great mistakes are often made, even by men of culture, in fixing
upon supposed causes of disease in particular cases. A single event
is selected as in itself effective to explain the whole disaster, when
that event alone was merely one of a whole train of causes. A
series of external events in concurrence with steadily operating
conditions within—but not a single event—an accident, a sorrow,
or need, or adversity—can all be regarded as adequate cause for
insanity . . . The seeds of insanity are often latent in the foundation of the character—may reach back through a lifetime or have
their roots in a foregoing generation. *Man gets much from his
parents in addition to the spark of life.**

"His father, his mother, are latent and declare themselves
within him: and it is upon lines thus laid on his nature that he

* The italics are mine. W.W.

will proceed. What would you think of a child's nervous make-up and mental equilibrium whose mother, upon the sudden death of her husband whom she loved to extremes, would marry in indecent haste her late husband's brother in name but not in quality of person or character? Would it be likely that we would find a well-balanced mind in the son of this mother who would urge him to join her in marriage festivities and rejoicings '. . . Ere yet the salt of most unrighteous tears had left the flushing in her galled eyes . . .'?"

After establishing the right of an organism, named Hamlet, to refuse to adapt to its turbulent environment, Charles Menninger attacked such thinkers as Dr. Samuel Johnson and Coleridge for suggesting that Hamlet had simulated insanity. "Without a single adequate reason," Charles said, "this notion has been handed down, like an heirloom, from one critic to another."

Charles attacked this subject with intensity; the source of his intensity must have puzzled him.

"The character and conduct of Hamlet are in the strictest accordance with the principles of human nature. Hamlet was no automaton but a living, human soul and, as in the cases of most distinguished men, his character is not easily read. The integrity of his chain of thought is marred by some intrusion of disease— the strong, deep current of his feelings is turned to eddies and whirlpools under its influence and his solemn undertakings are conducted to abortive issues. His clearest perceptions, his holiest purposes, his strongest determinations are followed by doubts, apprehensions and scruples that torment and distract the disordered mind. While his whole soul is occupied with the idea of revenge, he is forever finding excuses for postponing the moment of execution, constantly turning from his purpose by the merest whim and justifying his conduct by reasons too flimsy to satisfy any but a disordered intellect.

"His very remark, 'to put an antic disposition on' upon which the theory of Hamlet's insanity being feigned is mainly founded, indicates at most but an indefinite, half-formed resolve to accomplish a purpose by simulating a disease that was really overshadowing his spirit in all of its fearful reality. The final event of the piece most aptly finishes the story of Hamlet's irresolution, his vacillation, his forereaching plans, his inadequate performance.

The nearest object of his heart, revenge of his father's wrong—is at last accomplished, but by means of a contrivance he had no part in effecting. Such is the nature of insanity—to talk but not to act, to resolve but never execute, to support the soundest projects for action by the most imperfect performances."

As Charles defined the nature of mental illness in his last sentence, some of his audience must have been looking inward with a questioning glance, just as he must have at some time glanced inward at his own processes. Although the signs and symptoms of schizophrenia, or dementia praecox, had not yet been isolated from the chaos of mental aberration in general, Dr. Menninger on that night came near to doing so. At one place he said, "In the tumult of strange and contending emotions he [Hamlet] has lost the power of speech, for he has already lost the power to think and feel like himself . . . Insanity brings a change over the warmest affections of the heart and though it continues among men it is no longer of them. The fury and extravagance of mania, the moodiness of melancholia, Hamlet might successfully mimic; but to do violence to his affections, to desecrate and trample his idol that he had enshrined in his heart of hearts—this was beyond the power of mimicry."

Now in retrospect it is clear that the man who delivered that paper on *The Insanity of Hamlet* had a talent for and an attraction to psychiatry. At the time the paper was delivered, however, Dr. Charles Menninger's chief interest was in how best to improve himself as a general practitioner. Every spare moment was spent in reading and laboratory work that would enable him more adequately to meet the demands of the patients he was seeing. Because of his work with diabetic patients, nutrition was the chief study of this period, and Charles longed to go East where he could meet with the men who were doing outstanding work in this field. In the meantime he would study everything they had written and he was not shy about writing to them if he needed further information.

The biggest disappointment of this period was the discovery that other physicians were not always eager to share experiences. For example, Charles Menninger might be treating fifteen out of possibly one hundred and fifty cases of diabetes in Topeka. When he learned something that was of value in treating his patients he would have liked to share his experience with other physicians, and he would especially have liked to know how they handled certain situations. Although a paper on diabetes might be read at a medical association meeting and arouse some discussion, it was impossible to organize a meeting of the doctors who had a special interest in diabetes. At first Charles thought that this might be because of his homeopathic training, but when he attempted to organize meetings among the homeopathic physicians he had no better luck than with the allopaths. Slowly it grew upon him that medicine was competitive, and that few physicians wanted to share the discoveries that gave them superiority over others.

Medical practice in that day was at a junction in its history. While the road of scientific medicine seemed clearly defined and sure in direction, the general practice of medicine often followed trails that were known to lead to dead ends. Stubborn men persisted in using methods that had been proven not only to be of no value in the treatment of disease but often deadly in themselves. Such men could still dominate the medical community, and often did. Though no longer universal, bleeding was still practiced and leeches were used. It was not uncommon for an older physician, calling on a patient with abdominal pains, to place the patient in a chair, have a tin bucket and a glass of warm water brought in, then pull a stone of antimony, the *emetica eterna*, from his vest pocket and have the patient swallow it along with the warm water. In a few moments violent vomiting would ensue while the physician listened attentively for the clink on the bottom of the bucket that would tell him that his stone had been returned and could be used again on another unfortunate patient. If an appendix had been ruptured by this process, the physician would say that he had done all he could. As, indeed, he had. Such practices had to continue until the practitioners of the ancient arts of bleeding and purging died off.

Things were not as bad in Topeka as they were in many other parts of the country; in truth, Topeka seems to have been more receptive than most cities in accepting and furthering modern medical practice. There were physicians whom Charles sincerely admired, and who helped him. Dr. S. G. Stewart, whom Dr. C.F. respected above all other Topeka physicians, was a man he found always eager to share clinical knowledge. The friendship was professional rather than personal and was to last throughout the lives of both men.

Since Flo Menninger was a favorite teacher of the children as well as an educator who had attracted city-wide attention, it was only natural that parents should call in her husband when they needed a doctor. Without especially wishing to, Charles soon found that he was becoming something of a pediatrician and soon he was seeing more children than adults. The mortality rate among children was horrifying at that time. There was no such thing as a simple childhood disease. There were no antibiotics, no sulfa, not even aspirin. The best the physician could hope for was to bring a disease to a speedy crisis, while keeping up the child's strength and spirit as best he could.

In a time when the diseases of childhood were notoriously fatal, the panic and foreboding of the parents created a bad psychological situation in the child. Something resembling a deathbed scene often greeted Charles when he called at the home of a sick child. When the child should be resting it would have to suffer from being passed from the hands of one parent to the other as they held it to them in a parting grief. The doctor was called only as a duty; the parents expected no positive help. The child was ill, and scared out of its wits as well.

Charles appears to have been born with a nature that would not accept any situation as hopeless. He believed in life; he was optimistic about it. So long as there was breath there was hope, and he managed to convey this hope to others. As quickly as he could, he gave the child something to live for, if only a sugar pill. Wherever possible he put the parents to working on the side of life, preparing cool compresses, fixing a more comfortable bed, and cooking foods that the child could take. He let them know that he was not the forerunner of the undertaker they had expected, and that he would be with them as long as he was needed and on constant call. Many a time, he would spend the whole of the night with a child. Just at the moment when the child needed it, something dependable, hopeful, and warm had come into its life, and that child would not be returned to the parents until they had come to share the attitude of the physician. Again, an atmosphere of a patient getting well was created.

Most of the children Charles was called upon to treat lived, and often he did not know why. Certainly the medicines and techniques he had were inadequate to the situations he often found. In diphtheria, for example, it was hard even to be hopeful. When a child was strangling to death there was not much that could be done to reassure the parents, and the doctor's own helplessness could not fail to show. Fortunately Charles read an early report on the success of intubation—the forcing of a rubber tube into the child's throat so that it might breathe. When he discussed this method with Dr. Stewart, he found that equipment was available and quickly obtained a tube. Then, with the unstinting help of Dr. Stewart, he mastered the technique of intubation.

On his next diphtheria case Charles was met at the gate by a distraught father. "It's no use, Doctor," the father said. "You might as well go home. The child is strangling."

"Is he still alive?" Charles asked.

"Yes," the father said, "but don't torture him. Let his mother have her last few minutes with him."

"The child will live," Charles said, forcing his way past the father.

Ten minutes later the child was not only alive but was reaching for a toy Charles held out to it.

Intubation is forgotten now, but in those days it could make a doctor appear to be a god. But before Charles had learned of intubation, one or two local physicians had known of this lifesaving method and had used it to build their practices.

Before his first year of practice had run out, Charles was often called to see the children of other physicians. Most of the medical world of Topeka had forgotten that he had been a homeopath.

v

The struggle that came during Charles's first year of medical practice was not of the sort he and Flo had expected. Very early in that year he had had to buy a bicycle on which to make his calls. That in itself was a major investment and one that worried Flo, who could not believe that business could continue at the rate that made such an investment essential. The practice grew, and with the coming of the first snow and sleet, the bicycle was useless. For a time Charles made what calls he could by horsecar. But this means of travel was slow and the dirt streets of Topeka didn't help. Every few blocks the wheelboxes of the cars would clog with mud that had to be cleaned away while the passengers waited. Although Charles started a campaign for better streets for the city, that didn't help him in getting to his patients. In some emergencies he had to hire a rig from the livery stable and he couldn't very well charge the patient what this cost him. A doctor was expected to have good transportation.

There was a prolonged conference and much prayer before the savings in the brown jug were spent for a horse and buggy. Flo was still sure that their early good fortune could not last. When the horse and buggy had to be bought on time she was made extremely nervous; she had seen enough of debt and mortgages to have reason to be apprehensive. But, much to her surprise and delight, the rig was quickly paid for and she was proud of her husband's equipment.

As Charles's obstetrical and pediatric work grew it became necessary that someone be in the office to take calls while he was out. Flo was at school most of the day and could not do this. It appeared to Flo, and rightly, that having to hire a girl for the office constituted a direct threat to her own salary. A girl would cost at least half of what she herself earned. But if she were to quit teaching and stay in the office, she would be taking an equal cut. So a girl was hired. She was Sadie Dunn, a young woman who was to be Dr. Menninger's receptionist for the next sixteen years.

Charles's confidence was growing; his earnings were much greater than Flo's now, and he saw that he could well afford the expenditures that had seemed so hazardous. One of his great delights was to be able to buy things for Flo—a book, a picture, a knickknack. He loved to give her the little things that she had missed in life. To Flo these gifts were at once a delight and tokens of bad omen, for the thoughtful lover was also, in her eyes, a spendthrift. Tears of joy became tears of apprehension and Charles had to choose between the anxiety that sharpened his impulse to give and the guilt that came from giving. His choice was always the former. He had to believe in his masculine right and ability to give presents, and in Flo's willingness to accept them. Though Flo's excessive anxiety might well have tried the patience of another man, Charles was never perturbed. He listened to her fears and, when he could, attempted to calm them.

There is no doubt that Flo acted as a very necessary check on Charles's tendency toward extravagance or that she had real reasons for alarm. Until he had met Flo, Charles had never really known poverty; the necessities of life were always something that were dependably there. Charles liked good things, fine clothes, good equipment, the best magazines. When they had dinner out, and could afford it, he liked the better places. His bicycle had to be of the best make, and when he bought a horse and buggy, the animal and rig were something to be proud of. The young doctor was not pretentious; he was merely following his nature. He was fastidious about his person, and he believed that the physician should set an example to the community.

Where Charles was the aristocrat, Flo was the peasant. She knew the amount of money required to purchase every item of food and clothing and she knew that she would be free from serfdom only so long as she had the capacity to work and earn that money. *Culture* awed her; it was self-improvement, a form of prayer, really. She couldn't believe that one simply enjoyed a book, a painting, or a musical composition. One learned from it and then taught; there was a moral issue involved, a climb from darkness into the light. It was as if a new and essential crop had to be tilled, harvested, stored, and depended upon for life and strength. Flo would always be doubtful about anything that was persistently joyous. She was suspicious of any sort of display; to be fashionable was not, in her mind, a way of bettering oneself. She dressed plainly, shunned even such cosmetics as were then in use, and while she was proud of her husband she had no desire to be his match in elegance or manner. Seriousness was her forte.

In the matter of church affiliation, Charles and Flo struck a compromise. Because some Lutherans could drink and play cards, Flo mistrusted that church; on the other hand, she could not quite see Charles shining in the glum fundamentalism of the River Brethren. And so the Presbyterian Church was chosen as being comfortably in between, a pew was rented, and attendance was as regular as Charles's practice would allow. Flo was accepted into the social life of the church.

When she was invited to a large reception that was being given by a rich woman who had recently bought a house on Topeka Avenue, Flo protested to friends that she had no clothes for such a function. It never occurred to her that she should buy any, and she accepted the invitation only after she was assured that her ordinary clothes would be all right. This reception was a revelation to her. She was amazed at the amount of money that had gone into beautiful gowns, entranced with the décor and the spaciousness of the house, and, like an anthropologist visiting a strange and remote island, she studied the polite and empty conversation. The experience was entirely educational. Flo estimated the amount of money that had been spent for refreshments and wondered at the waste. She especially noted that there was no program and that the music that was constantly played was wasted because no one thought to explain it. The rooms were decorated with hundreds of roses, and when Flo left she took one and preserved it. At least she had something to show for her afternoon. Her first reception had been exciting, but not in the way it was for others.

Flo and Charles's social life was quite restricted, but in spite of this Charles became physician to some of the leading citizens of the town. Among them were Charles Kendall, the owner and operator of Kendall's Opera House, A. D. Robbins, a leading dry goods merchant, and Edward Wilder, an official of the Santa Fe and a leading businessman. When Wilder chose Charles as his physician, so did many other officials of the Santa Fe Railroad. Without any social climbing, and with none of the usual political maneuvering, young Dr. Menninger came to be not only accepted but depended upon by Topeka society.

Charles was also family physician to the T. E. Bowmans, an Eastern family which became prominent in Topeka's business life. One of the Bowmans' sons was Karl, who later became one of America's leading psychiatrists. The Popenoe family was related to the Bowmans, and one of its sons also made a name in the field of psychology. Dr. Samuel J. Crumbine, a physician who later attained a national reputation, was a great admirer of Charles Menninger.

Charles won acceptance not only because he was better educated than most Topeka physicians, but also because he was far more gentle and courteous than most. His seriousness inspired confidence. Both men and women felt that they could trust him and never hesitated to ask his advice in personal matters. He seemed to have a maturity that exceeded anything his personal experiences could have taught him. Although most people did not recognize it, his greatest asset was the quality of listening. Through talking to him, people heard and understood themselves for the first time. He was devoid of that anxiety that makes so many physicians feel that they must have prompt and ponderous answers for all questions or must at least make platitudinous suggestions; he knew that if you let people talk long enough they will answer their own questions and be the better for it. No matter how busy he might be, he was careful never to give the impression that he was hurried.

Charles's fees remained modest, but by the spring of 1891 the horse and buggy had been paid for and $300 had been saved. He was impatient to have a home of his own and tired of the winter days when the family wash had to be hung in the reception room of their office home. Flo wanted a home, too, but the idea of a mortgage terrified her. And once the home was established, children would be expected and her teaching career would be over. As it then seemed to Flo, Charles's success kept them in constant jeopardy. When she finally agreed to sign the papers for purchase of a little cottage at 1270 Topeka Avenue, she knew that she was taking one of the great steps of her life. There was much involved that Charles could not understand, and perhaps would never fully understand.

Flo remembered the little farm that her father and mother had happily bought and eagerly improved; then had come more children, her father's cancer and horrible death, and the debt-ridden grief of her mother. Flo knew all the horrors of having to depend on relatives, the humiliation of becoming a servant, and the widow's bitter and losing fight for independence for herself and her children. Only in Flo had that independence been achieved, and now she was to give it up. The papers that Charles happily brought home were much more than a mortgage to her. Only a courage that she had not known she possessed made her sign them.

CHAPTER FOUR

i

THE COTTAGE at 1270 Topeka Avenue consisted of one bedroom, a kitchen, and a combined living and dining room. There was no bath or back porch, and no barn for the horse. Charles's office remained at 727 Kansas Avenue. Flo was still teaching, having transferred to Garfield School, which was much nearer home, and she devoted all her free time to furnishing the house. As she bought furniture, made curtains, and laid carpets, her joy was overshadowed by a constant apprehension that the mortgage could not be paid. Over and over Charles had to say, "We can do it. I can pay for it." Though Flo tried to believe him, she could not still her ancient doubts.

Charles was so excited over acquiring a home and at last being able to start a family that he was not fully aware of the depth of Flo's anxieties. When she was most worried, he gave gifts in the greatest profusion. He wooed Flo as if she were a bride, but he was so busy that he often misunderstood her responses. He had to get up at five-thirty in the morning in order to go to the barn a block or two away and see that his horse was ready for his early calls. When he started a garden, which he did at the first opportunity, he often had to do his planting and spading by lantern light. His working day was so long that when he could persuade Flo to accompany him on a call, he was proud and delighted.

Before Flo had accommodated herself to the debt that was already contracted, Charles was planning improvements. His practice was growing, and his optimism with it. Flo, who had thought to teach school for at least two more years—a time in which her own earnings would have paid for the house—found that her income was no longer needed. There was no logical reason for putting off a family. Soon the decision of whether or not to teach school was taken out of her hands.

In December of 1892, Flo gave up a teaching career that had begun in 1879. She was twenty-nine years old; almost fourteen years of teaching were behind her. In that time her income as a teacher had saved her mother's farm, fed and educated her brothers and her sister, and had put her through college and her husband through medical school and early medical practice. For the first time since she was fifteen years old she had given up her independence. Furthermore, she felt that her pregnancy was a physical handicap.

Charles knew that Flo could not immediately settle down to the life of a housewife; at once he set about giving her something to do. The cottage was all but paid for, and it was now safe to improve it. Almost from the day she left school, Charles had Flo planning and directing the improvements that needed to be made. A larger kitchen, a porch, and a small bedroom were added, while she directed the workmen. When those were finished, a barn was built. But every time the school bells rang, Flo was reminded that the schools were going on without her. It didn't seem just or even possible. In spite of the fact that she should have had everything to be happy for, she was often depressed.

Thinking to allay Flo's distress, Charles bought books for her —the best sellers of the day—Holmes's *Guardian Angel, The Little Journey* series, and works on the Pre-Raphaelites; they offered self-improvement as well as entertainment. But Flo continued moody. A piano was rented, and a Miss Chamberlain was called in to give Flo lessons. At this point Flo's hands became numb. It was impossible for her to play the piano and nearly impossible for her to sew.

Flo's best times were in the mornings when she could accompany Charles on his rounds. She could then see the strength and assurance with which he addressed himself to sometimes hopeless situations. This made her immensely proud of him and glad to be his wife. He was very gentle with her and suggested that she have a woman in to help her during the last two months of her pregnancy. This Flo would not have—the idea that she should pay anyone to serve her seemed ridiculous.

On July 21, 1893, Charles took Flo for a long ride with him in the evening. He could not neglect his patients and he could not leave her alone. The night seemed endless, and the next morning Charles called another doctor to take over his patients as he sat with Flo. He had already obtained the services of the best obstetrician in town. The heat was oppressive and almost unbearable, and the labor was delayed. Then in the late afternoon of July 22 a boy was born. Big and healthy, he was given a robust name—Karl Augustus Menninger.

On that July evening it seemed to Flo and Charles that everything they had planned and hoped for had come to them. Excusing himself to make a call, Charles indulged in a clandestine passing out of cigars that Flo would have completely disapproved.

ii

Throughout the summer of 1893 the heat was continuous and oppressive. Both mother and child had a rash that only cool weather could relieve. Flo still resisted having a hired girl, so Charles hired a man to care for his horse and drive for him in order that he might be able to spend more time with his wife and child. But his presence was as much a threat to their peace as was his absence. He had a phone installed in the bedroom; just as mother and child were getting to sleep it would ring. If it didn't ring, Flo would worry for fear not enough money was coming in. Late summer in Topeka can be a fretful time even under the best circumstances; tempers often break before the weather does. Without rains to freshen the water supply, typhoid was a constant threat, and brought the young physician practice that he would have been glad to do without. Nevertheless, he remained calm and even optimistic with his patients and with his family. He never had to walk the floor with his son for long. His assurance seemed to flow into the boy and calm him. At times Charles's serenity was trying to Flo.

In the fall Dave Knisely was graduated from veterinary school, and Charles had a job waiting for him with the state veterinarian.

Dave had married while he was in school and he brought his bride, Laura, to Topeka with him. No sooner had they arrived than a child arrived too. Flo and Charles enjoyed having the young couple in of an evening. Then, just as the cool weather came, and Flo and little Karl were free of the rash, Dave and Laura came down with typhoid and had to be moved into the little cottage to convalesce. Two sick people and an extra child were too much even for Flo. Mother Knisely was sent for, and arrived just in time to take her son and his motherless child home with her.

In one of his attempts to counteract the effect of this disaster on Flo, Charles bought one of the first phonographs ever brought to Topeka, acquired the best possible records, and attempted to interest her in the study of music. This was partially successful. When friends were asked in to hear the records, Flo could tell them about the composers, the artists, and the intent of the music. Here was entertainment with a purpose, something she understood and could study. On one ambitious evening eight people were asked in for dinner and music, but Charles was called out, and Flo began to learn that she would have to do most of her entertaining without him. It saddened her to think that he could not share the things that meant so much to him, but she became an excellent reporter, able to repeat almost word for word the conversations that had taken place during his absence. Charles listened proudly.

The happiest event of the fall was the arrival of Grandmother and Grandfather Menninger. When the child was born they forgave Flo for her narrow attitude toward wine. In spite of his troubled beginnings Karl had grown into a big and seemingly healthy baby and Father Menninger had to be restrained from carrying him wherever he went. It seemed to him that his physician son and his grandson had crowned his life. Before the elder Menningers went back to Tell City, they inscribed their names in a family Bible and presented it to the young couple. Flo now felt at one with the warm and ebullient German in-laws.

iii

Soon after acquiring the cottage, Charles set up a more complete laboratory in his offices. He wanted to spend every moment he could with his wife and child, but he recognized that if he was to continue his studies he needed a place of his own. There were times when Flo's anxiety could keep him from concentrating. When he enlarged the laboratory he bought himself a long, white, silk laboratory coat; he found it comforting to get out of his heavy Prince Albert and into it.

Where the doctor of today takes care of most of his patients in a hospital and makes comparatively few house calls, the doctor of Charles's time had to treat most of his patients in their homes. Since there were no really well-trained nurses, and many of the patients in the homes were extremely ill, the conscientious physician had to call often in order to be sure that the patient was getting the proper care. There was no such thing as making a few notes on a chart, writing some orders, and then forgetting about the patient until the next day's ward rounds. Charles might have to make as many as four calls a day on pneumonia cases.

At one time Charles had three deliveries to make within a matter of hours, and all were made in homes. In these cases the doctor had to be prepared to act swiftly and decisively if complications arose. There was no such thing as a transfusion; sugar water given by mouth was the only method of replacing lost body fluids. Even though he had called in the best obstetrician in the city, Charles lost his first case of *placenta privia*—a situation in which the placenta blocks the delivery. The woman had lost too much blood; had he been able to act more swiftly and skillfully, she might have lived. As he made his rounds Charles would think of all the ways in which this case might have been handled and would rehearse in his mind the manipulations he planned to use on the next case. *Placenta privia* was rare, and skill in the handling of such cases certainly would not help his practice; patients had a way of blaming the physician for complications like that. But even if he got only one more case in his lifetime Charles wanted to be able to cope with it. As chance would have it, he got two more cases fairly close together and in both saved mother and child.

Charles gave himself completely to such problems. Many were the techniques he learned, rehearsed, and never used. Knowing that he could use them, however, gave him security. Whenever another doctor had a case from which Charles could learn anything, and would allow him to observe, time or expense were no object. When he had an opportunity to teach it was the same. Charles often referred patients to other doctors simply because he had to have time for learning as well as practice.

The young physician also had a tendency to spend what some doctors would have thought to be an excessive amount of time with patients, but Charles's conscience demanded that he take time to make the most thorough examination of which he was capable and keep the best possible history of each case. Even when his practice was large he still took time to check on patients after they had recovered. No prescription was ever written without a duplicate being kept, even when this meant time-consuming copying.

In his first years of practice Charles was as much in demand as any physician in Topeka. There were times when it was physically impossible to keep up his standards and see more patients than he was seeing. In the typhoid and pneumonia seasons he often worked around the clock; at such times a house call that could absorb as much as two hours of his time in driving and treatment would bring in less than five dollars. In a peak month Charles might take in as much as $450 while in the healthier seasons of the year his income might be half that, or less.

During the dull months Charles wanted to go East to familiarize himself with the latest developments in medicine. Even though it may have seemed like a needless expense, when considered from the point of view of his income from diabetic patients, Charles went to Cornell Medical School to study nutrition and metabolism, and at once he shared what he had learned with the local medical group. With one or two diehard exceptions, the members of the Shawnee County Medical Society now accepted him, even though he was still not admitted to membership.

The University of Kansas, located in Lawrence, Kansas, had no medical school at this time. In order to remedy this lack a group of Topeka physicians established their own medical school in affiliation with Washburn College, a small liberal arts school that was located in Topeka. This medical school, which was operated in a ramshackle building adjoining a livery stable, was later to become the medical school of the University of Kansas, but in the 1890s the Topeka medical group kept it going by contributing both teaching time and money. Because of the limited means at its disposal, the clinical and laboratory facilities of this school were even less adequate than those of Hahnemann. There were, however, some good teachers, especially among the younger doctors of Topeka who had attended the better medical schools of the East.

Although Charles was probably better prepared to teach most of the subjects offered than were the professors of the school, he enrolled at Washburn as a pupil and took all of the courses in which he considered himself deficient. Since the doctors of the town worked together at the school, Charles found some of the professional companionship he had missed elsewhere. The situation was strange in that he already had a better practice than most of his teachers. Some of these men could not understand his hunger for learning. Whenever there were medical conventions at which important papers might be read he attended them, going as far as Detroit. He took Flo with him to one convention.

Before leaving for the convention, Charles had made reservations at one of the better hotels of the city, a place where most of the doctors would be staying. Karl had been left with a nurse, and Charles wanted to give Flo a holiday in the most pleasant surroundings. As they got on the train in Topeka, just before lunch time, Charles tipped the porter rather well for carrying their bags and getting them pillows for the coach seats. This brought the first signs of displeasure from Flo. She couldn't understand tipping in the first place, and fifty cents was half of what the doctor got for an office call. Charles mumbled something about a physician having to keep up his standing, but Flo answered that this could be done by an example of conservative expenditure.

"Let's have a nice lunch," Charles said as a waiter came through, announcing that luncheon was served. Flo agreed. The style of the dining car brought out the quality of childish delight that Charles loved in her. Then when the menu came and Flo saw the prices, she paled and seemed to freeze. "What's the matter?" Charles asked, alarmed.

"I'm ill. I have to get back to our seat," Flo said in panic. Charles understood. With Flo in this state there was no use in attempting to eat. He surreptitiously left a tip for the waiter, who had only had a chance to serve them water, and then escorted her back to their seat.

In the doorway of the great hotel Flo froze again.

"We can't afford this," she protested. "I couldn't sleep here, knowing what it costs and how much we need the money for other things."

"But I've already reserved our room," Charles said. "We can afford to treat ourselves once in a while."

"Perhaps if you give them just a little money they won't hold you to your reservation," Flo pleaded. "We can find a much cheaper place. Why, this hotel would cost more than we took in in a whole week in the boardinghouse."

Again Charles gave way to Flo's panic over the expenditure of money. It wasn't a thing he could get angry with or quarrel about. At this moment her mother could use any money they could send her, and it was true that they had debts and their savings were small. At the expense of a pride that he felt guilty in having, Charles canceled the reservations and took Flo to a cheaper place. They had their meals in the least-expensive restaurants, away from where the other physicians dined, and Flo happily went to museums while Charles attended the professional meetings. But there was one expenditure against which Flo made no protest. An opera was being performed, and when Charles got tickets for it she never asked the price. Culture and self-improvement were a good investment. The opera was the high point of the trip.

In the more than fifty years of marriage that were to come the incident on the train and at the hotel was to be repeated many times. Charles would never believe that Flo would not enjoy the things he planned for her, and she would never believe that they could afford them. It probably never occurred to either of them that perhaps the strongest emotional motivation behind this seeming frugality was that Flo would never really think that she be-

longed in dining cars or in the great hotels and, indeed, she
cultivated a style of dress that would have made her seem odd in
such places.

In winter when Charles would be out making calls far into the
cold nights, he often looked into the windows of the houses he
passed and saw men luxuriously lounging before the fire, wearing
smoking jackets, enjoying their pipes. To the tired and cold physician these glimpses of the warmth and comfort of other homes
came to be a personal dream. Charles had no hope of ever being
allowed to smoke a pipe—his compromise was to chew gum, the
Kiss Me brand, popular in that day—but he did have a vision of
himself in a smoking jacket. It even seemed to him that Flo might
like to give him one as a gift, and so he confided his fantasy to
her.

Had Charles asked that a bar be installed in the house, Flo
could not have been more shocked. It hurt her that her husband
could think of such a thing as a smoking jacket when their stand
against tobacco and cigarettes was so well known. Perhaps the
intent was not overtly sinful, for he was tired and overworked,
but giving way to the regalia of a filthy habit could hardly be
said to strengthen the character. Charles didn't argue. After all,
an alpaca coat was comfortable, and at least it allowed him to
shed the heavy Prince Albert. There was no great issue involved
and therefore he contented himself with the things he *could* do.

iv

Soon the little cottage seemed all too small. The constant
ringing of the phone which wakened Karl at all hours of the night
was making Flo nervous and irritable. During the summer after
Karl's birth, some friends across the street were leaving their large
house for the summer and let the Menningers have the use of it.
This was much better. Flo was not disturbed by her husband's
getting in and out of bed during the night, and Karl was not
awakened so often. There were times, too, when the couple
needed to get away from each other. So that he could enjoy the
company of his family when he did have free time during the
day, Charles built a sunshade in the yard of the cottage; Flo and

Karl could rest under it while he worked in the garden. He was collecting roses and already had the finest peonies in Topeka.

The next year the couple rented a large house in the Potwin district of Topeka, and in August traveled to St. Louis, and from there, by river boat, to Tell City to see the elder Menningers. While visiting, they met Will Kircher, a fourteen-year-old nephew of Charles, who was just out of school and at loose ends. Charles and Flo both thought it would be fine if the boy could come back to Topeka with them, help around the house, and continue his schooling. For the boy this was an exciting opportunity, and when the Menningers returned to Topeka, he went with them.

With Will to take care of Karl, Flo had more time to get about. Often when her husband's patients needed cheering she would visit them and read to them. The cottage was put to good use even when they were not living in it. If for any reason some expectant mother needed a place away from home so that she might have her child in peace, the cottage was available. The first children of five different families were born there, and as time went on the cottage was enlarged. The family stayed in Potwin during the winter of 1895–96.

On March 18, 1896, Edwin was born. Living in the larger house, and more accustomed to her role of housewife, Flo was less tense and the birth was easier. The boy weighed ten pounds, and the only disappointment was that he was not a girl. He was a pretty baby, and Flo took great pleasure in caring for him. Edwin rarely cried unless he was hungry.

Though Charles wanted Flo to have a maid now, she still resisted every effort he made to hire one and as soon as the nurse was gone she did all the work, relying on Will for help with the children. Will was a good helper and Karl was very fond of him. Then one afternoon when Flo thought that Edwin was sleeping, so quiet was he, she looked at him only to discover that someone had put a banana in his crib and he had devoured most of it, skin and all. The doctor was sent for at once and was gravely concerned by what had happened. Edwin suffered no ill effects, but for once Charles really put his foot down. They were going to have a maid and that was that.

Years later Flo was to complain that one of the trials of her life was getting efficient help. As warm and sympathetic as she usually was to everyone, Flo was extremely critical of her hired girls. When she didn't drive them away with her impatience, she soon found reasons to discharge them. Of course, the money they cost was the real issue. Charles remained adamant. As soon as one girl left he would hire another. He knew that Flo would not willfully jeopardize the health and safety of the children, but he also knew that she would not admit that she had any limitations and would always attempt to do much more than her energies permitted.

With the passing of time, Charles was growing less timid about spending money. The old buggy was replaced with an attractive phaeton in which he could take his family for rides and which he could enjoy on his own long trips. He bought better horses, kept two instead of one, and hired a man to care for them.

In the summer of 1896 the Menningers met another young man, Foy Ernest. He was the brother of one of their friends, and he had been stationed in Topeka with the Army. After the Spanish American War ended, Foy Ernest came back to Topeka and it was decided that he would stay with the Menningers and go to Washburn Medical School. He was with them for four years and later practiced medicine in Topeka. Dr. Ernest later took up psychiatry and practiced in the West for the rest of his career. He, too, was very helpful about the house and good with the children.

v

Probably every young couple who have a hard financial struggle in their early marriage, but who work closely together toward a common goal, will feel that they are growing apart once the goal is reached. Many separations seem to come just as a home is acquired or when a growing business stabilizes itself. Certainly the years Charles and Flo Menninger spent in the little cottage on Topeka Avenue were the most hazardous of their life together.

While they had been struggling to get established, Charles could understand how it was that Flo could not give way to personal closeness. This was something he had expected to come after he had won economic security for them. Therefore he was deeply hurt when he discovered that even now the idea of emotional

and physical closeness only made Flo more anxious and more un-
reasonably insistent that they were in dire financial peril. When
she rejected him as a lover he couldn't help feeling that the companionship that had been the whole of their marriage was being
destroyed. She loved him in the only way she knew how and he
loved her in his way, but these ways were quite different.

On the nights when Charles was out on calls, Flo would keep
Karl up with her and read to him. The boy loved this. Even if he
didn't understand what his mother was reading, her nearness and
the sound of her voice were comforting. When his father could be
heard coming in from the barn, Flo would lay down her book
and clutch Karl closer to her. Coming in, bringing the cold night
air with him, the doctor would kiss her on the forehead and pat
his son. If he wanted to take Karl in his arms, Flo wouldn't let
him, or if she did, it would be only while she went to fix a hot
drink for the tired man. There was never much said. Charles
might remark on something or someone he'd seen in the part of
town where he'd been calling, or Flo would ask about the weather
or a patient who was a particular friend. Then the doctor would
go on to bed.

At such moments it was not unusual for Flo to clasp the boy
impulsively in her arms and assure him—to his consternation—
that his father was a good, a kind and generous man.

"But what's the matter?" Karl might ask.

"We soon may have nothing to eat," his mother would say. "He
doesn't know the value of money. If I had your father's ability
and learning there's no place I couldn't go, nothing I couldn't do.
But he's so slow, so overly conscientious that we'll all starve."

Her tears would flow and the child would puzzle. The words
meant nothing to him, but he could feel the emotional tension
between them like molten and uncooled metal caught between
the poles of a magnet. The child developed difficulties in walking
and fell often. It was as if he were never sure of what direction
to take, and sometimes when he fell and called out his mother
would punish him. In her diaries of that period Flo implored
God to keep her from "striking my little Karl."

When Karl was ill, and he often was, Charles called in the best
doctors to see him and at one time sent some distance for a woman
pediatrician who he felt might be able to talk to Flo. As a physi-

cian who did well with children, Charles was all too aware of what was happening to his son. "Don't confuse children by expecting them to understand adult problems," Charles had told other doctors in a lecture on child care. "If you can love them then you can reach them and accomplish anything with them. It isn't words that count, it's the quality of your acts and the sincerity of your interest."

But Karl was Flo's Karl. She made that abundantly clear. He had been her whole life in those first years away from the classroom when the resultant loss of independence and position were most keenly felt. He had been the symbol of her conflict and the answer to her conflict. She had truly and deeply inspired the son who was to write so eloquently on *Love against Hate*.

There was one thing Charles could not refute or argue against —Flo was *a good woman*. There was no flaw in her Christian perfection. She was charitable and kind when it counted most, and she never gave for display. She was pure in the sense that she never gave way to gross appetites, and although her code of conduct was narrow it was broad enough for her and she never broke it. She believed firmly in her God and she was careful that her prayers asked only for those things that she was sure were in the best interests of all, and obtainable through her own efforts or efforts she inspired. She was loyal and would serve Charles forever, in sickness and health. The great ambitions she had for her sons would be fulfilled if it were humanly possible; she would see that they had the very best upbringing and the maximum of opportunity. And yet something was wrong; it plagued Charles as he made his rounds.

Flo's anxiety over money was so great and constant and resulted in such deep depressions that he felt at times that the only solution was for them to separate so that she would not have to watch him earn their living or be threatened by his physical nearness. In that way he could give her an adequate income every month, of which she would have full charge. If it gave her more personal security, she could get someone to care for the children part of the time, and could teach. There were times in the last five years of the century when this matter was seriously discussed. The only thing that kept some such plan from being acted upon was Charles's optimism and a sense of responsibility that told him that no sacrifice could be too great if he could succeed in integrating his family into a healthy and growing unit.

Even at the peak of this crisis there were never any real quarrels or raised voices. During the lunch hours when Charles now felt that he was not welcomed by his family, he got together with two or three other young professional men and attempted to organize Topeka's first chamber of commerce. He also wrote letters to the paper and tried to get businessmen and others interested in improving the streets. To make sure that all his free time was taken up, he began to teach classes in physiology, neurology, and nutrition at Storemont Hospital and was active in arranging the programs of the medical society. And he gave Flo more gifts than ever before.

vi

In the summer of 1897 Flo made a discovery that had a great deal to do with saving her marriage. In August she and Charles took Will and the children to Ottawa, Kansas, where a Chautauqua was being held. Charles was physician to Bishop Vincent of the Methodist Church, the co-founder of Chautauqua, and through him he had become interested in this movement for adult education. One of the lecture series was called "Twelve Masterpieces." Flo attended it and found it a great experience. Even before she left Ottawa, she had learned where to obtain slides and reproductions of the "masterpieces" and had a reading list on the subject of art. At once she contracted to write a weekly article on art for the Holton *Signal*.

By the time the Menningers returned to Topeka the atmosphere was beginning to clear. Flo had found at least a partial outlet for her energies, and that took the edge off her anxieties. She discovered that the books on art in the Topeka library were almost never used and that she could borrow as many as she wanted and keep them as long as she wished. The hired girls became more competent; the children were happier, Charles seemed a different person. His gifts were art books and art reproductions, and he insisted that Flo should start teaching art to a small group of friends.

Through her writing for the *Signal*, she could both learn and instruct. The winter was busy and productive. Karl's health improved and he no longer had difficulty in walking; but in later years he has been heard to say that his lack of enthusiasm for the graphic arts was probably conditioned by the fact that his mother always kept her switch behind one of her art masterpieces.

vii

Charles had often thought of buying a larger home for his family, but the crisis in his relationship with his wife had kept him from acting on this plan. He had known, too, how Flo would have reacted to going further into debt, and therefore nothing had been done except to rent the larger house in Potwin. With Will Kircher and his own two sons, as well as himself, Flo, and the hired girl, the cottage was crowded to the bursting point. The size of the art classes Flo could teach there was limited, too.

One thing Charles Menninger was sure of: if he made a decision to buy a larger home his lot with Flo would be cast for life. It wasn't fear of her financial anxiety that kept him from getting such a house; it was his own indecision about his marriage. He felt that something about him had made Flo unhappy, and at times difficult with Karl. He didn't believe then and he was never to believe that he was good enough for Flo.

With the discovery of the art masterpieces, Flo had undergone a change that made him hopeful. And he was beginning to see just how much her teaching had meant to her. The world threatened her when she wasn't instructing it, supporting it, or in some way managing it. She would never adapt to the society around her. She had chosen one style of dress that suited her, and she copied it over and over even though it had the plainness of a Mother Hubbard. It was a garb that declared her social intentions. Her friends would be attracted to her by things of the mind and spirit or not at all. Although Flo's way of life imposed limits on his own activities, Charles admired her for the firmness of her convictions and wondered if he did not need her just because of the restrictions she imposed on him.

In the summer of 1898 Flo had an opportunity to take the children up into the Colorado Rockies and out of the heat. A friend, Mrs. J. H. Miller, had rented a cottage there and asked Flo if she wished to share it, thus cutting down on expenses. Charles was all for this idea. He needed time to think things through.

For Charles, to think things through meant to pray. As he stood open to God, he stood open to himself also; as he asked for help with his imperfections he was forced also to find the source of those imperfections. It was not enough for him merely to ask God for guidance; it was also necessary to explain why he needed that guidance and what his goal was. Charles's God answered him with questions, and when Charles answered these questions for himself, his prayer had found fulfillment.

viii

More than a week before Flo and the children were due to leave Colorado, she got a telegram from Charles asking her to come home at once. If it was a matter of illness or disaster she felt that he would say so, but since he did not, she was puzzled. Packing swiftly, she left as soon as possible for Topeka.

The Charles who met his family at the station was a different man. He seemed more sure of himself than ever. There was a difference in the way he embraced Flo and a fatherliness toward the children that he had not shown before.

"Why did you send for us?" Flo asked, sensing that he had exciting news.

"Because I have bought our home," he said. "I couldn't wait to tell you about it."

Flo embraced Charles now. She knew what it meant when he said he had bought a home. It was more than a house; it was the pledge of a lifetime of undivided devotion. She had prayed, too, and she didn't ask the price of the house or how much they had gone into debt.

CHAPTER FIVE

i

THE HOUSE Charles had bought at 1251 Topeka Avenue had thirteen rooms in addition to a large attic and cellar. There was also a yard and an adequate barn. The living and dining rooms were enormous and, since they were divided by large sliding doors, could be used as one room for classes or receptions. Although the house was large it wasn't ornate or pretentious; it was just the sort of home a busy and growing family would need if each person in that family was to be allowed a maximum individual development. Charles had a right to be proud of the place he had selected, and Flo had every reason to agree with his choice.

As a means of calming Flo's worries about money, Charles let her take over his bookkeeping and agreed that she should set aside a certain sum each month as savings. They were to act as if this money did not exist; it could not be used for current expenses. On the months when this set sum of money was not readily available for deposit, Flo would insist that they were destitute and must live as paupers until the money was deposited. But all in all the new arrangement made things much more comfortable for everyone and gave Charles the freedom to spend his extra money without too much explanation. Spend money he did.

One of the first things he bought for the new home was a Kimball grand piano. At about this time Annie M. Perry Bundy, a young pianist of talent who had just returned from a year of study abroad and wished to teach music in Topeka, came to live with the Menningers. "She is an artist," Charles said. "There aren't many of them and we're fortunate to have her." During the three years she stayed with them, she gave recitals in their home that were enjoyed by as many as one hundred people at a time. Always, before she played, she would tell the story of the composer, with special stress on the aspects of his life that showed that genius could always overcome poverty, antagonism, and perfidy. After the piece was played the literary content of the composition would be discussed. Topekans could not be content unless they felt that music described something, but they enjoyed it none the less. It was only that there must be a lesson, and that there could never be waste.

Another child was on its way, and this time the Menningers were determined that it would be a girl. Flo was further determined that it would be a girl of the finest quality. Somewhere she had read of pre-natal influence, so while she carried the child she read only the better books, thought only the deeper thoughts, and exposed herself to only the finer influences. Nothing gross was to mar this child. There was an implication that Karl and, to a lesser degree, Edwin had been marred, but both boys were to benefit by this pre-natal regimen. Flo read aloud to them and helped them with their preparations for the German lessons which their father conducted at the dinner table.

Edwin had an innate charm and a wonderful disposition; he was bright, active, and agile. Where Karl tended to be an obsessive and insatiable student who would follow through on one thing at a time, Edwin was an eclectic. He was delighted with everything and rarely bored; Karl was easily bored and if he wasn't using himself to his full capacity he seemed to sink into a sort of torpor. His mother had made him dependent on her, and he had learned that the best appeal he could make for her attention was to ask to be instructed in something. For this reason he had learned to read before it was time for him to start school. Watching his mother keep his father's books had given him an aptitude for figures that made her hope that he might someday be a banker.

From the beginning, the big house was a center of productive activity. From it, the father went out to a flourishing medical practice and a place in community life; the two boys who had been taken in were busy in school as well as active in housework and caring for the children; the children themselves were occupied in one way or another during all of their waking hours, and Flo, through art instruction and music, was again finding herself in the role of a teacher.

Flo had been teaching a primary Sunday-school class at her church, but she realized that she was not a thorough enough student of the Bible even though she had studied it almost every day of her life. At the time Blakeslee's outlines, a series of books on Bible study, were much in vogue, and Mrs. Countermine, the minister's wife, was giving Bible lessons according to their methods to a class of young unmarried women. Flo asked if she could join. Having heard of this advanced course in Bible study, she would no longer teach her primary class until she had taken the new course in its entirety. There was only one objection; the young unmarried women would not have a married woman in their class. Taken aback by this, Flo assembled a group of young married women and had Charles go with her to Dr. Countermine, the pastor, and insist that Bible study be made available to them. The answer was that such young women must organize themselves and provide their own teachers. Flo at once got Blakeslee's works, and her study of them was part of the pre-natal program.

So sure were Charles and Flo that their next child would be a girl—they had already agreed that it would be the last child—that the name Clara Louise was chosen long before the birth. The Menningers had not been able to afford an engagement ring at the time of their marriage and therefore had planned that when a daughter was born a diamond ring would be bought for Flo. If a son was born, a copy of a famous painting would be bought for the home. This ceremony had been agreed upon in Holton. Greuze's Broken Pitcher and Bodenhausen's Madonna had been acquired at the births of Karl and Edwin.

Even the weather collaborated in making the birth of this last child pleasant. It was a perfect October; the big elms were shedding their leaves outside the upper windows of the substantial Menninger home. Downstairs there was music; everywhere there was happy activity. The baby was born on the fifteenth of the month, a time when the budget was sure to be balanced. But it was a boy. Only the new peace in the household made this bearable. If Charles was glad to have another son, he at least had the good grace not to say so. Corot's Spring was the picture selected in honor of the new son.

When Foy and Will were allowed upstairs to see the boy, Flo tried to be casual about the rebuke she had received from fate. "Will," she said, "the baby is here but the name is wrong."

"Cut off the Louise and make it Will," Will Kircher said, and the problem was solved. The boy's name was William Claire Menninger. It seemed never to have occurred to anyone that the child might bear his father's name.

ii

Before making a final affiliation with the Shawnee County Medical Society, Charles attempted to organize the homeopathic physicians of Topeka, hoping that they could be made acceptable as a group to the medical society. The rift between the homeopaths and the allopaths could not be mended. The group he had proposed offered no special protection to the homeopaths; its sole purpose was to band physicians together for a better sharing of knowledge. Charles could not believe that anyone would be so hidebound as to practice homeopathy according to the old doctrines, but many men were still doing just that. In 1898 he made his final break with that sect and was accepted into the County Medical Society as a full member.

At this same time he left the staff of Storemont Hospital and went to Christ's Hospital, where he could practice under the men he most admired, Doctors Stewart, Bowen, McClintock, and Peers. At medical society meetings Charles became more articulate and more confident. There were fine, friendly arguments with Dr. McGee, his old teacher in pathology, and when sides were taken on any subject he found that Dr. Stewart's position and his were usually identical. They never became close friends, but they were the town's outstanding physicians and the most willing of collaborators when one had something to offer to the other. In this their relationship was unique in a day of highly competitive medicine.

In 1900, Charles was elected president of the Shawnee County Medical Society, an office that usually went to a much older man, and certainly had never been given to a man with a homeopathic background. Something else had happened in the meantime.

While at a national medical convention, Charles noted that the men who were closest to his own views of medicine, were beardless. Going directly to a barbershop, he had his beard removed and for the first time in his adult life stood barefaced to the world. As soon as he got home, and his family had become accustomed to his beardlessness, he divested himself of the Prince Albert and the batwing collar. A tasteful Chesterfieldian suit replaced the Prince Albert.

Even though he was the president of a medical society that was predominantly allopathic, Dr. Menninger did not hesitate to use homeopathic remedies when he thought they were needed. He was interested in what best served the patient, not in creeds or schools. Although preventive medicine had been ignored by his school, Charles was one of the first physicians in Topeka to insist on proper sanitation. Two typhoid deaths in his own family had made an impression on him, as had the many other deaths he had seen. He started and persevered in a movement to have the plumbing in the schools brought up to date; he studied the art of plumbing, and became the town's examiner for licensed plumbers. At the same time he delivered to the Saturday Night Club a paper on the backwardness and viciousness of the anti-vaccinationists. In 1900 he was also made president of the Board of Health and although some of his closest friends were merchants of the town his first act was to condemn all the oysters that were on sale in cafés and stores. Although sea food was heavily loaded with unhealthy preservatives, it rarely survived the long trip to the Plains in a safe condition. There was some grumbling, but most people agreed that he had acted wisely.

Dr. Charles Menninger was a busy and conscientious man, but no one could call him a meddler. In many ways he was a puzzling figure to his fellow Topekans. On one hot summer day a drink-crazed man stole Charles's finest horse and ran it to death. Charles had been proud of the horse and had loved it; it had cost him $200. Nevertheless, when the time came to prosecute the man who had stolen it, Charles would not appear against him. This seemed to many to be an odd turn in someone who was known to be an ardent prohibitionist and extremely religious. Charles knew that the culprit was an alcoholic and, as such, a sick person; he also knew that it would have been futile to attempt to explain this to his townsmen. Though he might pray for guidance in treating a patient, he would never inflict his religious beliefs on the patient. While he could be firm with his patients about following the orders he had given them, he never sat in judgment on them.

Some of his actions might have bewildered people, but they trusted him because they recognized him as a mature human being. When a leading citizen went into frothing fits because a hired man had ruined one of his prize trees by trimming it too close, the family knew that Charles was just the man to call. He would understand the emotional nature of the illness, and also, he was a lover of trees and could know how the assaulted householder felt. The fits were severe and continued for several days, but Charles succeeded in stopping them, and in the meantime did some preventive medicine by giving the offending hired man lessons in pruning.

Trips to New York, Battle Creek, and Chicago clinics for study had given Charles a new understanding of nutritional diseases. He was becoming a much sharper diagnostician, and he had always had a good grasp of diseases of the heart. Although pediatrics was not yet really considered a specialty, Charles read everything he could lay his hands on in that field and attended conferences on childhood diseases. By rights he should have been a specialist in internal medicine and pediatrics since that was the work he knew best and enjoyed most. In that day, however, it was difficult to specialize.

The part of his practice that plagued him most was obstetrics. For the amount of time spent the return was small, and Charles felt that there were many other physicians who could do much better than he could with these cases. An obstetrical case at the usual fee of fifteen dollars, which covered pre- and post-natal care as well as the delivery, might cost him from fifty to one hundred dollars in fees from other patients that he would have to turn away. And yet, as a family doctor, he had to take obstetrical cases. There were people who had faith in no one but him, and he could not let them down. In a sense he was part of their family, and he recognized the emotional values involved.

Another facet of medicine that interested Charles was neurology, perhaps because the neurologist of that time was the forerunner of the psychiatrist of today. In any event he studied neurology wherever he could and went to the expense of having slides made to illustrate his lectures to the medical society. There were many diseases that were difficult to account for, and sometimes neurology seemed to offer a clue.

It would have been difficult to convince an outsider who observed Dr. Menninger's standing in the Topeka medical community that this was a man who fifteen years before had never thought of medicine as a vocation.

If Charles ever had family troubles, no one in the town would have guessed it. Certainly no patient ever had reason to feel that the physician who called on him came fresh from a family scene that had disturbed him greatly. In one situation, at least, Flo's financial anxieties had contributed to his community standing. When some businessmen of the town wanted to launch a building and loan society, Charles was the one physician they called upon to join them. He did, and was one of the founders of the Capital Building and Loan Society.

Dr. Menninger never tried to modify his wife's social peculiarities. They seemed to have become his own. Social obligations were taken care of by inviting people to his home to receive instruction in whatever it was Flo was teaching. Refreshments and entertainment were secondary. There were always many people who were willing and eager to accept the Menningers' type of social life.

iii

Charles had little time to spend with his family, but he made the most of the time he had. At breakfast he would read a verse or two from the Bible; as soon as the boys were old enough they were required to memorize and contribute a verse at each meal. The doctor also kept a notebook in which he jotted down interesting facts or inspiring ideas from his omnivorous reading and he often read from it. He always encouraged the boys to talk about whatever it was that interested them at the moment. When he bought books for them, as he often did, he familiarized him-

self with the pictures and text before making the gift. He wanted
to be able to answer promptly and satisfactorily any question
that might come up.

At as early an age as possible, Karl was given piano lessons.
Though these were initiated by Charles, it was Flo who had to
see to it that the child practiced. Because of ill health Karl did
not start school until he was seven. His parents felt sure that the
boy would be a prize scholar. Then came a shock.

The first-grade teacher from Karl's school came to call on Flo
and was so nervously cordial that it was obvious that she had
some bad news to communicate. Flo suggested that she come
right out with whatever it was she had to say.

"This is painful to me," the teacher said. "At home one often
has no opportunity to compare a child's development with that
of other children, and you know the difficulties that can cause."

"Yes," Flo said, "but I don't see what that has to do with Karl.
He has two brothers and he plays with other children. He's nervous at times, that's all."

"No, it isn't all," the teacher blurted out. "Your son simply
hasn't the capacity for learning. There's some mental deficiency.
He just sits in a sort of stupor and has no interest in anything."

Flo couldn't reconcile this picture of Karl with the Karl she
knew.

"Just where is he deficient?" she demanded.

"He won't do any of the exercises or recite the alphabet. He
has no interest in learning to read or write," the teacher said.

"But he can read and write," Flo protested. "You'd better move
the boy up a grade or two," she suggested. "I know it sounds
strange, but remember I'm a teacher, too."

Karl was advanced three grades and had no more trouble in
school. He became happy and active as he set himself to catching
up with his class. This experience caused Flo to visit the school
rather often and gave her an idea. Why not become a sort of
class mother? With this plan in mind, she gave parties in the
Menninger home for the boys in Karl's class. They would be going
all the way through school with Karl; a little extracurricular soli-
darity might be a good thing. This started a practice that was to
be followed with the other Menninger boys and their classes.
There were times when the big house seemed far too small.

The doctor had set about improving the yard of the big house, indulging his passion for flowers and trees. If Flo had known the price he paid for some plants and bulbs she would have been frantic. Charles's peony collection was the finest in the state, and he had some of the rarest roses. As a boy, when he had worked with his father's flowers, he had been made to respect all growing things, and he expected his boys to do the same. The only trouble was that he had forgotten that Topeka was not Tell City and that the boys had no meadows or woodlands to play in. Karl, Edwin, and their friends raced and rolled in the garden, and when the doctor saw the havoc they caused he was almost in the state of the citizen who had had frothing fits over the ravishing of a tree.

"Those boys will have to learn where to play," he said emphatically. "They'll have to learn respect and reverence for flowers right now."

"I know you love your flowers, Charley," said Flo, "but I also know that you'll have to make up your mind whether you want to raise flowers or raise boys. In the city like this, with only a yard to play in, the two don't go together."

After a few futile attempts to separate the boys from the flowers, Charles had to agree. He gave most of his plants to the gardener at Christ's Hospital and then went over to the other side of town and bought three lots where he started gardening again. If the boys wanted to go with him when he worked this new garden, well and good, but if they did they had to understand that they were on sacred ground. They did, and the new garden flourished.

That is, the garden flourished until the next Decoration Day. When Charles went to his gardens to see his precious peony collection he found a shambles. It appeared that everyone at that end of town had stolen flowers for the occasion. That self-respecting citizens could be vandals was something that exceeded the bounds of the doctor's tolerance. And yet he could not strike out at a whole neighborhood. The best he could do was to hire a watchman to protect the remaining plants.

Much to Charles's surprise, Flo took the denudation of his garden—an expense of which she had not wholly approved in the first place—as a lack of commercial astuteness on her part. "Why, we could have sold every one of those flowers," she exclaimed, "made the garden pay for itself, and you wouldn't have had to hire a watchman." Charles could not have been more shocked if his wife had said that she was going to cut out the illustrations in the family Bible and sell them. But by the time he had finished his rounds that night, when he had had a chance to review the situation, he knew that the die was cast. Flo had a new and possibly lucrative project; he would have his flowers—up to a point. Was this compromise, or was it surrender? For fifty years to come the issue was to remain in doubt. But of one thing the doctor was sure: he was going to stop feeling guilty over what he spent on plants and see to it that the garden venture suffered a healthy loss each year.

Charles couldn't help buying plants and trees. He studied seed and nursery catalogues with the same seriousness that he studied medical books. Every year or two he would select new orchard plantings for Mother Knisely's farm at Industry only to have each lot fall before bugs, drought, and storms. But so long as there was anyone on the farm, he never gave up. As a consultant to Dr. Eastman, at Topeka State Hospital, he continued to select and supervise the planting of the many great trees that were to make the hospital grounds as beautiful as the finest park.

Mother Knisely came to visit the Menninger home and was told that she would be welcome to live there and give up the uneven struggle of the small farmer. But Manda Knisely had bought her independence dearly and wouldn't give it up. Although Topeka was only a city of 35,000, it seemed too crowded for the old lady. The city and its ways made her nervous. One of the city's innovations that especially offended her was the serving of bottled soda pop in the summertime. To her mind, no beverage that came out of a bottle could be innocent, and she wouldn't stand by and see her grandchildren corrupted by such city ways.

When Mother Knisely left, she told Flo that she was determined to live out her days on the farm, and that if anything happened to Leah, who was staying with her, she wanted Flo to get some old friend to come and live with her. She wouldn't come to the city under any circumstances. It is doubtful that the soda pop really determined her attitude; she loved the land and she wanted a farm for her grandchildren to come to in the summertime.

iv

Three weeks after William Claire was born, Flo started her Bible class, and thirty young wives enrolled. Linking her new interest in art to Bible study, she searched everywhere for pictures to illustrate the lessons. The class was an immediate success, and before the year was out eighty more women were enrolled for another class. Flo taught both classes and Karl was recruited as a runner to deliver the lessons to the ladies. No Bible class in Topeka had ever been so well attended or so methodically administered. Flo had her hands on the reins again.

In order to assist Flo with her art classes, Charles bought a large MacIntosh Stereopticon projector and helped her obtain the best slides for it. By hanging a sheet between the two big rooms of the house it was possible to have an audience on both sides of the screen. The doctor soon had to buy folding chairs to accommodate the crowd that these art lectures attracted. Whenever it was possible, he ran the projector and he saw to it that travel slides were bought for the boys.

As Charles's reputation as a diagnostician spread, his office practice grew. He could demand slightly larger fees, and, as he learned to organize his time better, the income from his practice increased markedly. Still Flo's apprehensions persisted. The doctor came home for lunch in order to be with his family for at least an hour and at lunch he would get out his appointment book to check the number of calls he had made and had yet to make. As he did this, Flo would watch him anxiously and count the number. When there were few house calls, she would become quite agitated over the seeming lack of business and if there were too many calls she would become equally agitated, seeing herself as a widow because of Charles's overwork.

It appeared to his sons that their father was quite oblivious to their mother's worry over the appointments or the lack of them. He spent money for anything he thought might please and educate his family; in an attempt to check this habit Flo increased the sum of the monthly savings to $250 per month. Soon the doctor knew that failure to turn the full amount over to her would result in discomfort for everyone. He strived mightily to have this sum available so that his family should enjoy life as much as possible.

In 1901, William Claire, or Claire as he was usually called, was boarded out, and Edwin and Karl were sent to the farm while their parents made a grand trip through the East. That year the American Medical Association Convention was held in Richfield Springs, New York. After attending that, the Menningers went on to Buffalo to the Pan-American Exposition, and then visited Flo's old home in Pennsylvania. On the Fourth of July they made a pilgrimage to Gettysburg where Flo had heard Lincoln's famous address from her mother's arms. Whenever they could, the couple stayed with relatives or friends. Since Charles had learned not to attempt to get Flo into the good hotels any more often than he had to and Flo had learned to avoid diners by packing lunches, travel was less hazardous. People who saw Charles and Flo Menninger while they were traveling were not likely to forget them. The plain and unattractively dressed woman became vivid through her interest in the things that were going on around her, and she betrayed an obvious pride in the tall, distinguished man who was with her. The man's pride in the woman was obvious, too, and his solicitude was constant and genuine. Physically, they seemed to inhabit different worlds and yet it was obvious to all that they shared a world of their own. Often they were thought to be brother and sister, and people were always startled when the handsome man introduced the plain woman as his wife. When they made friends on a train or at a hotel, Charles was always careful to restrict the conversation to those things that were of especial interest to Flo.

At the Exposition, Charles saw an Appolo Piano Player, a mechanism that was attached to the front of the piano, operated with rolls, and powered by foot pedals. Nothing would do but that he take one back to Topeka with him. He was as stubborn about things like this as Flo was about saving money. The piano player delighted everyone. Charles loved to pump it and the boys were fascinated by its machinery.

Having read about sleeping porches, and having inspected some in the East, Charles was determined that his family must have one. And so the house, big as it was, was added to, and the whole family could now sleep outdoors in the summertime.

v

It is possible that a fear of tuberculosis was partially responsible for the sleeping porch. Flora, one of Charles's twin sisters, had gone through college and had just begun teaching school when she became ill with tuberculosis. It was recommended by her physician that she go to Colorado Springs, Colorado, to rest and recover. The girl made the long trip alone, but when she arrived she was unable to find proper accommodations. She died not long after her arrival. The other twin, Emma, had been very close to Flora and was greatly affected by her sister's death. She almost immediately joined a Lutheran nursing order. When she had completed nurse's training, Emma went directly to Colorado Springs where she helped found a nursing home that took care of tubercular newcomers and found homes for others. When she entered upon this career she wrote to her physician brother for advice. Charles gave what advice he could and intensified his study of tuberculosis.

In about 1897 Charles's mother's health began to fail. A list of questions he sent to his father indicates pretty well what his fears were. He wanted to know the nature of his mother's fever, about her appetite, if she had night sweats, about the cough and what it produced, whether there were pains and where, and many more things that related to tuberculosis. It seemed unlikely that she was suffering from this disease, but it was obvious that a life of hard work had taken its toll. Charles sent medicine that would bring his mother some comfort. In March of 1902 she died. Taking Edwin with him, Charles went to Tell City for the funeral. His mother's death was a loss not only to her family but to all the people of the town.

On their return from Tell City, Edwin contracted scarlet fever and brought it home to William. The family was under quarantine. For a time it seemed unlikely that William would survive; his father worked with him day and night. When he recovered, the doctor was allowed to break the quarantine and move to his office so that he could go on with his practice. The house was quarantined for six long weeks; during that time of enforced separation

Flo and Charles had a chance to experience what a real separation would have meant. It now seemed impossible that they had ever thought of such a thing. This period of quarantine brought a new unity to the Menninger household. Cut off from playmates, the brothers learned how much they meant to each other. Playmates were all very well but real closeness was to be found only in the family.

i

KARL AND EDWIN went back to the Knisely farm in the summer of 1902. When their father came to visit them he interested them in nature studies. Since the birds in Kansas were a menace to the crops, there was no restriction on the collecting of birds' eggs and nests. Both boys ranged over the farm and competed with each other in collecting. When their father could make them stand still for it, he began to teach them a little geology and botany. He always brought gifts of some sort. There was a strong competitiveness between Edwin and Karl, and during these summer interludes both were striving for their father's approval rather than their mother's. Generally speaking, this competition was without much point; the father divided his affections equally between the two and encouraged the boys in joint endeavors.

While the boys were at the farm, Flo was having a vacation in New Mexico and had taken Will along. Hugh U. Mudge, general manager of the Santa Fe, was a patient of the doctor and a next-door neighbor. Mudge's family was going to Glorieta, New Mexico, by private car, and their cook became ill just before the time they had planned to leave. Flo had volunteered to take her place. The Mudges were delighted and the summer worked out perfectly. Flo had work to do and was with people she enjoyed. Will had a dog and the run of the camp and was completely happy and healthy.

As a rule Charles chose the times when his family was away to go East to study or to do concentrated research and reading. Although he participated in clinics, taught classes at Washburn Medical School, and organized study groups in the medical association, he was beginning to have a sense of isolation. The practice of medicine was becoming too broad to be mastered by the family physician. Although competitiveness could be valuable in that it kept physicians on their toes, at the same time it created a situation wherein the individual physician enforced his own limitations upon the patient. There was always a fear that after a consultation the doctor would lose his patient to his colleague. Since there was little inclination to refer the patient to another doctor for specialized treatment, other than surgery, the specialists had difficulty in earning a living and often returned to the general practice of medicine.

Charles felt that it should be possible for a group of physicians, each of whom excelled at and kept up with some special phase of medicine, to band together and share their knowledge. As it was, when Charles saw a patient with skin disease he would be forced to study dermatology, a field in which he had no real interest, when he should have been devoting more time to the study of metabolic diseases or pediatrics. At the same time, a doctor who was good at diseases of the skin would be trying unsuccessfully to treat a case of diabetes in a family to which he was physician. In each day of practice either physician would have cases that should be referred to the man who had complete current knowledge of the disease from which they were suffering. A great deal of time was wasted and, of course, the patient was denied the best of treatment. All physicians were aware of this, but when Charles suggested that a sort of clinical club be organized he ran against a blank wall.

There was a good reason for this. In a time when the physician had so few effective weapons with which to attack disease it was the personality and the intuition of the doctor that accounted for most recoveries. When a family respected and had faith in a physician its members often got well *for* him. The skillful practitioner often made recovery seem a personal obligation and that sense of obligation on the part of the patient often worked, where today antibiotics given by indifferent physicians sometimes fail. An intimate knowledge of the patient and his family could give the physician an insight into the nature of a disease that would result in accurate diagnosis, proper treatment, and eventual recovery. Actually these insights or intuitions were a part of a highly personalized and not easily communicable scientific method. Since most case histories had no existence outside of the physician's memory, and few physicians kept anything resembling a treatment chart, many important discoveries were passed by unnoticed. The methods then in use were not systematized, but they were often remarkably successful, and doctors were reluctant to experiment with new methods.

Charles was especially alert to the psychological factors that entered into medical practice and would have been the last to relinquish his status as family physician. What he wanted was to be a family physician and at the same time have the totality of medicine available to those patients who trusted, respected, and believed in him. He believed that he did not deserve their faith if he knew where better treatment was available and kept them from it. When someone was referred to him by another physician he scrupulously saw to it that the patient returned to that doctor when the treatment was completed.

Through his Eastern trips, Charles had learned more of the value of specialized medicine and the fruits of research within a limited field than most of his fellow physicians. He also subscribed to all of the medical journals, many of which were just being launched by new specialists in various areas of medicine. Added to the American medical periodicals were those from Germany and some from England. Probably no other Topeka physician had an equal library of periodical literature. A wider knowledge of what was going on in medicine created in Charles a wider sense of responsibility, but it was a sense of responsibility few other doctors had a chance to feel.

As a means of fulfilling this responsibility Charles set about preparing papers on metabolic diseases to present wherever he found an audience of physicians. Since he was dedicated to the study of nutritional and metabolic disorders, he wanted to offer to other doctors the knowledge he had acquired through his research, but that did not keep him from feeling lonely and inadequate when he knew that somewhere there must be doctors who would be able to save the lives that slipped away from him in spite of his best efforts in research.

ii

The spring of 1903 was rainy and there was high water on the Kaw River. Day by day the residents of North Topeka watched the papers, hoping that the next issue would report that the river was going down. Each day the river rose and by Decoration Day men were frantically filling sandbags, trying to stay the flood. It was a futile effort; the time could have been better spent in getting everything out of the houses in the flood area. For a day or two Charles made many house calls by boat. This, too, was a losing battle.

"Get the house ready for twelve or fourteen people," he wrote in a note he sent to Flo by messenger, "I'm sending them on to you. Buy all the ham, flour, bacon, and other foods that you can get. The flood victims may have to stay with us for some time and we may be feeding others."

The doctor was too modest in his estimate. Before nightfall there were over thirty flood victims in the Menninger home, many of them ill. All of the Menninger family and their wards pitched in. Meals were served on schedule, and Flo called on her Bible class to contribute bedding. Whenever he could be spared from the flood area, Charles was at home caring for the people there. There was no sleep or rest for anyone but the guests.

It was over a week before permanent places could be found for the refugees, and the flood had taken all that most of them owned. Flo brought order out of chaos; she organized everything and everyone. As in every crisis, it was she who had to take charge if things were to be resolved. At such times she gave no thought to money, for when people were in want or suffering, anything she had was theirs to command. She was truly illustrating her Bible lessons and making her students work out the text.

Before the flood victims could be moved, measles broke out among the twenty-three children in the house and of course they had to be quarantined. All the fathers moved out, and four of the mothers stayed. Charles now found himself operating a hospital upon which he called from his headquarters at his office. The children were to stay in the Menninger home for almost a month. Charles was rarely there except when he came to treat them. As a

member of both the state and city Boards of Health it was his task
to see to it that every sanitary precaution was taken to prevent
the spread of typhoid. At the same time he was keeping up his
regular practice. He was a stranger to sleep, but always when he
appeared on the street or made his rounds he was immaculately
and perfectly dressed and shaven. Neither hell nor high water
could make him set what he considered a bad example to his
patients. He was equally fastidious about his emotions and no
one ever saw him upset or ruffled in a crisis.

When the crisis was past, there was no letdown. The boys all
lent a hand in cleaning the house, family schedules were at once
resumed, and Flo's classes went on just as before. No one in the
family ever discussed the "good" they had done or mentioned the
"sacrifices" they had made. There were only two questions in their
minds: had they done enough, and had they been efficient in
what they had done?

iii

One morning the boys saw a pony tied to the hitching
ring in front of the house. Excitedly, they ran out to see it and
found that it was a gift from their father. There was a cart to go
with it, and Edwin, who was a good hand with horses, at once
took charge, somewhat to the dismay of Karl and Will. But by
taking charge, Edwin had also assumed the responsibility for the
care of the animal. Things had a way of equalizing themselves in
the Menninger family.

The pony was not the first animal the boys were to have, or the
last. It joined a veritable menagerie in which there were pet
ducks, guinea pigs, rats, dogs, and cats, not to speak of their father's horses. The boys were allowed to have any animal they
wanted, as long as they took good care of it and trained it properly.

Since the pony had given Karl and Edwin an incentive to enter
into the life of the barn, their father suggested that they earn some
money by taking care of his horses. He would pay them fifteen
dollars a month per horse, the going rates for the care and feeding
of a horse. Out of that sum they would have to buy feed and

bedding for the horses. Whatever was left would reimburse them for the necessity of being out in the barn at five-thirty every morning to have an immaculately groomed horse hitched to the carriage and ready for their father's first call of the day, usually at eight. Since feed came to about ten dollars a horse, they would have five dollars a month for their efforts. Of course, they would have to care for the horses in the evening as well as in the morning.

This project in horse care was not to interfere with any of the boys' other duties. They were still expected to be neatly dressed at the seven o'clock breakfast and prepared to recite a verse of the Bible. Their rooms had to be straightened, and before breakfast there had to be a period of practice at the music lesson of the day. Karl was still studying the piano and Edwin had taken up the violin. For a time both Karl and Edwin had paper routes and when Karl dropped his in order to be a runner for his mother's classes Edwin incorporated Karl's route into his own.

If either of the older boys was following any particular hobby, he had to give it his best efforts and keep all the paraphernalia of the hobby in order. The homework from school had to be done under the eyes of two professional and instinctive teachers. There was no possibility of a Menninger boy, or a boy living with the Menningers, ever being behind in his schoolwork.

The doctor encouraged hobbies and often sought to launch them by indirect methods. If the boys were interested in telegraphy and in having a telegraph system between their rooms and the homes of their friends, they not only had to learn the Morse code until they were perfect in it, but they had also to study the principles of electricity and learn enough chemistry to be able to construct and maintain their own wet-cell batteries. In the case of chemistry, their father would push it along a little further than the battery formula by bringing home chemicals and doing experiments for them.

No opportunity to implant knowledge or curiosity in young minds was overlooked. When the boys asked for books they could be sure their father had not only read them before they did, but had already assigned collateral reading. Once he set them to the task of learning something, it fell to Flo to follow through and see to it that they did a thorough job of the study prescribed.

When one of the boys thought it would be fun to collect stamps he found his father ready to give some money to start the collection and supply the basic books on the subject. At the beginning this would seem to be a relatively easy hobby and one which offered an opportunity to barter. Then, suddenly, he would find that stamps had to do with geography and that he had to know all about the country from which each stamp came. Since this geography simply called for a practical application of what was being learned, or had been learned, at school, that wasn't bad. Then, however, it would turn out that the faces and symbols on the stamps were of historical importance and that stamps could be separated and indexed not only by country but by other categories as well. There could even be a collection of stamps that commemorated great scientists and physicians. What could be learned from stamps was endless. When the boys found themselves with a surplus of stamps and had some for sale, still another learning experience reared its head. In order to avoid quarrels about whose stamp was whose, incorporation papers and the rules of the stamp firm had to be drawn up. The doctor hadn't studied law for nothing and so the business had to be on a sound legal base. Flo was the business director, of course. To this day Dr. Will Menninger is an ardent stamp collector, specializing in issues commemorating great physicians.

The irritable query, "Mama [or Papa], what can I do?" was never heard around the Menninger household. Nor was there any quarrel between the parents as to policy once any project was introduced into the daily schedule. Their father might be present only long enough to say that a certain thing must be done, but once he had made his decision their mother would see that it was carried out. Charles, for example, believed that he could teach German by simply writing it, speaking it, and inspiring it. He expected successful results, and when they didn't come quickly enough it was Flo who had to teach the boys grammar.

On Sundays the boys kept just about the same work schedule they kept on weekdays. That is, the horses had to be cared for and one of them harnessed, since their father tried to get all his calls for the day over as early as possible. Of course the music practice had to be observed. Then there was Sunday school and the lessons had to be prepared as carefully as all the other lessons.

When time for the regular church services came, the Menninger family marched into their pew dressed in their best and with their shoes freshly and personally shined. After church, and while Flo was getting dinner ready to serve at two o'clock, the boys were expected to give their father a musical recital or join him in playing some previously announced and practiced piece. Charles did rather well on the flute. During the recitals the father would tell the boys something about the theory and history of music. At dinner another verse of the Bible would be recited by each of the boys, and perhaps Charles would read something from his notebook. As soon as dinner was over, and the boys had helped with the dishes, there would be a trip to the country if the weather was good. Flo would take her knitting or some book she was studying, and when an attractive shaded spot was found she would take her ease while father and sons went into the fields for nature study. The boys might run, play, and wrestle a bit, but when they stopped, their father was waiting with an interesting plant, a rock, or an example of bird migration. Meteorology wasn't overlooked. Weather is important in Kansas and there is a lot of it. As best he could, the doctor told the boys where it came from and how. When, at last, the family rode home in the gathering darkness there were stars to be seen from horizon to horizon and their stories could be told.

On Sunday evenings, if the next day's schoolwork was done, there might be games of crokinole, carom, Flinch, or Authors. No playing cards were ever allowed in the house. The only competitive game the father ever joined in was crokinole and at this he was a champion. The boys liked to play with him, for it was the only time that they ever saw their father play at anything. Their mother played no games. At most she might, as if for her own entertainment, go to the piano and accompany herself with one finger as she sang "Sweet Alfareta" or "Two Little Girls in Blue." No playmates or callers came in on Sunday; the family had that day to themselves.

iv

The boys played just as hard as they worked. The attic, basement, and extra rooms of the big Menninger home were turned into boys' clubs. Flo's hot breads, cakes, and cookies were waiting for the dozens of boys who were friends of her sons. Karl, Edwin, and Will all had their separate gangs, which somehow resisted Flo's efforts to organize them for moral betterment and cultural progress. Her best role was that of traffic manager and referee of disputes. If the tennis net in the back yard interfered with the baseball diamond that was also laid out there, she would rule as to which could be used and when. If the boys became unruly her theory was that it was because they didn't have enough to do. The solution was to put them to work and punishment was seldom necessary.

Although the boys admired their father and were proud of him, they knew that they could never count on his being able to participate in their plans. They were much closer to their mother, and it was she who made most of the decisions in their lives. She encouraged them to talk things over with her and felt hurt when they didn't, and so she was let in on most of their plans. Since she was a worrier, they reported to her frequently and tolerantly accepted her directives. In this they were reflecting their father's attitude. It would be more accurate to say that they were thoughtful of their mother's wishes than that they were dominated by her. In self-protection they learned to anticipate and modify her wishes.

Karl had of necessity been closer to his mother than had the other boys and was, for that reason, more influenced by her. As her moods fluctuated so would his. He was always anxious about his mother's welfare and sought to please her, a task that was at times impossible. Her moods seldom stemmed from anything he had done, but out of the moods would come her hopes of what he should be and the sort of man she wanted him to become. The boy could guess that the mother's desires for his future were a direct reproach to his father, but he could seldom see that there was anything in his father that warranted reproach. In reality Flo was not reproaching Charles; she was protesting against her own limitations—and he seemed to be one of them.

At times Flo wanted Karl to be a literary genius who could recreate the life she had lived and wring some ultimate truth out of it; at other times she wanted him to be a powerful figure and a great voice capable of leading America to the light. Then there was a dream that encompassed all the other dreams. Karl would be a great banker, a financier, a Gibraltar of security who would accept his wealth and power as something given him to administer in the name of the Lord. Never once did she suggest that he become a physician.

From the time Karl could talk and understand her, Flo had drilled into him the necessity for telling the truth. Karl had taken this literally; the truth was that which you could see, hear, taste, smell, and feel—reality, the way things were. Moreover, he believed that most people told the truth at all times in all ways. He was an extraordinarily naïve child and even if people he loved warped the truth to fit the social situation, he believed them completely. He told the truth as he saw it and believed that they did the same. And he was hurt and puzzled when he saw that other people were always more socially adept than he was. That his social bluntness might hurt his friends never occurred to him. Nor could he see why it was that some boys would think he was stupid just because he honored them enough to believe their exaggerations. Often he was quite at odds with the world, and his mother was never able to explain to him just why this was. Like Karl, she was socially blunt, and also had a tendency to believe anything if the sentiment was on the right side. She liked the idea of Good conquering Evil and was never likely to question a story, no matter how implausible, in which Good was the victor. Both she and Karl suffered greatly if they thought they had injured or offended anyone.

Edwin and Will somehow escaped the direct onslaught of their mother's truth-teaching. They were truthful children, but they also knew how to use charm and understood that *little* falsehoods need not be vicious, and could, indeed, be a kindness. Thus they had the edge on their older brother; they were better liked. Neighbors called them in and gave cookies and sweets to them, but never to Karl. It was up to him to attract attention by excelling at whatever he attempted. When he played, he played harder than the other boys, and when he assumed leadership he went all out. He was in command and that was that. In short, his bids for attention had to be made through exaggerated effort, and he was often restless and nervous.

He did not, however, have to compete with his father for his mother's attention. When his father was at home his mother was apt to be more attentive to the boy. In this there seemed to be an emotional survival from the early days when Karl had been her whole life. In many ways Karl's feelings toward his father were conditioned by those days. When his father would take Karl with him as he made calls in the country, Karl would become upset and fearful if his father were in a house for too long a time. He would be sure that the patient had robbed and killed his father and that the family's source of income was gone. If the calls were few and swift he worried, too. The father never talked about medical practice with his family. The greatest moments of closeness the boy knew came when his father would share his Kiss Me gum with him, something which his mother did not wholly approve. Karl did find his father was a good listener, however. There was approval in his quietness as he listened to a boy's story and though he might offer a suggestion as to how this or that could be done better the next time, he was rarely critical of what had been done.

Flo, on the other hand, could be quite critical of what had been done and could, because of some past mistake, move in and take charge of the activity under question. She could never quite believe in anything that she did not in some measure control. When the boys confided in her they gave away control of whatever it was that called for the confidence. "We'll do it this way," Flo would say, and the boy would know that his club or sport would be invaded and perhaps improved. She could make plans that were beyond a boy's scope. Karl probably confided in her more than the other boys did. Edwin was a diplomat, and as such could at times manipulate and control events. Will had a peculiar sort of independence. He got along with everyone; at the same time he steadfastly pursued whatever line he had chosen to take. While Karl and Edwin might quarrel on occasion, neither of them ever found much reason to quarrel with their younger brother. In the first place, he rarely tried to do anything that threatened either of them and, in the second place, if he had, he would have planned it through to a point where there would be no use in trying to divert him. It was obvious that he gave some thought to whatever decisions he made. Put him in any group and he would emerge the leader, not because he would assert himself as such, but because he would be the only boy with a well-co-ordinated plan of action. Others would soon recognize that he knew what he was doing and that they didn't.

Will could make quite frightening decisions and see them through. One day, for instance, he was down in the basement playing with his dog when he ran across a cache of his father's discarded homeopathic pills. Some of these were plain sugar pills and as such a delicacy. Will ate a few and, being of a benevolent spirit, gave a few to the dog. Then, reasoning that if white pills were good pink ones would be better, the boy and the dog enjoyed a few dozen pink pills. And so it was with the blue pills, the green, and the scarlet. Hahnemann's theory of the thirtieth potency was really protecting the boy and the dog. It took both a long time to eat their fill.

When Will was called for supper he went upstairs to wash, even though he had little appetite for food. He knew that he should have asked his father about the pills and that they would not be an adequate or acceptable excuse for a loss of appetite. The dog had followed him to the bathroom and suddenly began to run around in circles, frothing at the mouth. Will knew that it was the pills that were causing the fit and tried to get hold of the dog so that he could flush him out with water. But before he could reach the animal it had dived under the bathtub and died in a horrible convulsion. Will was heartbroken, but he knew that his heart-break would not last for long, that he would soon join the dog. If he went to his father and asked for help he knew that his father would blame himself for leaving the pills in the basement and that his mother would blame him too. Innocent people would suffer because of what he had done. There was only one way out and that was to keep quiet and die. Keep quiet he did, even though he was sure death was at hand. The family wondered why the boy was so subdued and thought they had discovered the reason when they found the dead dog. It was years before they learned the real reason for the boy's quietness that night.

Edwin was steady and a hard worker, but was perhaps more imaginative than the other two boys. Legerdemain was his forte. He liked the drama of sleight of hand and magic; he liked chemical experiments. He was more successful at business, too. His paper routes were well organized; he had an excellent system of collecting and getting subscriptions. Even as a boy he seemed to have an affinity for the newspaper business.

Karl, as the oldest boy, was the first to find social life outside the home. As he entered high school, he joined the Epworth League, went to the parties of this rather liberal church group, and began to have occasional dates with girls. From Bach, Mozart, and Beethoven, he turned his piano to ragtime and was quite a success. Dramatics also attracted him. Though his mother, who watched closely over the boys' schoolwork, knew that Karl was at the top of his class, his father could not believe this to be true when he saw his son playing so much and often coming home in a flippant mood. One night when Karl was supposed to be mastering some difficult algebra lessons his father could hear him whistling and humming ragtime. This was too much for his scholarly German soul. The lessons, he reasoned, must be suffering. He told his wife that he wanted his son and the algebra lesson brought to him; it seemed to him that Flo was protecting the boy.

When Karl came into the room, still whistling, Charles said, "Give me those lessons and sit down and be quiet."

Karl obeyed. "I'm just feeling good and the lessons are easy," he said.

As his father studied the lessons a look of amazement spread over his face. The lessons were perfect. He could only lecture his son on the seriousness with which matters of scholarship should be approached. The doctor had always had a reverence for learning, but still there was nothing to do now but compliment his son on having done the lessons well. Even though he abhorred his son's taste in music, he said nothing about that.

Karl knew that his mother had been prepared to defend him against his father, but he had not wanted that defense. He wanted just what he had achieved: recognition for having done his lessons well. Perhaps, without knowing it, he had been bidding for his father's attention by whistling and humming. As he grew older he found that he needed his father's respect.

While he was in high school, Karl was given an expensive overcoat. He was tall now, over six feet, and he wouldn't be outgrowing his clothes so rapidly. The coat had cost thirty-five dollars, a great deal for those days, and Flo had been reluctant to approve such a large expenditure. Soon after he had been given the coat,

Karl was bringing a girl home from a party on the outskirts of town. As they drove along—Karl had been allowed to use his father's spare horse and buggy—they passed a grass fire that had got out of control and was threatening a house. Caught up in the drama of the moment, and going all out to impress his girl, Karl took off his coat and began to beat out the fire with it. His attempt was both valiant and successful and won the admiration of the girl. But when Karl was riding home alone he knew that his mother could take only one view of what had happened. Thirty-five dollars had been destroyed and nothing was worth that. His father would be berated for having bought so handsome a coat in the first place, and Karl for having been so careless. It was a scene the boy could not face.

That night he managed to conceal the fact that his overcoat had been destroyed, and the next day he went to his father's office to tell him what had happened. As he sat among the waiting patients the enormity of his crime grew on him. He was in tears when his father called him into his inner office.

"What is it, Son?" Charles asked. "Nothing is worth what you're feeling. Tell me about it."

Karl managed to get the story out to his father, admitting the vanity that had motivated him.

"Karl," the father said, "thirty-five dollars is only money. We'll go right over and get you another coat and keep this matter just between you and me. Whatever there was to learn from this incident has been learned. There's no use punishing yourself."

Flo never knew about the overcoat; an implicit understanding had drawn father and son closer together, and the boy knew why it was that other troubled people had been in the waiting room waiting to see his father.

Each boy was to have an experience something like Karl's. Behind their father's seeming sternness was a tolerance they would never find in their mother. The boys knew, too, that their father could always be depended upon to be the same. Their mother's moods might fluctuate, her financial worries might disrupt the peace of the household for a few days a month, but their father would always accept such situations with a quiet firmness, tolerance, and gentleness. By example, he adjured the boys to be gentle with their mother. This is not to say that he ever allowed them to look down on her in the slightest. By word and act he taught them that she was the greatest woman who ever lived and that it was through her heroic efforts that they were all together, fed, and well. Week in and week out it was she they would have to depend on, their father made that clear. His work was such that he could not be with them as much as he wished.

The truth was that Flo Menninger ran her home so that all who were in it might have economic and cultural security. There would always be food and shelter and the better things in life as she conceived of them. Her husband had a great deal more freedom than most men. He was practicing a profession he liked in accordance with standards that were acceptable to him. Flo saw to it that bills were collected, savings put away, the education of sons prepared for, and that the household was as perfectly organized as possible. In his free hours the doctor could study without fear that his family would suffer from his absence. He never had to neglect a patient and hurry home from a call because of family trouble, and if he decided to go away for a little study he knew that the necessary money would be available. Once, back in Holton, Flo had refused to let him join the Oddfellows because they were a secret order. Now in Topeka she let him join the Masons. This made sense to the doctor when he looked back and saw that the Oddfellows would have been a waste of time and substance, and that he had been allowed the Masons when he had no time to waste and would eventually drop them of his own volition. There was a safety in moving within the restrictions that Flo placed upon those close to her. The father saw to it that his sons respected their mother's wishes even when her attitude seemed old-fashioned.

v

On that morning in 1908, when Dr. Menninger returned from his trip to the Mayo Clinic and announced that his sons would be doctors and that they would have their own clinic in Topeka, it is doubtful that the boys were consciously impressed with what their father said. Their mother's Bible classes had much more reality than had Mayos' and the practice of medicine. Their mother had never suggested that the boys might become doctors; therefore they had never given the matter much thought. They knew that their father was a successful and respected man, but they didn't know why. Many of the fathers of their friends, on the other hand, were connected with the Santa Fe Railroad, and every passing train emphasized the romance of that industry; it seemed far more attractive than the practice of medicine.

It could even be that in an excess of emotion Charles Menninger was going against his wife's wishes when he made that breakfast-table announcement. So far as Dr. Karl and Dr. Will can remember, their father never again mentioned the clinic or the practice of medicine during their boyhood. Even when the boys rode with him as he made his calls, as all of them did from one time to another, the father never spoke of medical practice or of their future as physicians.

Once, when it seemed likely that Washburn Medical School might go under, Charles Menninger had pledged $1000 to it, to be paid in over a period of time. That incident proved that he considered medical education important, for his contribution cost him dearly. To Flo, the thousand dollars represented the cost of a trip to the Holy Land that she had long wanted to make. More than that, it represented four months' savings. This was a thousand dollars that both the father and the boys were to hear about all their lives. But never once did Charles say, "I gave it so that my sons might have a school to go to." When Charles Menninger believed in something he dedicated himself to it, no matter what the penalty, and he took it for granted that his act carried its own explanation. He never defended his gift to Washburn, nor did he seem to regret having made the gift in spite of the prolonged objections.

Perhaps Charles Menninger's lack of inclination to force a profession on his sons came from his own experience in having the law forced on him as a boy and young man. He knew how painful it had been for him to reject that profession, and he knew by what a roundabout route he had arrived at his true vocation. Nevertheless, he must have wanted his sons to be physicians, and it must have cost him dearly to keep this wish to himself, except for that one disclosure that morning in 1908.

CHAPTER SEVEN

i

By 1908 Dr. Charles Menninger was as successful as any doctor in Topeka. Certainly he was one of the most highly regarded. That he was physician to the families of most of the medical group in Topeka attests to the esteem in which his colleagues held him. In his middle years, and established in his profession, the doctor could easily have felt that he was entitled to relax a little. Where another doctor might have taken a younger man into his office so that he could give up night calls, Dr. Menninger went on alone. Nothing his sons or his wife said gave him much hope that he would eventually have a son in practice with him, but he had faith and patience.

While Charles Menninger had reasons to wish that he had more time to spend with his family, he never regretted that he had become a physician. In him there was a deep need to serve mankind and his constant prayer was that he might better serve man for the greater glory of God. In this his vocation was intensely religious and in addition it offered him full scope for his powers as a practical scholar; he could constantly study and teach. He liked people and his profession took him out among them and brought him close to them, but the thing that was most important to him was that in the practice of medicine he was forced each day to take the measure of his powers, both personal and professional.

In Sir William Osler's book, *A Way of Life,* he found a poem taken from the Sanskrit, *A Salutation to the Dawn.* It expressed his living philosophy. He had thousands of copies of it printed and distributed them among friends and patients. This is the poem:

Listen to the exhortation of the dawn!
　　　Look to this day!
For it is Life, the very Life of Life.
In its brief course lie all the
Verities and Realities of your existence:
　　　The bliss of growth,
　　　The glory of action,
　　　The splendour of beauty;
For yesterday is but a dream,
And tomorrow is only a vision,
　　　But today well lived makes
Every yesterday a dream of happiness,
And every tomorrow a vision of hope.
Look well, therefore, to this day!
Such is the salutation of the dawn.

Usually, Charles Menninger wrote, "Have firm faith in God," at the head of the poem. In that and through the poem he stated his simple philosophy, and every act of his life was an expression of the principles that sustained him. Because he was able to confine them to one day at a time, Charles had been able to endure the troubles of a marriage that fell beneath his romantic expectations. And so it was with medical practice; he was well aware of his inadequacies, and although he knew that they could not be overcome in one day, he would not rest until he had found in that day the best remedy then available to him. Tomorrow did become "a vision of hope" as he developed better methods of finding out what he needed to know. A thousand nights at ten thousand bedsides could have been too much to contemplate, but without the burden of the morrow Charles was able to carry heroic patient loads during epidemics.

Flo was, at times, irritated by Charles's optimism, for his philosophy certainly bred that in him. This optimism struck at the core of the anxiety that supported her, and indeed gave her the caution and thriftiness which would always keep Charles's optimism intact and sure of itself. In a strange way the couple supported each other; Flo knew that she and the boys were dependent upon her husband's reliable ebullience. Still, it was difficult to live with a man who had never known a defeat that had outlived its day, and who was always calm no matter what threats the future might seem to hold. Also, Charles had a way of believing that other people lived by his philosophy and if by chance he did say or do anything that might bring offense or injury to anyone he was sure that all would be forgiven and forgotten when a new day dawned. Certainly he forgave and forgot those who injured him, but there were people who thought him to be somewhat insensitive on this score. No one, however, could say that he was ever insensitive to the needs or the suffering of the ill, or that he was insensitive to the needs of his family.

By his every action he told his sons that he was there if they needed him, and that they could always come to him unquestioned.

When Flo had dropped her resistance to fraternal orders, Charles had joined the Masons and taken most of the degrees. For a while he enjoyed this, and then, as his professional activities made more demands on him, he had to resign from his lodge. The building and loan society gave him some outside activity and a feeling of the business world, and with the organizing of the chamber of commerce he entered briefly into civic life. For a time he joined the local band, but only to play in the rehearsals, never in the parades. Playing the flute, he said, was his way of letting off steam. His interest in flowers and trees continued. Whenever he went away to study, he visited the gardens and parks of whatever city he happened to be in. On almost every occasion he brought home plants and trees for his own gardens, and for others. He was the sponsor or founder of some of the first garden clubs in Topeka. The fact that his boys' activities would not permit him to have a garden at his own home was probably a blessing to the city. It was a rare patient who was not the gainer by a plant or tree if he called in Dr. Menninger. Anyone who wanted a horticultural consultation could have it without a fee, and perhaps a free medical consultation as well.

Though Charles Menninger had never been a horseman in the true sense of the word he did like good horseflesh and fine rigs. He had patience with animals; he knew how to talk to them and train them. To a degree, he also understood their ills. Often he was called upon to help Flo's younger brother, Dave Knisely, who had now become one of Topeka's successful veterinarians, and had even had a chance to make a contribution to animal medicine. At Charles's suggestion, and with his help, Dr. Knisely had devised what may have been the first stomach pump ever used on a horse.

Every one of Charles's horses had been trained to step to one side just as the doctor stopped and was preparing to get out of the buggy. Thus a muddy or dusty wheel, as the season might have it, would be pulled out of the way so that it would not soil the doctor's clothing. Charles trained his horses carefully and he would not stand for any mistreatment of them. The moment Karl and Edwin became frivolous in their job of caring for the horses and devised a harness drop, such as was used in the firehouse to lower harness onto the fire horses, they were dismissed. He could see the humor of the boys' plans, but no horse of his was going to be frightened just for the entertainment of his sons. In any case the harness drop they had fixed up was just as likely to get the breech in the horse's mouth and the bridle under its tail as it was to get the harness on straight.

Before 1910 some Topeka physicians were using automobiles, but since they also had to keep their horses for emergencies, Charles couldn't see the wisdom of such an investment. What finally aroused his interest was the vacation trips people were able to take by automobile. His family was away every summer, and in recent years had been going to Winona Lake, in Indiana. With a car, he might be able to take them there or bring them home, and thus have more time with the boys. And there was no doubt that the boys would like the idea of a car. After many consultations with friends and mechanics Dr. Menninger bought his first car, a 1910 Cadillac. It was a proud day when he drove it home. From the way the boys took to it, he could see that he would never lack for assistants when it came to cleaning and polishing; there was brass to be shined and gadgets to examine while they worked. As quickly as possible Charles mastered the principles of internal combustion engines so that he would be able to answer the many questions the boys would inevitably ask.

If Flo objected to such a large outlay of money for a vehicle, the excitement of a trip to Washington, D.C., to attend the International Sunday School Convention made the car seem a small matter. The Bible class was paying her way.

ii

With a huge house, three growing boys of her own, and the various boys who lived with the Menningers while they went to school, Flo Menninger would have seemed to have all that one busy woman could take care of, even if she did have a hired girl. The keeping of her husband's books might have been a burden to another woman, as might the chore of being class mother for three separate sets of her sons' schoolmates. But to Flo Menninger these activities were essential. Not one moment of her time was wasted. If she went calling, her knitting went with her, and the products of that knitting were the next season's Christmas gifts. As she walked from one room of the house to another, there was no reason why she couldn't carry a water can and irrigate the potted jonquils and hyacinths that would eventually go to shut-ins and friends who needed cheering. At Christmas time, with a little extra effort, as much as 200 pounds of candy would be made for gifts. At such times the doctor and the boys cracked nuts whenever their hands were idle. Mending and washing that would have seemed monumental in any other home were minor weekly incidents when fitted into the Menninger routine. When there was work to be done whatever hands were present were put to work.

Flo Menninger's life seems to prove that anyone who wants to do anything strongly enough, and makes its accomplishment the reason for his existence, will also accomplish all of the little things that so often seem to get in the way of the major aim. Her life also proved that a conscientious person can do many things well, and, in fact, must do them well if he is to have a solid base. The Bible classes were no hobby with Flo Menninger; they were an act of vocation, a way of life, something that she had to do in order to live at all. She could be a housewife only if she was a teacher and a leader—and she wanted mightily to be a successful housewife and mother. Her teaching was by way of being a compulsive act. It was as if she said, "If I do not teach and lead, the threatening forces of life will set upon me and destroy me in my entirety."

Had this necessity existed in another woman it is possible that her husband and her sons would have been destroyed by it. As it was, the sons were led, through their father, to understand and respect this necessity, and to honor it. Moreover, there was something in Flo Menninger that kept any act of hers from being selfish. The gratification she got from teaching and leading would have been as nothing if she could not see that what she was doing was for the greater good of all. She was incapable of enjoying any success that was achieved at the expense of anyone else. Whatever it was that kept her from being a wife to Charles in the fullest sense had happened long before the Bible classes came into being, and she never knew that she was not that. Certainly she was a loyal wife and a proud one. Her man meant as much to her as the most uxorious husband could have meant to the most submissive wife.

Even as she had succeeded with her first classes, Flo had been discontented with her Bible-teaching ability and equipment. In 1903 she had gone to Chicago to study at the Moody Bible Institute. After that the Blakeslee outlines no longer sufficed. They explained too much when all the explanations a Bible student should need were to be found in the Bible itself. Often Flo needed extra material, such as illustrations, and these she had to pay for from her own money. The class members paid only for their books, and this went against Charles's grain. It was not that he resented the expenditure; it was that he felt that if people really wanted to learn something they should be willing to make some investment in it, especially if they were to maintain an emotional tie with their studies. The ones who were just wasting time would think twice before they put money into something that didn't mean anything to them, and would thus be weeded out. Flo agreed, but she was afraid of losing students and, in the early stages of her teaching, numbers were still important to her.

While she was in the Colorado mountains one summer in the early 1900s and the boys were at the farm, Flo had time to give some serious and consecutive thought to Bible teaching. It seemed to her that if she could outline the book of Genesis in her own way, without relying on any of the methods she had previously used, she would have developed a way of teaching that was entirely her own, a way that would lead as directly as possible into the text of the Bible. The great test came one day at noon when she decided to put her first thoughts about Genesis down on paper. That night while the others slept she was still writing by the campfire and by candlelight. By the light of the rising sun she read what she had written, and knew that what she had done for Genesis she could do for every book of the Bible. The words that were written by that campfire still appear today in the Menninger Bible Lessons that are printed every Friday in the Topeka *Daily Capital*. Thousands of students have memorized those words and have been grateful for the experience that they have brought.

But the early days of the Menninger Bible Lessons were difficult. When Flo met with the church council that fall and told them that she was going to use her own lessons and charge five dollars per student so that she could have some working capital for the preparation of texts, she was firmly voted down. No one had ever charged a fee for a Bible class, and certainly no Topekan had ever been presumptuous enough to think that he could improve upon the accepted ways of teaching the Bible. Flo did not argue with the council; she simply sent the two local papers a notice that she would be at home every afternoon to enroll members for a Bible class for which she would use her own lessons and charge a fee. The classes were to continue for four years. Church people shook their heads knowingly; such a plan would not attract more than a dozen people, and those would be attracted by the novelty. By the end of the next week they were shaking their heads for a different reason. One hundred and twelve women had enrolled and, before the year was out, the class numbered 198. And this was the smallest the class was ever to be.

Although Flo Menninger taught the Bible in its entirety, she always remembered something her grandmother had told her when she had been puzzled by the many seemingly disconnected stories that make up the Bible. "You'd better just read about Jesus," her grandmother had said. Flo had taken this advice seriously and veered away from strict fundamentalism. Certainly the Sermon on the Mount had found its way into her sons' spirits and was accepted by her husband as the basis of true Christianity. When Dr. Karl Menninger says to students of psychiatry, "If we can love . . ." and tells them that this is the basic precept upon which they must proceed, he has not strayed far from his mother's teachings.

When Flo went to the International Sunday School Convention

in Washington in 1910 she was a personage in the world of Bible
teachers. She was a guest of Senator Charles Curtis' family and
shared a room with his sister, Dolly. The Curtises took Flo to meet
President Taft and when she went home they gave her a copy of
Thomas Jefferson's *The Life and Morals of Jesus of Nazareth.*

iii

Karl was graduated from high school in 1910 near the
top of his class. Unlike his brothers, he was not social in the conventional sense, and his mother's organizational activities had
centered less around his classmates than around Edwin's and
Will's. Flo thought that she saw something special in Karl that set
him apart from other boys. Although she hoped that he would be
an organizer and leader, she saw that for the time being he seemed
to excel at solitary pursuits. He wrote well and was good at
photography. He was interested in areas of human endeavor that
were then little explored. Once, when there had been a series of
articles on psychology in a women's magazine, Karl had been able
to explain them to his mother when she herself could not clearly
understand them. He was articulate, and when the opposition was
brisk he was the best member of his debating team. His mother
realized that he functioned best on the zealot's monorail, just as
she did. In her diary she made shy remarks about what some
genius in the family might do, and quite obviously related those
remarks to "her Karl."

During the summer after Karl's graduation from high school, it
seemed to him that his father was waiting for him to bring up the
subject of his future education. Not being sure of what line he
wanted to follow, Karl avoided discussions with his father until it
had already been decided that he would take a liberal arts course
at Washburn College, of which Washburn Medical School was a
branch. If his father was hurt because Karl did not launch into
pre-medical courses he gave no indication of it. Flo seemed sure
that she would be asked for counsel when the time came for Karl
to decide on his preparation for professional life.

Karl had not been a full-fledged member of the group of boys
from his high school class who were to enter Washburn with him.
Some had belonged to the Epworth League, others had come to

parties at his house; with still others he had engaged in school politics, dramatics, and sports such as tennis and back-yard baseball. It was not a closely knit group, even though the boys did come from the upper segment of Topeka society, to which the Menningers belonged. His father was physician to many of their families. Karl took it for granted that because of his family's position he would be rushed for the fraternity upon which he had set his heart, Phi Delta. Perhaps he was even more confident of immediate acceptance into the upper social stratum of college life. It never occurred to him that he had not participated in all the activities of the other boys, or that the taboo in his family on card playing, dancing, and the like, might have made him seem strange.

During his first weeks at college, Karl went into one of the depressions that always beset him when his mind was not fully occupied and challenged by new situations and problems in learning. Little was offered in his freshman classes that he did not already know, yet when he was asked the simplest question he often couldn't find the answer; he had already answered the question, more elaborately, to his own satisfaction long ago. Only the science courses made a demand on him, and these were few. The dullness that beset him in the classroom carried over to his campus life. He waited painfully for his call to join Phi Delta, feeling that fraternity life would bring out the energy and enthusiasm that were usually his.

One by one, he saw his classmates join the fraternity until finally it became obvious that he wasn't going to be rushed. The one other fraternity had not interested him, and now he was too proud to compromise and join it. His rejection by Phi Delta wounded him deeply and his family worried about his health. He could not confide in his mother, for fear she would take matters in her own hands and worsen the situation. Nor did he want to go to his father. He knew too well that his father viewed education as something more than fraternity life. And perhaps his father thought that he was having a struggle in choosing a career, and therefore might force an issue that Karl was not willing to face at that time. Charles was concerned only for his son's hurt, but the boy had no way of knowing that.

Finally Karl decided to go directly to some of his old high school friends and ask why he had not been invited to join the fraternity. He felt sure that the reason must be some misunderstanding which he could at once rectify. He was puzzled when the boys were embarrassed by his question. They evaded the issue until Karl said, "I don't care what the reason is. I have to know and I have a right to know."

"Well, if you've got to have the cold truth," a classmate told him, "it's because most of the boys think you're just plain feeble-minded. A couple of us have tried to say you're not, but we can't convince the majority. When you come right down to it, you *are* mighty odd."

Karl listened in disbelief. Hurt and furious, he went from boy to boy and the answer was always the same. "They think you're a feeb, Karl," was the consistent answer, but no one would come right out and say that he was one of those who thought so.

For a week or two Karl wandered about the campus, an outcast, a pariah. If he had ever been sure of anything it was of his intelligence. He had always felt that other boys looked up to him for just that. And now he was deprived of his chief point of pride.

In thinking about this experience in later years, Karl said, "Not being accepted [by the fraternity] was one of the most valuable things that ever happened to me . . . You will remember the passage in Isaiah about the stone that was rejected by the builders becoming the head of the corner. I have always held that this was probably the most important thing for psychiatrists to remember about their patients. If they can realize that they can be fitted in somewhere else, such "fitting in" may be of enormous importance —much more than they had ever hoped for in the lesser adaptations at which they failed."

But in his college days, Karl could not think of his rejection in such terms. What had happened to him was a canard, a slander, against which reasonable argument and evidence had no effect. It was a situation that momentarily alienated him from his family and became an issue which he could meet with no weapons but his own. His two younger brothers looked up to him, and he had the family honor to maintain. The boy suffered from excruciating feelings of loneliness, but in that loneliness he found a resolve.

The extracurricular life of Washburn had never experienced such a whirlwind as Karl Menninger became. He plunged into campus politics with an awe-inspiring energy and zeal. Where he could not hold office he worked behind the scenes. The drama and literary groups were bowled over by the impetus of his attack; he acted and wrote, directed and edited. Where there was a musical group, there he was. He barely concentrated in his classes, getting passing grades and little more. He was active in church groups and at the same time he learned to dance.

Grace Gaines was the most sought-after girl on the campus, but it was the boy who had been called a feeb who dated her steadily. As if fearing that someone else might gain her attention for a moment, he attended her constantly. Perhaps she had been a little sorry for him, but she learned that she might as well have been sorry for a hurricane. Though she might solace and reassure him, she could not stop the human storm he had become.

Flo Menninger, who was apt to measure health by zeal, was not especially alarmed at her son's great outburst of energy. Indeed it may have seemed a fulfillment of the very quality she had hoped for in him. But Charles Menninger was no casual student of psychology, and he knew that only a very troubled boy could be capable of such an output of energy. Still, he felt that it would be wrong for him to intercede until whatever it was that ailed his son had made him desirous of help. It took all the doctor's patience to watch his son fritter away the educational opportunities that surely must exist in Washburn. He could not agree with his wife when she said that Karl's activities at Washburn were a response to an opportunity for activity and leadership. To be a leader, a man has first to lead himself, and Charles Menninger did not think that his son was doing that. And yet he waited almost two years before he interceded.

Washburn Medical School had given Dr. Menninger a medical degree in 1906 when he had become a full member of the faculty. He had a certain loyalty to the school; perhaps he hoped that his son would arrive at this medical school by some route, however devious.

iv

As their older brother went on to college and into a swirl of activity, the two younger boys went their own way. By being

younger children for whom their brother had, in a way, run interference, they had certain advantages. Their tie with their mother
was less charged with emotion. Also, they had been born in more
favorable economic circumstances. Flo had probably made Edwin
slightly more dependent upon her than William, for William had
developed at the time that Flo was organizing the Bible classes.
Both boys, however, were better able to cope with her than Karl
was, since neither had been made to feel so anxious over her
moods, and were thus less subject to her own anxiety.

None of this meant that they were slighted in the least. It meant
only that their mother's concern for them was not so intensely
personal. She wholeheartedly assisted them in group activity.
Edwin had a group of boys who called themselves The Stags,
who wanted to have a regular meeting place after school hours.
Of course the Menninger home was the place. A large clubroom
was set aside on the ground floor of the house and Charles saw to
it that it was equipped with adequate furniture, books, and games.
The boys provided their own logs for their fireplace, but the food
they ate before the fire—ice cream, cake, candy, and pumpkin
pie with whipped cream—came from the Menninger larder. This
clubroom was to be kept up long after Edwin went on to college.

While he was in high school Edwin kept on with his paper
routes and worked on all the school publications. He was a natural
businessman and he had a flair for writing. Like Karl, he was also
interested in his father's flowers and trees.

In 1910, Will and his friends were already using the back yard
of the Menninger home as a campground, and on warm nights
more than a dozen boys might have pitched tents there. Charles
Menninger bought some books on scouting, and this group became the core of the first boy scout troop in Topeka. Since the
doctor had no time to become a scout leader, much as he would
have liked to, Will became a sort of in-the-ranks leader until The
Boy Scouts of America was started and an adult leader stepped
in. Whenever he could not be present, his mother took his place.
Will took naturally to scouting, and the Menningers' house was
the home of the scout movement in Topeka. It seemed only natural that he should eventually become a military leader and a member of the National Executive Board on Scouting. A time would
come when he would seriously think of making scouting a career.

Both boys were good students, and they were joined by another good student, Charles's nephew, Charles A. Menninger, who was to make his home with the Topeka Menningers until he finished school and took a job the doctor obtained for him with the Santa Fe Railroad, of which he was later to become treasurer. Will Kircher had gone East to study journalism and Foy Ernest was in medical practice in Topeka.

When he could, Charles took the boys out on calls with him, and most of the trip would be spent in answering questions of personal concern to the boys. They seldom asked a question that touched upon medicine. As Charles watched Karl he must have wondered if the quiet influence he intended to have was all that he thought it to be. Flo seemed to feel that it was she who would have to help the boys choose careers; she had never consulted the doctor on the possibility of their becoming physicians. Still, he was not the sort of man who would make a contest of anything, no matter how dear it might be to him. He respected his sons' personalities. If they were to be doctors they would prevail against their mother, and he felt that she would accept anything about which they felt real conviction.

v

In 1912 the doctor took the family on a trip by Cadillac to Colorado. Here was an ordeal that would have tried the tempers of most families. Farmers were still fighting against hard-surfaced roads because of the damage they did to horses' hoofs. Flat tires and boiling radiators were routine, and 150 miles a day was a heroic run. Camps had to be set up late and struck early, and the heat in the long, level stretches of western Kansas and eastern Colorado was intense. Nevertheless, the Menningers made it an exciting trip. On such occasions Charles was as thoughtful of Flo as a lover, and she was able to respond with a certain girlishness. The boys were given chores to do, and the chores were not a source of quarrels: each was simply someone's job, and that was that.

Wherever there was a rock, a leaf, a flower, or a bird, the doctor had an opportunity to teach. The Rockies were a magnificent introduction to geology. Flo could tell stories of her early days in Kansas that made rough beds and quickly thrown together food seem elegant. Will's scouting ability found a practical outlet, and Karl and Edwin could display their skill with the car. A stretch that could now be covered in one day took six days then, and the family were on intimate terms with the country they passed through.

Shortly after this trip, the doctor felt impelled to call Karl into his study and talk with him very seriously about the frivolity that had marked his first two years of college. "You've got off to a wrong start at Washburn," he told Karl, "and I doubt if any amount of resolve would alter your pattern there. Grace is a good girl, but this isn't the time for either of you to monopolize each other. What you need to do is go to a school where you don't know anyone and where you can do something to earn your way, instead of spending all your time in extracurricular activities. Your mother thinks that you want to go in for economics, and that will take some hard and diligent study. You should also get the feel of other subjects so that you can be sure you're on the right path. An education isn't a thing to be played with; it's the basis of life."

Karl had no defense to offer, no matter how unhappy he felt about leaving Grace Gaines. Only he knew just how bad a start he had made at Washburn, and the scholar in him was eager for a fresh chance. In a place where he wasn't known, and where his subjects fully engaged him, there could be no charge of feeble-mindedness.

"How does the University of Wisconsin strike you?" his father asked. Wisconsin was making an outstanding name in the sciences.

"Fine," Karl said. He was grateful to his father for rescuing him from a bad situation—and he wished that he had suggested the idea himself.

Flo did not like the idea of so much distance being placed between her and her son, but she could see her husband's wisdom, and Karl would be taking a course she had wanted him to take.

When she was packing Karl's extra clothing in a box that could be checked through on his train ticket, she packed some apples, of which he was very fond, in the same box. The doctor insisted that Karl say his good-bys to the family at the house and that he drive him to the station alone. He knew how he would have felt had he been in his son's place. At the station, after the ticket was bought, father and son went into the baggage room to check the box that contained the apples and clothing. It was packed in such a way that both apples and clothing showed from the outside. A regulation against checking fruit was posted on the wall of the checkroom.

"Clothing?" the baggageman asked of the doctor, preparing to check the bag without further question.

"Yes," Charles said, blandly.

"And apples," said Karl, highly offended at his father's carelessness with the truth. When his father nudged him to keep quiet, Karl persisted, "Well there *are* apples in the box."

"You'll have to repack the box," the baggageman said, and, with a wink at the doctor, left the room.

"Karl," his father said, as he and his son bent over the box, "no matter what your mother has taught you, you don't have to tell the whole of the truth all of the time. The baggageman was asking us not to tell him that there were apples in the box. You did him no favor by insisting on the truth and you would have done the railroad no harm if you hadn't told him. You actually hurt a man who wanted to do us a favor. You've got to learn that the truth is a matter of principles you believe in and not of details in which you have no belief but only a useless knowledge. You'll get along better with people and life when you discover that. Here, take an apple."

The father handed his son an apple from the box, took another for himself, then nailed the lid shut on the box of apples and clothing. The son started to protest, but as his father bit into his apple he bit into his own and their eyes met. They walked out of the baggage room arm in arm. Karl suddenly had less fear of the strange university he faced and more respect for his father than his conscience would immediately allow that he had any right to have.

The doctor saw no reason to point out that Flo, who had packed the box, had done so with a full knowledge of railroad regulations, and that the son who was following her precepts was betraying her. As Charles Menninger put his son on the train, he had a feeling that his patience would sooner or later be rewarded.

CHAPTER EIGHT

i

ALTHOUGH HE REMAINED a general practitioner, Charles Menninger was now bringing most of his study to bear on diabetes. His study of diatetics at Battle Creek, Michigan, had covered all nutritional diseases. He had also gone to New York to study under the famous German gastroenterologist, Dr. Carl von Noorden, and in his studies of pathology in Topeka he had given special attention to the pathology of the pancreas. Diseases of the kidney and bladder engaged him for a time and he made a special trip to Chicago to learn the technique of using the cystoscope, a recently developed instrument through which one could examine the bladder. Charles finally dropped his interest in the genitourinary field because this work led directly into surgery. The study of diabetes remained his principal interest.

His most intensive study of diabetes took place at Bellevue Hospital in New York, under Dr. Graham Lusk. Using what seemed to be the best available text on diabetes, Charles, aided by Lusk, searched the wards for clinical equivalents of the textbook cases and studied them, observing the way the doctors in the great medical center handled diagnosis and treatment. When the other doctors had gone home, Charles would be in the laboratory where he had a chance to experiment with animals. In his spare time he read case histories. When he left New York at the end of three busy weeks, he knew that diabetes would remain his most active medical interest.

In reality, Charles had been obtaining physiological data in order that he might better follow a psychological bent that was already well fixed. The diabetic could be treated primarily through his mind, and that challenged Charles—it brought out the psychiatrist that was latent in him. Even in the early days of his practice he had noticed that patients with diabetes invariably suffered from a feeling of hopelessness that had been conveyed to them by every physician they had seen. In talking with other physicians, he realized that their fatalistic attitude toward diabetes made them halfhearted about its treatment. This attitude was an affront to Dr. Menninger's constitutional optimism. He felt that diabetic patients often died of despair rather than of their illness and that in any case they had little encouragement to follow the strict and punishing diets that were necessary if the diabetes was to be controlled. Many physicians also assumed that it would be useless to explain the nature of the disease to the patient; he could not possibly understand. To Charles Menninger it seemed ridiculous that a man could not be made to understand something that to him was a matter of life and death.

In Christ's Hospital, Dr. Menninger had some beds set aside for diabetics, and went about training nurses and a dietician to assist him in the treatment of the disease. The Menninger method of treating diabetics was a refinement of what he had learned from his studies and reading; added to this were his teaching ability, his optimism, and his endless patience. The moment diabetes was diagnosed—and the doctor had perfected methods that aided him in making an early diagnosis in many cases—the patient was hospitalized and was made to submit to a course of treatment and instruction.

As the patient's diet was cut down to the bare minimum that was required to maintain life and slowly brought up to the point where an adequate diet could be given without a diabetic reaction, he was taught just what the diet meant in terms of his own metabolic process. He would learn, for example, and be able to recite, all the common and pure carbohydrates as well as the 1 to 5 per cent, 5 to 10 per cent, and 10 to 15 per cent carbohydrates, and the sugar content of fats and proteins. All this information was given in an intensive training course in which an atmosphere of hope persisted. Hope was given a basis by the improvement in health that came about while the doctor and his staff were supervising the diet of the patient. This improvement was the incentive for the patient to try to equal or excel the skill of the physician and his dietician.

That such treatment required the utmost in patience from the doctor goes without saying. Day in and day out the same things had to be repeated over and over, as the patients were made to see that life was worth the effort they were putting into it. The psychological factors were many, since for purely physiological reasons diabetics may run the emotional gamut during reactions. Where there was a predisposition to emotional extremes, emotional problems had to be dealt with directly, and only an extremely mature and dedicated man could consistently cope with the problems of these unfortunate people; love and concern had to be expressed through firmness and perseverance and in this Dr. Charles Menninger was at his best.

In the first decade of this century, before there was insulin, Dr. Menninger's reputation as a man who could treat diabetes successfully spread not only to communities around Topeka but beyond the borders of the state. And while he functioned on a level that would have brought fame to any Eastern physician—fame and enforced specialization—he continued to deliver babies, lance boils, treat measles and mumps, and give families the counsel they expected from their doctor. Charles Menninger's zeal in this special field was carried on at the expense of time he would have liked to spend with his family and his flowers. Whenever he had an opportunity he tried to instruct other physicians in the use of his method; he tried particularly to instruct them in the art of giving hope to their diabetic patients.

ii

The letters that Karl wrote to his father and mother from the University of Wisconsin told them that he was living a completely different life from that of the year before at Washburn. He had a job playing the piano during mealtime in the main dining room of the school. He had joined the Presbyterian Church in Madison and had made friends with its pastor, the Reverend Richard Hunt, and a student pastor named Matthew Allison. Allison and Karl had become especially close friends, and played chess together twice a week. The courses he had enrolled in were those that would best prepare him for a career in banking—economics, accounting, business-letter writing, and the like. There was also a course in chemistry, the subject he had enjoyed most at Washburn. His parents were pleased with the change in him, his father believed that the course in chemistry would overthrow the courses in business methods. Unless he was mistaken, Karl had scientific curiosity.

By the time the second semester had begun Karl had forsaken the piano and was working as a waiter in the dining room. While his letters quite obviously showed the effect of the course in business-letter writing, their content certainly betrayed no great interest in the world of business. Karl was now enthusiastic about his courses in chemistry, but what seemed to interest him most was religion. It appeared that he now thought of religion as a possible career, for he often spoke of the necessity of reconciling religion with science.

Flo was beginning to worry a little. At one time or another each of her sons, in attempts to please her, had spoken of going into the ministry—something she did not want. Too many of the ministers she had known had been so handicapped financially as to be rendered useless in their vocation as their families suffered deprivation for no great gain on the part of the world. She was especially alarmed at Karl's sudden religious turn since he was likely to plunge into things with an intensity as great as her own.

In Madison, Karl was thoroughly enjoying himself. The conflicts he felt were primarily philosophical and were borne on a rising wave of idealism that could break only on the shores of science or religion. He was tempest-tossed and he loved it; all his senses were quickened and his mind was finding material that really engaged it. In spite of the business courses he was taking, Karl considered himself a scientist and took that side in the friendly debates that he and his friend Matthew Allison had about religion and science.

Karl wondered whether religious knowledge and scientific knowledge belonged in the same world. He would point out that a knowledge of chemistry was something you could do something about. It was capable of growth and advance; it furthered man's knowledge of the natural world around him, and it particularly aided the healing arts. Religion, he maintained, was something that was always present when you called upon it; it was like a bed to rest upon or ham and eggs for breakfast—a dependable substance. With this his friends did not agree. They pointed out that religion had directly to do with man's responsibility to the world, even though, as they saw it, man's primary responsibility was to God. As each evening of argument ended, Karl found himself on the verge of saying, "Almost, thou persuadest me."

In fact he was so much persuaded that before the year was out he found himself standing in a rural pulpit, preaching a sermon. Hunt and Allison had prevailed on him to try his hand at preaching and told him that there were small churches that were eager for even such words as a student could give them. Standing in that pulpit had a profound influence on Karl. The people did need him; their little community was starved for word of God and of the world outside. It wasn't necessary to be an ordained minister to have influence upon these people; to them even a college student was a man of great learning. Karl did well in the pulpit. The years of having fresh Biblical verses ready for each meal had given him a better knowledge of the Bible than he knew he possessed and he had, of course, learned much from his mother. Campus politics, the drama groups, and the debating team had given him a certain eloquence. He could feel his powers as he preached, but his idealism made him question whether he was using his powers properly.

Other things were happening at the university. He had joined the International Club, and his view of the world was broadening. As he talked to people from various countries he began to wonder if he might not be most useful as a missionary. For a while he became possessed with the idea of studying those things that would enable him best to serve the people of backward lands. There were thoughts of teaching, thoughts of practically everything but the practice of medicine. Karl felt that his mission in life would have to be one of great scope; he had no doubts of his powers if he put them to use, and he already had an inkling of the energy and zeal that he could command.

Fortunately the University of Wisconsin abounded with men who could inspire a young man of an idealistic nature. Karl avidly sought everything from any source that would feed his idealism. There were times when he almost forgot Grace Gaines, but they weren't lasting. She was not enthusiastic about his feeling that he might have a vocation in the ministry or in missionary work. And she was important too. So was his mother; she wasn't in a position to disapprove wholly of the new trend in her son's life, but she certainly did not give him the approval he had felt he would get from her when he offered to enter into the religious work that had meant so much in her life. Only his father was quietly approving and seemed to understand. Karl was a puzzled young man.

iii

In the summer of 1913 there was the usual trip to Winona Lake, Indiana, where Flo Menninger could enjoy association with other Bible teachers. The boys could fish, swim, and play, as well as take courses in natural history and the like. The lake was an interdenominational religious meeting place which tried, in a small way, to emulate Chautauqua, in New York State. Charles enjoyed going there and made it a point to arrive before the Fourth of July, bringing fireworks. This was a practice of his every year, no matter where his family was. In 1913 it was more important to him, for he could see that his sons would not be sharing his summers for long.

Edwin would be entering Washburn the next year and Will in another three years. Charles hoped that Edwin would move quietly and directly into those college courses that would prepare him for the study of medicine. The boy's outgoing personality and his talent for getting along with people would be a great asset to a physician. Perhaps he would be a surgeon; he was attracted to science and he was good with his hands. It was, of course, too early to tell just what direction Will would take, but one thing was sure; once he made up his mind there would be little chance of deviation. The boy seemed to have been born with a strange maturity and there was no doubt that he, too, would make a fine physician if he chose to be one. But Charles Menninger could only look on and hope.

The doctor did not feel as his wife did about the ministry. Had one of his sons chosen to enter the Church he would have given him his wholehearted backing. Charles Menninger had stood by too many bedsides and known too many troubled people to be one to discount the value of the minister. Flo's idea that everyone should be an independently practicing Christian, and as such an amateur theologian, was well and good, but there were times when people needed the things that only a dedicated minister of the Church could give them. Perhaps, second to becoming doctors, Charles Menninger would have chosen that his sons go into the ministry or into teaching, another vocation at which Flo Menninger now looked askance.

Charles Menninger did know that the older his sons grew the more he enjoyed them. It seemed to him that they came to him more and more often, and that even if nothing much of importance was said a greater understanding was established with each year. Karl obviously felt more free to discuss his college experiences with him than he did with his mother. As his son talked of the Church and of missionary work, the doctor simply listened, allowing the young man to explain things to himself. When he did this, he remembered that his own youth had been more lonely and confused than need be, simply because he had had no one who had made him listen to himself. The closest he had ever come to experiencing this had been through prayer, when he had sensed God's pattern of guiding best by guiding least.

Charles Menninger was frequently in pain that summer, but only he knew about it. And he knew the cause of it. His gall bladder was troubling him, and something drastic might have to be done about it, but he was not going to worry his family until that day came.

iv

In the late summer Karl had still not decided on just what courses he would take when he returned to school. He did know that when he was at home he could feel again the rejection that he had suffered at Washburn, and he knew that it affected all his efforts in that town. He knew that he wanted acceptance, but not on the same grounds as before. He wanted Grace Gaines, too, and his confusion only confused her. There was also a slight alienation from his mother which he found it difficult to explain, for it seemed to him that she was waiting for him to tell her something that would please her even if he did not know just what it could be.

And then came an incident that was to change his life. He had a tremendous toothache. An appointment was made with Dr. Fred Koester, who was an old family friend as well as the family dentist. As Karl got into the dental chair, the doctor asked him what he was doing at the university, and was told about the courses in banking, and so on. When Karl described these courses the disgust he felt was so great that he must have conveyed it to the dentist.

"It's strange that you should have so much trouble deciding what to do," Dr. Koester said. "Your father is a devoted scientist who gets great satisfaction out of his practice. He's respected by everyone. You could have the privilege of practicing with him— and that's something a lot of young men would give their eyeteeth to do."

Karl was thinking through pain now, but the thought he had was startling enough to break through clearly. "Why haven't I thought of that before?" he asked himself. "Of course it's the thing to do."

As he left the dentist's office, he said, "I am going to become a doctor."

"Of course you are," Dr. Koester agreed.

That night Karl found his father alone, and, after an embarrassed moment, said to him, "Father, I've made up my mind to go into medicine. I'm going to become a physician."

For a moment the father could find no words. He embraced his son. There were tears in his eyes as he said, "I'm glad, Karl," and then turned away.

A week later Karl heard himself saying to his mother, "Something has happened to me. I'm sorry if I hurt you, but from now on I have to go my own way."

v

Early in the summer of 1914, Charles Menninger was operated on twice, and, for the first time in his adult life, was forced to stay in bed for more than two consecutive days. It is even doubtful if he had ever been allowed to stay in bed the entire night during most of his years of medical practice. For a change people were concerned with *him;* he was an object of their attentions and affection. Flowers, fruit, callers, and cards of greeting and encouragement told him how well loved he was in Topeka. But in bed in the hospital and in bed at home, while he recuperated from the operation, and rested from the weariness of the years, he had a chance to survey his resources. And he learned that he could not truly rest while he stagnated. A vision of what enforced retirement would mean presented a fearful reality.

A man whose profession gives him reason to move about in the city he loves, helping its people and walking among trees and flowers planted by him, or at his suggestion, can feel very lost when walls imprison him. He can become cantankerous and moody, or else he can find something within his new and narrow environment that will engage his mind and spirit. The doctor chose to engage his mind. Sending for mineral specimens and books, he gave himself a more complete course in mineralogy than he'd had before. This led into geology and suggested that plant paleontology might be an interesting field—something to look forward to studying. He whetted his appetite for it with a book or two.

Of course, he was studying the catalogues of the nurseries and seed houses, looking for ways to improve his garden. Also he had plans for landscaping the grounds of the house, since the boys would soon no longer need the yard as an athletic field and plants would be safe. This kind of study and planning, he could see, was of the sort that would get an invalid out of bed, or shake a retired man out of a depression. The doctor was very studious of his responses to invalidism; things that he learned made him wish that he had been ill earlier in his career so that he might have used the knowledge he was now gaining for the greater good of his patients. He was incapable of wasting anything that happened to him.

Of course he was catching up with his medical reading and comparing his experiences of the years with any new material that confronted him. This was an added incentive to activity. The doctors who had taken over his patients called on him regularly and were often amazed to learn that their incapacitated colleague would have new knowledge to impart to them at almost every visit.

As the doctor recovered, one thing was clear to him: health always depends on the ability to keep one's curiosity alive. There must always be something to look forward to as one goes to sleep at night. Each day must end with at least one question unanswered, one lesson yet to be learned. There must always be things that need one's individual care, whether they be plants or human beings. When he dressed and went to his office again, he was no longer afraid of retirement.

Another thing that gave him a new hold on life was the letters Karl wrote about the things he was learning in school. Some of the letters were naïve, but all showed that Karl had the makings of a sound physician—he always seemed to know what the courses he was taking would mean in relation to the courses to come, and he was giving himself a solid groundwork, neglecting nothing.

At that time the University of Wisconsin did not have a four-year medical school. The first two years of medical school were taught and then a master's degree in science was presented to the student doctor, who would then have to find another medical school for his last two years.

Charles Menninger wanted his son to have the best possible education and if he deserved it, the cost wouldn't be a consideration. He encouraged his son to choose a school for his last two years that would accept him only on the basis of superior scholarship. Much to his father's delight Karl chose Harvard, one of the schools with the highest scholastic requirements, and from the first year of medical school on there was little doubt that Karl would be admitted to Harvard.

It was clear to Charles that Karl had his mother's zeal. He had not abandoned religion because he had chosen medicine. Even as he took the heavy medical courses and kept up with laboratory work, he had taken on the job of occupying the pulpits of rural churches on Sunday. In one rural village Karl was particularly liked, but filling its pulpit was not simply a matter of delivering a sermon. To reach this village, Cambridge by name, he had to get out of bed at four on Sunday morning, walk across town to the railroad station, and catch a milk train to a town called London where his parishioners met him at seven. Often the trip had to be

made by sleigh and through terrific cold. It would be eleven on
Sunday night when Karl got back to his room. But as he wrote to
his family about his experiences and the need the people had for
him, the father could see that Karl's greatest gratification came
not from the ten-dollar fee that he earned but from the love he
had for the people and they for him.

Karl had, in the meantime, become engaged to Grace Gaines.
She came from a well-established family and was a levelheaded
girl; she had the full approval of Karl's parents, and especially of
his mother. Grace was practical enough to do what she could to
discourage Karl from going into the ministry, and now that he
sometimes spoke of becoming a medical missionary she acted as
a buffer against that impulse. His mother's lessening influence
with Karl was supplanted somewhat by the growing influence of
her future daughter-in-law. Whatever he may have felt, his father interfered not at all with his son's sporadic impulses to become a medical missionary.

With Karl's decision to go into medicine a precedent had been
established for the other two boys. Although Edwin didn't enter
Washburn as a pre-medical student he was taking courses that
could be quickly adapted to that end. He did show a decided
penchant for chemistry. Will was curious about his eldest brother
who was a medical student, and that curiosity augured well for
his future. As the doctor looked back on the pronouncement he
had made on the morning of his return from the Mayo Clinic, he
could see that his prophecy had become a dream that was constantly with him. Now it seemed likely that the dream would be
fulfilled; the boys could choose their own specialties in medicine
and he would adapt himself to them. Between them, the four
Menningers could master large areas of medicine, even a medicine that was becoming more and more involved.

Flo Menninger did not oppose the idea of her boys going into
medicine. Perhaps the idea had never occurred to her, or perhaps
she felt that she had created one doctor and that with the boys
she could venture into other fields. She could not help feeling
that there was something a little unfair in having to relinquish
the boys to their father after all her years had gone into forming
their lives. Where they had been lucky to have the doctor's day-
by-day attention, they had demanded and received her attention

hour by hour. They had made her close to them and had, indeed, made her as dependent on them as they were on her. Even the feeling of having one son drawn away from her was a little like the experience of hearing the school bell ring and knowing that she would not be under that bell waiting for a class, that grade after grade of pupils would go on without her. While she was glad to see Charles happy she could not help feeling a pang of jealousy.

Flo Menninger could never guess what strange influences she had on her sons. Her lessons in frugality and the careful management of money had impressed them not at all, for she had succeeded only in making them feel that home was a place of security and that her worry about money was excessive. None of the boys was a spendthrift, but on the other hand none of them was good at saving money, unless it was for something especially desirable. She had no way of knowing that one of the things that made Karl swerve toward the career of a missionary, which she dreaded, was his memory of her worries when she thought that his father didn't have enough patients. Karl had a vision of a line of patients stretching out into infinity, if he became a medical missionary. He wasn't very realistic about relating medical practice to the money it might bring in.

Even though Karl was partially lost to her, Flo had the other boys with her. For a while Edwin's fraternity used the Menninger home, and when the fraternity found a house of its own it was she who did most of the work in fitting it up. This gave her a proprietary interest in the fraternity house when Edwin went there to live so that he might enter more fully into college life.

Edwin often talked to his father about the chemical experiments he was doing at school. He was intense about chemistry, and perhaps he was competing with Karl, who now seemed to claim most of their father's attention. Some of the chemical stunts that Edwin discussed with his father were of an extremely dangerous nature; Charles had often tried to modify his son's enthusiasm for strange chemical combinations that could be explosive. Edwin was not averse to carrying chemicals about with him and doing tricks with them. While his father could only encourage the boy in anything that had to do with science, he did have forebodings that led him constantly to caution his son.

vi

At eight-thirty on the evening of March 2, 1915, Flo and
Charles Menninger were in their study, and Will was doing his
homework, when the phone rang. Charles went to the phone.

Flo, who was expecting a call from one of her Bible students,
waited as her husband took the receiver from the hook. Will was
also alert, for he expected a schoolmate to call about some business
that had to do with scouting. As they watched the doctor while
he listened to the phone, they saw his face go white.

"Yes, yes," he said into the mouthpiece, "I'll be right there. Call
an ambulance."

"It's Edwin," Flo said in panic, as her husband grabbed his
medical bag and coat. "I'll go with you. What is it?"

"There's been a little explosion," the doctor said. "The boys are
excited and it may not amount to much. You stay here and pray.
I'll call you as soon as I know what has happened. Have faith
in God."

He was gone before they could say anything more.

The Topeka *Daily Capital* told the story the next morning.

"STUDENT LOSES EYE IN A LABORATORY EXPLO-
SION," said the headline.

"Upending a test tube filled with chlorate, an explosive with
which he was experimenting, about eight o'clock last night, caused
Edwin Menninger the loss of his right eye, the ring finger of his
left hand, and left him in such a condition that his father, Dr. C. F.
Menninger, feared that more serious conditions might result.

"Menninger's face was full of small holes where possibly pieces
of glass from the test tube tore the flesh. His right eye was cut
and bruised by the force of the explosion. After an examination,
Dr. Menninger said there was practically no chance to save it.
The amputation of the finger was made necessary because of the
badly mangled condition of the flesh and bone.

"Marshall Sanders and Menninger, both assistants in the chemistry laboratory in Washburn College, were experimenting with
explosives in Rice Hall. After mixing phosphorus and potassium
chlorate to make an extremely dangerous explosive, they went
out on the campus north of Rice Hall to test it. Menninger was

carrying the test tube. He held it in his right hand. In changing it to his left hand, he accidentally turned it upside down, allowing the solution to fall to the other end of the tube. The slight force of the concussion caused the explosion. Sanders who was nearby was uninjured . . . Menninger had been warned by his father to use great caution in the experiments . . . Menninger is associate editor of the Washburn Review and is a member of the Alpha Delta Fraternity. He has studied chemistry for three years and is now doing organic work."

The newspaper story could have added that there was little doubt that Edwin Menninger would eventually enter medical school. It did say that his brother, Karl, was a student in medicine.

In the days that followed, Dr. Menninger stayed at his son's bedside most of the time. He had called in the best physicians from both Topeka and Kansas City. His encyclopedic knowledge had enabled him to telephone to any physicians who might have any suggestions to make about the treatment of his son. When surgeons suggested drastic surgery as a means of preventing gangrene, Dr. Menninger resisted. He knew the danger, but he also knew what it would mean to his son to be further handicapped. It wasn't merely a matter of saving him for the practice of medicine, it was a matter of saving him for life.

Charles himself had to administer the treatment in which his colleagues had no belief. There was a theory, and at that time it was not much more than an untried theory, that gangrene could be prevented, or arrested, if oxygen could be injected into the infected flesh in the form of peroxide. This meant putting dozens of hypodermic needles into the muscles of the boy's arm. Seldom has so much pain been inflicted with so much love. No one can ever measure the father's feelings as he hurt his son in order to save him from a lifetime of pain, knowing that he might be wrong, and that the pain might be needless.

Flo Menninger was at her son's bedside whenever it was safe for her to be there. Prayer, which most of her life had been a reinforcement for wishes that she knew were feasible and which she was determined to carry out, became something of a different order. She was asking God to give her back her own and to keep him whole. She put herself at God's mercy and at His service. And when she was not praying or at the bedside she went about life as she always had. The boys at the fraternity were to benefit by the extra baking she did, and her Bible classes marveled at the way she carried on. If she stopped working, she knew that she would have time to let bitterness seep into a mind that had in its time had adequate reason for bitterness.

Will responded to the accident by quietly keeping out of the way. Already he could guess what this accident meant to his father, for he had heard his father tell his mother that it would probably be unwise to think of Edwin going into medicine now, and that if any further maiming took place it would be impossible. It may have seemed to him that he might have to be twice as good a doctor, to make up for Edwin.

vii

Karl had received a wire telling him to come home, that his brother's condition was critical. As the train moved toward Topeka he was suffering for his father and mother. From what his father had said in a phone call, he knew that Edwin might be maimed and that he could never become a doctor. By now Karl knew better than anyone else what it meant to his father to have his sons become physicians, for his father had confided in him his hopes for Edwin. He knew, too, how much it hurt his father to have one of his children suffer over anything. It seemed to him that this patient and gentle man was very vulnerable in this respect.

The nearer the train came to Topeka the more Karl dreaded the moment when he would have to face his father. He thought that his father's suffering would be too much to bear, that his grief and pain would have broken him and that he would expect a greater solace than Karl knew how to give. The young medical student was actually sick with dread as he got off the train and took a taxi to the hospital.

When the girl at the reception desk of the hospital sent for the doctor, Karl waited in an agony of fear. What could he say; what could he do?

And then he saw his father coming down the stairs. In place of the grief and despair he had expected to find, he saw instead a

man whose concern was turned on him like a warming light. The
young man who had expected to be called upon to give compassion was receiving compassion.

"Karl," Charles said, "it was good of you to come. But you must
be dreadfully tired. You don't look well at all. We'll have to get
you to bed."

When he embraced his son, it was the son and not the father
who was shedding tears. There was a great gentleness in his face
as he held his son at arm's length and looked at him.

"Everything will be all right, Son. Don't worry," he said. "What's
important now is that you get some rest."

When Karl was home and in bed, he knew that he had seen the
great physician, a man whose concern for all suffering things is
the essence of his being. Before that night selflessness had been
only a word to Karl; now he had seen what it was in reality. His
father had healed his fear, put him to bed, and while he was
doing this he had calmly and clinically discussed Edwin's condition. Then he had gone back to the hospital before Karl had a
chance to inquire about the great weariness his father must have
felt. He realized that his father would have been puzzled and
embarrassed had he been asked about his fatigue or his feelings.
That trip home was to remain one of the most important experiences in Karl Menninger's medical training and education.

viii

Charles Menninger's resistance to drastic surgery had
been right. Edwin recovered without additional surgery. He was
not seriously crippled, but the injury to his hand and eye were
such that they would handicap him as a physician. One of the
most difficult adjustments Charles ever had to make was that of
accepting the idea that his son would have to go into some other
profession. The boy had grown even more dear to him as he had
treated him for his painful injury and seen his bravery and faith.

Just what that profession would be was not hard to foresee.
Edwin had always liked newspapers, and had he stayed at Washburn he would have been editor of the school paper. The next
fall he entered the School of Journalism at Columbia University.

CHAPTER NINE

i

EARLY IN 1918, when he had finished medical school, followed by an interneship at Kansas City General Hospital, Dr. Karl A. Menninger took over his father's office and practice for a month while the older doctor went East to a medical association meeting. After this month of practice, Karl returned to Boston for graduate work and teaching in the Navy, and wrote this letter to his father:

Dear Father:

After a pleasant and profitable period of nearly a month in your office and practice, and after cogitation over the subject for something more than that, I am moved, dear Father, to make the following suggestions, which I hereby respectfully submit for your consideration.

1. I would raise my fees for obstetrical cases to $50.00 or more, require them to go to the hospital, insist on at least a month of prenatal examination and care, make thoro prenatal examinations of general physical condition, pelvis, urine and B.P.

2. I would refer all surgical cases to Stewart or Stoors, and enter into an active and avowed co-operation with the former. This entails absolute severance of present relations with anyone else, except as demanded by certain patients with preferences.

3. I would announce myself as confining myself to Internal Medicine (and obstetrics if you wish to keep it) and diagnosis.

4. I think it will be of vast time saving value to you to put up a card and have it neatly printed thereupon, "Dr. Menninger prefers to see all patients by appointment. Speak to the office girl. To do so will save yourself and others much unnecessary waiting," or at least the first sentence. Personally, I tried all this month to see everyone this way, and have succeeded to the extent that on one day, June 22nd, I saw ten patients in the office; I had had ten appointments and one failed and one came in. Several others came also but I sent them away

as I was too busy to see them. They got appointments for later in the week and returned to keep them.

5. I would throw the burden of correspondence on Mamie; either get her to learn shorthand or else dictate to her slowly in longhand, or give her the sense of the letter; let her do all the typewriting and addressing of envelopes, and stamping, etc. Then you need only sign the letters. The same applies to having her make out all checks for bills to be paid, and then you can sign those you wish her to send forth.

6. I would certainly make an effort to keep the office, office desk, and waiting room table, especially the former, as free from litter, and as well arranged and as orderly as possible. This, for the reason that the patients, particularly new ones, are much impressed by their first impressions of order and disorder. I think that the stacked up papers, blotters, magazines, etc., especially in haphazard fashion, create a very bad impression.

7. I would discontinue subscriptions to all medical periodicals except those bearing on my particular field, i.e., Internal Medicine. These I would keep neatly filed in the cases, and preserved for future reference in yearly volumes. I would immediately dispense with such worthless magazines as the —— and such entirely unnecessary ones as the —— and such irrelevant ones as ——.

8. I would decrease materially the medical stock on hand. If a patient needs medicine at all, he can be given a prescription. If he doesn't need one, he shouldn't be given any. I except, of course, such individuals as demand some medicine in a small bottle, of which of course I realize there are not a few, homeopathic and otherwise . . .

9. I would charge more for office visits of people who can well afford it. They will respect you more and have more respect for the opinion or advice professionally given them. I would either charge such people $2.00, or more, or nothing.

10. I would have Mamie send out notices or letters to all back number patients on whom you did careful work, reading something like this, "Dear Mr. Jones: I should like very much to see you to make observations on your general physical condition, and particularly with regard to your improvement or otherwise since you professionally consulted me. Will you arrange to call in my office at your convenience, or if that is impossible write me of yourself." Something like that only better worded. I am rattling this off fast and cannot think of the best way to word it.

11. I would continue just exactly as you are doing of late years in spending more time with each patient, charging them more and doing more for them, even at a loss NUMERICALLY of the pill chasers and the 18th Century variety of patients.

12. I would certainly take life leisurely as possible and compatible with an interesting professional life. From now on you are going to

have a rushing business. Pick and choose. Why take everything that comes? Take what you like.

13. I would cultivate the diagnosis and treatment of syphilitic cases for these reasons: they are so obscure; they are so often missed by the other fellow; they are so much in need of help, they are so genuinely helped by treatment . . .

14. In addition to the reasons just given, remember that few men realize as you and I do, the large number of neurosyphilitic involvements. And as I shall be in that work with you before many years, keep tab on them. For Example: Mrs. X. See record. Did you think, 3 years ago, that I would be treating her for early tabes in 1918?

15. Be sure to keep your lab. reports, especially the Wassermans. Last of all I want to say that I am more impressed each year of my life, and this year each month of it, of the remarkable progress you have made up from a meagre medical education to an educational endowment, entirely self-acquired, that puts you far ahead of the average medical man, and alone with one or two in this state and a few in Kansas City. I can tell you Father, that this makes me, your son, extremely proud of his father, and the more anxious to come and be with you and practice with you and think and act with you in mutual help and strength. I want you to know this, and to be sure of it, and to reflect on it, remembering that your practice, numerically speaking, has no attraction for me because I could probably acquire such in other places, e.g., with some man in K.C. But nowhere in the world will I get the help and pleasure from medical co-operation that I will from working with my father. I could not say this if you were like most medical men. Your self-education, constant study, and vast experience make you a medical man with an enviable fitness; most men of the old schools I would have no pleasure in working with because it would be like new wine in old skins. If anything, I think you are ultra-progressive, if such is possible. But I'm glad of it. For while I do not think highly of your extension of interest into other fields than your own in the purchase of apparatus, etc. (e.g., roentgenology, surgery), I am awake to your interest in everything new that is proposed and to every new idea. and thought and apparatus and method, not forgetting the value of the old. And so I shall proceed with what the USN gives me to do until the war is over and we can begin an elaboration of the plans and hopes which you have cherished so long, and I so fondly. I love you as I write as more than a son . . . as your official and eternal partner in business.

KARL A. MENNINGER, M.D.

The variety of Charles Menninger's emotions on reading this letter can be imagined. Here was a son who had graduated *cum laude* from one of the great medical schools and who would have been a Phi Beta Kappa had he remained long enough in any one course as an undergraduate. He had acquitted himself well as an interne in Kansas City General, and he could have had his choice of practices in that city. Already he was as fine a physician as a school could produce, although, perhaps, a little cocksure. But why not? He was his mother's son, too, and blessed with her best endowments.

It amused Dr. Menninger, Sr., that his son should consider him as an ultra-progressive and himself as somewhat of a conservative. The boy had an impulsiveness that had caused him to go ahead and marry Grace Gaines while he was still in medical school. And he had certainly thrown himself headlong into utilizing whatever new diagnostic and treatment methods had come his way. The colloidal gold curve, for example, by means of which syphilis could be detected in the spinal fluid. It was this that had interested Karl in neurosyphilis, as well as in syphilis in general. And the way in which the mental patients had responded to the attention this method of diagnosis required had given Karl a general interest in mental illness that he was now following up in Boston Psychopathic Hospital under Dr. Ernest Southard. The Navy had assigned him to this work and it counted as training toward the specialty of psychiatry. Conservative, indeed!

As the father looked over the list of things his son had suggested that he do in order to improve his practice of medicine, he was touched at the boy's brashness. How could he know that you couldn't require women who had become accustomed to having children at home to go to the hospital? That was something for another generation of women. In the matter of limiting his patients to one surgeon, how could Karl guess the years of careful observation that had made it possible for him to select the right surgeon for each case? It might be all right, as the young physician suggested, to announce that he was limiting his practice to internal medicine, but that wouldn't impress the families to which he was the family doctor.

The suggestions on running the office were more to the point. There should be more order to the appointment book. People walking into the office were a nuisance, but their illness was a nuisance to them, too, and it might need taking care of on just the day they called. Mamie wasn't much of a secretary, but she knew Charles's patients and she had a concern and warmth that made

up for her lack of secretarial training. When Karl came back, they
would have to get an extra girl.

It shocked Charles that his son should think that he was disorderly, even about his desk, for Charles was the most orderly
of people. Everything that he carried in either his pockets or bags
was always in place. He never had to make a false move. When
he took off his clothes at night he placed them so that he could
get into them in the darkness and emerge perfectly dressed in a
minimum of time. As for his desk, perhaps it did look littered,
but there was an order in the litter. The records were the ones
he knew he would need and the magazines were those that contained a paper that referred directly to a case in one of the records.
The blotters, as anyone should be able to see, were markers. He
wondered if after a year of practice his boy would be as critical
of the desk as he was now. As for the periodicals, especially the
medical ones, the same son who praised him for keeping up with
medicine was now suggesting that he cut off his major source of
information. The texts Karl had used in medical school had had as
their sources articles Charles had once read in the periodicals. It
might be that several people were alive in Topeka just because
of his good memory and apparently irrelevant reading. Charles
could not think of one magazine he was willing to do without.

Then there was the matter of dispensing medicine from the
office. Karl had carried on at length about how the patients in
Kansas City General had responded to the attention that was required to get a needle into their spine and yet he thought it odd
and old-fashioned that his father should give people the special
attention that went into filling a prescription by hand and giving
it to the patient with love.

On the matter of fees, Karl was no doubt right. Some people
could be charged more, but there were others who would be hurt
if they weren't allowed to pay a little something, even if the sum
was so small as to be almost meaningless. Respect, Dr. Charles
Menninger had learned, came from another source than that of
money changing hands. But Charles had learned never to charge
people so small a fee as to insult them.

That Karl should suggest that he spend more time with patients
and do more for them, even if he lost some, was ironical. Flo
had always had the opposite attitude, and the doctor had so

played down his tendency to spend too much time and do too much that it had become invisible to his son. He had always given the patients the maximum of what he had to give in either time or skill. As for writing to ex-patients and suggesting that they come to the office for a check-up, it had always been his practice to see those patients when he was in their neighborhood or to inquire about their health when he met them on the streets. At any given time he knew just exactly how most of his patients were doing. It was his business to know, the business of the family doctor. Karl must have read some peculiarly convincing book to come up with a suggestion such as that. As for taking life easy, in so far as it was "compatible with an interesting professional life," the doctor didn't know what Karl meant, and the suggestion that from now on there was going to be a rush of business was funny. It seemed to Charles Menninger that he couldn't remember when there wasn't a rush of business. Pick and choose, indeed. Dr. Menninger would have chosen never to have had one case such as the hundreds he had had during the flu epidemic, or any of the childhood diseases for which he had so few answers, or obstetrical cases on stormy nights. Charles Menninger had lived in a day when families chose him as their physician and with that choice all choosing was ended.

There was something far beyond youthful brashness in Karl's letter, of that the father was sure. His son's sincerity and loyalty was unmistakable. There was no doubt that he would have gone elsewhere to practice if he hadn't believed completely in his father. That he was already trying to improve the practice showed where his inclination was. The line in the letter that the father read over and over was, ". . . we can begin an elaboration of the plans and hopes which you have cherished so long, and I so fondly. . . ." Will was in his last year as a pre-medical student, and there was little doubt now that he would feel the same way.

ii

In the summer of 1918, Flo Menninger's hands were again affected by a numbness. It was the same as that which had beset her when she had given up her teaching and her independ-

ence in order to have Karl, and, indeed, she was in almost the same
position. Will, the last of her children, would be going away to
school. Edwin had been graduated from the School of Journalism
at Columbia University and was employed as assistant editor on
the cable desk of the New York *Herald Tribune,* a job that he
had held even while he was in college. Moreover, he was married
and a child was on the way. The chances of his coming back to
Topeka were very slender. When he had been forced to abandon
the idea of medical practice he had apparently also dropped the
idea that Topeka could ever mean anything to him.

Except for sporadic periods when he had played with the idea
of becoming a medical missionary and had talked to his mother
about that, Karl had moved almost completely into his father's
world. His energy, vitality, and certainty about himself were almost frightening to Flo. He was the kind of son she had wished
for, but he had gone a very long way from her. When he tried to
explain to her that the missionary and the psychiatrist filled almost the same role, she could not understand him, and she wondered whether he was not moving dangerously far from medicine
as she and his father knew it. But Charles did not seem worried,
and he had a way of being right about such things.

Flo had found herself moving closer to her husband. When they
had visited Karl in Boston for his graduation, she had stayed in
the best hotel without protest and had managed to enjoy the city
immensely, even though she had thought that the graduation exercises at Harvard were pretentious and impersonal. The things
she remembered best were visits to see Sargent's Frieze of the
Prophets in the Public Library, and the homes of some of the
famous men. Then, of course, there was Bunker Hill Monument
and the Arnold Arboretum. The latter, because it gave the doctor
such joy.

The big house on Topeka Avenue seemed empty with only
Will remaining in it. The doctor read to her on some evenings
now, and occasionally he talked about the future. If they had an
electric car for Flo there would be no reason why they couldn't
live in the country now, on the outskirts of town, and have a fine
garden and a place for their grandchildren to come. Leah was
still on the old home place where the Menninger boys had often
gone in the summer but that, Charles and Flo agreed, would be

too far away to have the grandchildren go. By staying near To-peka, Flo could continue with her Bible classes, which were still growing, and further her Bible-teaching methods. But she would need companionship during the day while the doctor was gone, for even as he approached retirement he wanted to spend several hours a day in the office with Karl and, eventually, Will. He hoped to live to see some sort of clinic formed, and he wanted to have a hand in it.

It happened that in the summer of 1918, Pearl May Boam, a member of Flo's Bible class and the daughter of a physician who had recently died, was convalescing from appendicitis and was making a poor recovery. She was a good friend of Flo, and Flo often went to see her and interested the doctor in taking care of her. When the doctor had seen her only once or twice, he decided that the girl simply lacked a home and some new attachments in life. And so it was suggested that she come and stay with the Menningers while she was recuperating. She made a remarkable recovery and was asked to stay on. As a cultivated and active person Pearl gave Flo some badly needed help and companionship and she also gave the couple something like the daughter they had wanted. With a third person present, the evening conversations were enlivened.

iii

Charles Menninger had never openly discussed with Karl his plans for a clinic, nor had he attempted to guide Karl into any specialty while Karl was in school or in his interneship. At one point Karl had been interested in becoming a surgeon, and his father had helped him by writing to doctors in various parts of the country to find out where the best residencies could be taken. Karl's idea, at that time, had been that a surgeon was the perfect complement to an internist like his father, that the father's diagnostic skill could best be used if he had a surgeon son. And then Karl had decided against surgery as being too mechanical and limited. It was apparent from what Karl now wrote from Boston about his experiences under Dr. Ernest Southard that psychiatry would claim him.

This did not frighten Dr. Charles Menninger. Instead, it had interested him in the new field and he was reading all the books that Karl suggested and tempering the thoughts they contained with his experiences as a general practitioner. There was nothing in psychiatry that he could see that would keep him and the boys from having their clinic. Indeed, if he read his psychiatry right, it, more than any other specialty of medicine, called for the total application of all medical knowledge and experience. It was, in fact, a natural outgrowth of medicine as it had been developing during all Dr. Menninger's years of practice.

But of one thing Charles Menninger was sure. He was going to place himself at the service of his sons, come what might. The education they had received was more than a summing up of all he had learned or unlearned during the years and only constant search and study had kept him abreast of medicine at all. He could see how his own teaching had kept him alert and caused him to make many trips East in order to give his students the benefit of the latest knowledge. Karl and Will would, in a way, be starting where he stopped; it might be a good idea to keep them on their toes and learn from them for a while. Of course his clinical experience would always be theirs to command and, by example, he could teach them his techniques of practice, if those techniques were good.

As he summed up what he felt, Dr. Charles Menninger could see no reason why it was not fitting that the doctor in late middle age should not become the student of the young. Karl's letter had reminded him that the young have forcefulness and a fresh point of view. Maybe the very things that their elders so often wanted to beat out of the young—the brashness, the freshness, the high idealism—were just the things that could serve medicine best. For a long time Charles had been aware that much of medical practice moved in a self-chosen rut, using a weary fatalism as an excuse for sloth. The young believed, and that was more than half the fight.

On his recent trips East, Charles Menninger had studied under Elliott Joslin and, dissatisfied with that great man's teachings in the treatment of diabetes, had gone to see a student of his who was doing the same work in what seemed to Charles Menninger a more modern and enlightened way. Ideally this young man should never have broken away from Joslin. At least, so Dr. Menninger thought. It was experiences like this that made him determine that he would continue his studies under his own sons and partners and wherever possible let them direct the way.

Since the number of diabetic patients he was treating successfully was growing from year to year, they could provide a basic practice and income until the boys were ready. As it was, it seemed that he had gone as far as possible in the treatment of diabetes. Unless something entirely new was developed, such as Cushing had hoped for in his work with the pituitary, or such as had been attempted with pancreatic extracts, there were few refinements that could be added to the work he was doing.

The whole idea of having sons in practice with him was more exciting to Charles Menninger than the idea of going to medical school had ever been. It was as if this were his real start and all else had been preparation. His prayers now were that he and his sons be spared to practice together and, although it seemed presumptuous, he was already seeing cards and letterheads with "Topeka Clinic" emblazoned on them, and the three Menninger names, and perhaps others, beneath. It had been a long wait and he was impatient for his son to come home and join him. He felt a little guilty over his good fortune when he thought of Flo and saw what had been taken out of her life. But, as always, he conceded that she was the strongest of them all. She had put him through school, and the money she had saved had made the boys' educations possible. All of them were repaying her in the best way they could.

iv

The son who came back to Topeka in June of 1919 to enter into medical practice with his father stood out in contrast to his father. Both were tall men, over six feet, and they shared an aristocratic bearing. Dr. C.F., as the elder was to be known to Topeka after Dr. Karl had joined him, had gained a little weight since the sickly days of his youth, but he retained his carriage. Physically, his son was slighter; still he gave an illusion of size. Anyone who saw the two men separately would have sworn that Karl was the larger, although that was not the case. Perhaps this was because Dr. Karl had a quality of command and authority that was lacking in his father, at least in an overt way.

The elder Menninger won people by his concern for them and by his earnestness and the quiet command he had of his knowledge. The younger doctor had the same qualities, but in him there was a restlessness, a desire to move onward from any given moment and from one idea to the next. There were people who would have said that he was a man who was perpetually ahead of himself, when in fact they would mean that he was ahead of them. Even when young Dr. Menninger was sitting still there was a feeling of motion, of onward movement and impulse. He took things in at a glance, and he seldom altered his view of them. The fact was that he grasped things more quickly than did most men, and he knew what to do about the things he grasped. An uncanny associative process, formed perhaps during an anxious youth, enabled him to translate almost everything into one sort of action or another.

As one schoolmate of Dr. Karl was to say, he was either "all mind or all matter." If a situation engaged him mentally, everything he had ever learned, heard, seen, felt, or read, was at his command in the instant. If his mind was not engaged he became pure matter and as such incapable of action. Once anything engaged Karl, as psychiatry did, he could not and would not let down for a moment.

Though his father was not one to let down, he was a man who could sustain one solitary thought, or look at a flower or tree for a long time without having to do anything about it. If Karl saw a flower that pleased him, he would at once have made an arrangement to have more such flowers in better surroundings. In his inability to leave things alone, he was like his mother, but the things that interested him were more likely to be the same things that interested his father.

On the surface it would have seemed that Dr. Karl's personality might have been upsetting to patients; that his restlessness would further disturb the emotionally distraught. But this was not so. The personal electricity generated by Dr. Karl's active mind somehow created a magnetic field in which the patient was caught and in which he felt a warmth. Instead of waiting for the patient to give out information, Dr. Karl might reach ahead and probe. His impatience with small talk led him to sense and elicit the significant at once. As he did this, he had a way of making the patient feel that he was triumphing over himself and that he and the doctor made a wonderful pair.

But Dr. Karl's skill in working with patients did not carry over to his relationship with some of the physicians of the town, for there were those who thought him to be pretentious, a sort of quack who was trading on his father's reputation. Men who had been jealous of Dr. C.F. and had never dared say so, now had a target for their resentment of the Menningers. On the whole, Dr. Karl was oblivious to this. He felt, and perhaps quite rightly, that Topeka was lucky to have him, and he never for a moment let anyone doubt that psychiatry was a speciality with a significant future.

Dr. C.F. was a man whose relationship with all people, patients or friends, was consistent. He emanated concern; he personified patience, at least so long as there was any justification for patience. People spoke of him as being a thoughtful man, one who made slow and sure selections from a vast field of knowledge and who would be able to remember each decision he made and his reason for making it. In this, certainly, he seemed quite the opposite of his son. Because of this reputation people were apt to consider Dr. Karl, in contrast to his father, as flighty.

Dr. Karl, in a survival from his days of unblemished honesty, was apt to be tactless. In this he was very much his mother's son. If a colleague was wrong, Dr. Karl was apt to point out where and why. No one ever said, "We ought to do this or that" without hearing Dr. Karl say, "But why don't you do it?" He couldn't understand that conjecture was a form of conversation. There were doctors who avoided him on the street, and there were many people who felt sorry for Dr. C.F. for having such a son.

But Dr. C.F. was never for a moment sorry for having the sort of son he had. He was grateful to Dr. Karl for joining him in practice; he believed that the boy could have done much better almost anywhere. Since he worked closely with his son he knew just how good he was with patients, and that what might be called the healer's touch was present in the young physician, however cocksure he might seem.

Had not Dr. C.F. decided that he would subordinate himself to his son, there might have been clashes. But he was happy to put Karl in command and even to study under him. There had never been a question of how the partnership would be arranged. From the beginning it was made clear that Dr. Karl would be the boss and that all proceeds would be divided fifty-fifty. Quietly, Dr. C.F. would go ahead with his routine practice and his special treatment of diabetes without forcing this phase of his practice on Karl. At the same time he would apprentice himself to Karl as a psychiatrist and learn that specialty from him. This was the way he wanted things to be; he did not expect his son to show any special gratitude.

Karl's first response to command was to announce that the old office at 727 Kansas Avenue where Dr. C.F. had practiced for almost thirty years was dingy and no longer adequate. Better quarters must be found at once, and in a place that would lend itself to expansion. Even as he talked of the move, Dr. Karl was talking in terms of group practice, almost as if it were his own idea. Humbly, and somewhat sadly, Dr. C.F. agreed that a move should be made. Lest he get in the way of Karl's plans, he announced that he was thinking of taking Flo, Pearl, and Will on a drive to the Pacific coast that summer, and suggested that that would be an ideal time for Dr. Karl to set up the new offices in the Mulvane Building. This was tantamount to saying, "When you are ready, I will come back and join your practice." At that time, however, Dr. Karl did not fully understand his father's tactfulness.

CHAPTER TEN

i

In EARLY APRIL of 1920 Dr. C.F. prepared and sent out
a letter announcing the formation of the Menninger Diagnostic
Clinic. In part this letter said that the clinic was founded on the
principle "of co-operative medical specialization," and would be
guided by the strictest ethical principles. Any patients referred
to the clinic for diagnosis or treatment would be returned to their
own physicians. Fees were to be moderate, and there would be
one inclusive charge even though the patient might see all the
specialists in the clinic. The specialists were: C. F. Menninger,
M.D., internal medicine, director of the clinic; Karl A. Menninger,
M.D., neurology and psychiatry; E. W. Netherton, M.D., general
practice, with special attention to dermatology and syphilology,
director of laboratories; A. K. Owens, M.D., roentgenology, X-ray
diagnosis and therapy. The offices in the Mulvane Building had
been somewhat enlarged, and new equipment had been installed.

The Menninger Clinic was born. It had not been an easy birth
and, indeed, the Menninger Clinic in its announced form was a
compromise with the clinic Doctors C. F. and Karl Menninger
wanted. During most of the summer of 1919 they had been inviting Topeka's better physicians to meetings in their offices in an
effort to interest them in forming a group in which every specialty
of medicine would be represented. The plan was, of course, too
idealistic for the time. None of the established practitioners of
medicine could see any point in putting their fees into a fund
and getting back only a prorated share of the proceeds of group
practice.

These meetings were not without gain, however. Dr. C.F. insisted that a case be presented at each meeting, as a means of illustrating the merit of medical co-operation. The doctors liked this idea; often the presentation of a case would absorb an entire evening. These meetings were to continue even after the larger idea of group practice had been shelved. The group was called The Topeka Medical Club.

Doctors Netherton and Owens were not true specialists; they were young men, just out of their interneships, who wanted to gain experience under a successful doctor like Charles Menninger. They were, in a sense, residents. Netherton had access to a laboratory and equipment that he certainly could not have had in a practice of his own. Owens had the very best of X-ray apparatus. They felt fortunate, too, to be working with a young doctor, like Karl, who had held an instructorship in neuropathology at Harvard and whose medical papers were already attracting attention.

The Menningers were not launching the clinic in search of more practice; they had all the practice they needed. Their aim was to supply Topeka with the finest and most economical medical service possible. But medicine, as the Menningers practiced it, was costly, and the net income of each doctor was much less than the earnings of the average physician. Long before, Dr. C.F. had taught Mamie Johnson, his receptionist, most of the laboratory techniques he used in his practice with diabetics, and her place in the front office had to be taken by another girl. With four doctors in the office, a nurse was needed. Equipment was expensive, especially when only the best was used, and replaced the moment improved models came out.

The Menningers had had a busy summer. In the spring Dr. C.F. had been given a doctorate in medicine by the University of Kansas Medical School. This was his third degree in medicine. Karl was delivering papers before a variety of medical groups in the region, and as a result he was often called out of town for consultations. On many days he came to the office directly from a train or went from the office directly to a train. He was also preparing a course in mental hygiene for the next term at Washburn, as well as a course in abnormal psychology. As if this were not enough, he had a Bible class of young college men. On his rare evenings at home he worked on new medical papers.

During the summer, Will, home from Columbia and already

Dr. C. F.'s mother, Mrs.
August Menninger, 1887

August Menninger, Dr. C. F.'s
father, 1887

Dr. C. F. and Flo, April 1885

Karl, Edwin, and Will Menninger, 1900

Dr. and Mrs. C. F. Menninger, 1909

Will, Edwin, Karl, and Doctor C. F., 1914

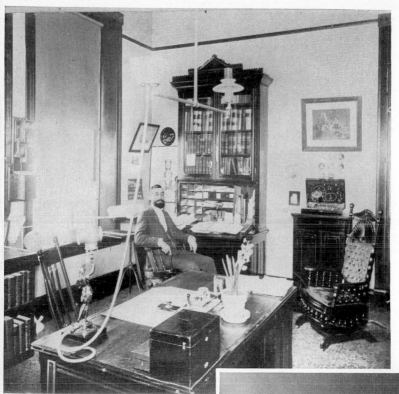

Dr. C. F.'s private office in 727
Kansas Avenue, Topeka, 1895

C. F. Menninger, M.D., 1895

Clinic building where Doctors Karl
and Will still have their offices

Dr. C. F. breaking ground for the
new hospital, July 1952

Looking west above new hospital

C. F. Menninger Memorial Hospital (1954)

The South House, Southard School

Dr. Will, 1944

Dr. Karl and 7000th patient at Winter V. A. Hospital, 1948

Dr. C. F. at 90

accepted by Cornell Medical School, did professional work with the Boy Scouts and for a time thought of giving up medicine and making that his career. He was a natural leader. As he looked at the swirl of activity that had caught up his father and brother, however, he may have realized that the Menninger Clinic would need his administrative ability.

Flo was busy, too. Her Bible classes were more crowded than ever, and the birth of Karl's daughter Julia had given her a grandchild, whom she went to see every day. But the big house on Topeka Avenue was beginning to echo, and talk of a country place became a favorite topic since Flo now had her electric car and could drive to her classes.

ii

Aside from the state hospital, there was no place in Topeka where mental patients could be hospitalized. At one time there had been a ward on the grounds of Christ's Hospital with a capacity of ten beds, but people in the neighborhood complained about having "maniacs" so close to them, and an injunction was issued forbidding the hospital to take mental patients. As secretary to the staff of the hospital, Dr. Karl was in a position to alter its policy. There were certain mental patients who could be called neurological cases, while others, requiring more restraint and separate supervision, could be kept in the old psychiatric section without anyone being the wiser. The only difficulty was that he would have to hire his own nurses. That he did, and quietly hospitalized patients who could afford private hospitalization and who had some chance of recovery. Since hydrotherapy was at that time one of the best ways of calming disturbed patients, he also refurbished the hydrotherapy department and hired his own physiotherapist. Even when he was functioning in a small and surreptitious way, he gave his patients almost everything they could have found in the large institutions of the East. He had to be a good psychiatrist; if one of his patients had become too disturbed or had escaped, both Karl and the hospital would have been at odds with the law.

Dr. C.F. always had between six and a dozen diabetic patients in Christ's Hospital, and when he called on them he would call on the mental patients also. When Karl was out of town he took charge of them. He was good with such patients; they responded to his gentleness and concern, and to his eagerness to learn from them. As he read psychiatry he needed clinical material for study, and the patients at the hospital provided it. Unlike Karl, he could not give time to the state hospital in order to get more clinical experience; he was too busy during the day and he needed his rest at night.

Both Netherton and Owens had left the Menningers after the first year, and Dr. C.F. was doing all the physical and neurological examinations for Karl, in addition to taking care of his own heavy practice in endocrinology and internal medicine. Karl, on the other hand, was not of much help to him with his diabetic patients. In order to keep up with the latest developments in the treatment of diabetes Dr. C.F. had gone East in 1920 to visit Johns Hopkins. He was taking no chances that any improved method of treatment might pass him by.

Whereas at first Dr. C.F. had wished to defer to Karl in everything having to do with their practice, aside from the treatment of his own patients, he was learning that it was best that he hold the reins in matters of policy and expansion. Dr. C.F. had never been a very good businessman; Flo had always taken care of that side of things, but now he had to devote more time to the everyday matters of practice. Karl would make inspired suggestions and forget them a day later; he needed guidance and support. The elder doctor was not director of the diagnostic clinic because of seniority only; he was in fact the director, even if he was often the director of his son's ideas. Karl, who was just beginning to earn money as a doctor—and to him it must have seemed a substantial sum—did not realize that he might have diminished his father's income, as he certainly had. Not that Dr. C.F. would have had it any other way, since he was practicing medicine as he had always wished; also, with Karl as his partner, Flo was less alarmed by increased expenditures for equipment and help.

The first two years of practice with Karl were more trying for Dr. C.F. than he let anyone know. Over the years he had worked out his own system of managing his practice, and even though it may have seemed awkward and inefficient, the routine had become as easy as breathing. Mamie, in her easygoing way, had learned order from him. As he taught her simple laboratory procedures he also made sure that she cleaned up the laboratory when she had finished working, and insisted that the expensive dyes and stains he had imported from Germany for special procedures, which he did himself, be kept in their places and in perfect order so that he could find them in the dark if need be. The doctor collected these preparations as other men collect stamps. If, in his reading, he found a reference to any new stain, he would not rest until he had it, even though such a stain was unlikely ever to be of any use to him.

Mamie had always known his patients well, and he rarely had to tell her what laboratory work should be done with the diabetic patients. She would go out to the hospital, take specimens for blood-sugar tests, and have reports ready for the doctor on anything unusual she had noticed about a particular patient. If bills went out a few days late, it made no great difference, and the fact that Mamie could not type well bothered the doctor not at all. His own handwritten notes were enough, since he was the only one who had to read them, and when he prepared a paper an outside secretary could be hired.

Of course, the system had changed when Karl came into the practice. Duplicate case histories were required, and Mamie could seldom anticipate Karl's needs as she did those of his father. Her deficiency in general laboratory work was not noticeable as long as Dr. Netherton was in the office, but when he left, Karl found that his father was often acting as his lab technician, and that often he had to wait until the older man had time to do the work. Oddly enough, as inefficient as Mamie seemed to Karl, even though he was personally fond of her, it was obvious that it would take two people to replace her, a receptionist-secretary and a graduate laboratory technician. Even at that, Mamie would have to stay on; she was almost one of the family.

Dr. C.F. tried to see to it that a change was made gradually. It was not until July of 1921 that a graduate technician, a young woman named Mildred Law, was brought from Kansas City. She too was to become a part of the Menninger family, and an important voice in all Menninger projects. But the beginning was not easy. The laboratory was small, and there was Mamie standing sadly by, seeing herself stripped one by one of the things that had made her valuable to the doctor. Karl was given to periodic spells of demanding order. At such times he would often suggest to Mildred that the collection of imported stains must be removed from the shelves and boxed. There were standard American stains for any work she was likely to be asked to do. Miss Law considered Karl's suggestion reasonable and acted upon it.

Whenever Dr. C.F. had a few spare moments he would don his white coat and make for the laboratory. He always had on hand some strain of bacteria that he wanted to subject to special tests. When he was in the laboratory he always hummed a tune as he went about his work. When he stopped humming everyone knew that he had found something startling.

On the day after Miss Law's cleanup of the lab, the doctor's humming did not last long. Indeed it died out on something like a growl. When he stuck his head out of the door he looked straight at Mildred Law and asked, "Where are my German stains?"

"I——" Miss Law started an explanation which she had no chance to finish.

"They are to be kept in their place," the doctor said grimly. When they had been replaced, Dr. C.F. started to hum again. He bore Miss Law no ill will; with great relish he explained the origin and purpose of each stain.

The matter of keeping the stains on the shelves was never discussed by father and son. Miss Law, caught between the two, bore the whole burden of their being on or off the shelves. Both men felt that she had a peculiar streak of stubbornness, and tolerated it because she was an excellent technician and a fine worker.

It was this way with many things. The father and son never clashed directly; the employees were always a buffer between them. When Karl issued written memos, the policy they stated was accepted wherever possible.

In Karl's Bible class, and in his classes at Washburn, he had an ardent admirer in a young man named John Stone. Stone, an iconoclast and a rebel, had to have something to worship, and Karl became the object of his devotion. The two men became close friends, and Karl convinced Stone that he had a future in psychology. Stone, however, thought that college degrees were just symbols and, as such, beneath him. He refused to take his degree at Washburn, although he had more than enough credits. It was many years before he bowed to convention and accepted the degree.

Wherever he could, John Stone helped Karl with his work, and, finally, after Stone had spent a lot of time investigating a criminal case in which Karl was interested, he went to work for the Menningers, taking histories and bringing some order into the business. For all his pretense of unconventionality, Stone was a good business administrator, and while Dr. C.F. did not like the intrusion of a layman into the medical field, he did see Stone's value in handling business details.

Through his work with Dr. Southard, Karl had become interested in child psychiatry. Dr. C.F. had also had a special interest in younger patients, and often had as many as a half dozen diabetic children in Christ's Hospital. Through his work in large psychiatric hospitals, Karl knew the value of psychological testing and often wished that he could have a psychological evaluation of his patients. Since there was no psychologist available in Topeka it was decided that it would be worth while to send John Stone to Chicago where he could learn testing in the Institute for Juvenile Research. It was accepted that Stone was a fixture in the Menninger firm.

In 1922 Mamie Johnson left the Menningers. The office had become too modern for her, and she found it difficult to adapt to new ways. She remained a friend of the family, and even Karl went to her for advice at times. She had been the first Negro receptionist in Topeka, and in her way had contributed a great deal to the Menninger medical practice. She had a soothing way with worried and suffering patients, and she was a master of tact on the many occasions when tact was needed.

Will came home from medical school for the summer and another new member was added to the firm. He took Miss Law's place during her vacation and assisted in some research in polio.

A report for 1923 lists the staff of the Menninger Clinic as follows:

C. F. Menninger, President; Internal Medicine and
    Endocrinology
Karl A. Menninger, Neuropsychiatry

William C. Menninger, Research Fellow
M. S. Gregory, Assistant Neuropsychiatrist
Mildred Law, Laboratory and Clinical Director
Bess Cowdrey, Secretary and Record Clerk
John Stone, Treasurer and Business Manager
Francis Hoy, Office Nurse and Historian
Ingeborg Lindquist, Physiotherapy
Stella Boyd, Hydrotherapy and Special Psychiatric
    Nursing
Mrs. Bonine Titus, Special Psychiatric Nursing

The number of new patients seen that year was 438; there were
2367 laboratory procedures.

To many people it seemed pretentious that a father-and-son
medical practice should bear the title of clinic, and that the employees should have such impressive titles. But the dream of a
real clinic was so strong in both father and son that they were
throwing up a framework that seemed awkward because it was
bare. It was a clinic in the rough, half hope and half reality.

iii

It must have seemed to physicians outside Topeka that
the Menninger Clinic was a full-blown research institute. Medical
papers poured from the place; Dr. Karl spoke wherever doctors
were gathered and would listen to him. His experience in the
pulpit and his missionary zeal found a purpose as he became a
local pioneer in his specialty, and gave many Midwestern physicians their first opportunity to meet a practicing psychiatrist.
Wherever there was any interest in the treatment of diabetes, Dr.
C.F. would speak. Reprints on his papers, "The Modern Concept
of Diabetes Mellitus" (1921), "The Glucose Tolerance Test in
Diabetes" (1922), and "The Restoration of Pancreatic Function"
(1922), were circulated widely. There was another printed paper
that was a collaboration of Dr. C.F., Dr. Karl, and William Claire
Menninger, M.A., titled "The Diagnosis and Treatment of Acute
Anterior Poliomyelitis," which summed up almost all that was
known at that time of the disease. Dr. C.F. wrote on diagnosis,

Dr. Karl on treatment, and Will on laboratory tests and experiments with serum.

A few of the papers published by Dr. Karl in the first five years of practice were: "Psychoses Associated with Influenza"; "General Psychiatry for the General Practitioner"; "Mental Diseases after Influenza"; "The Treatment of Mental Disease"; "Ataxic Paraplegia with Pernicious Anemia"; "The Dandy Method of Localizing Brain Tumors by the Roentgen Ray"; "Syphilis of the Nervous System"; "Epidemic Encephalitis"; "Melancholy and Melancholia"; "The Thyroid and Psychiatry"; "Paranoid Psychosis and Uremia"; "Practical Mental Hygiene"; "Static Seizures of Epilepsy"; "Heredosyphilitic Osteoporosis"; "A Mental Hygiene Clinic"; "Postencephalitic Manifestations." There were also articles for the popular press and a paper or two on forensic psychiatry for law reviews. In 1923, Dr. Karl published an abstract of Freud's *Group Psychology and the Analysis of the Ego*, his first venture away from the precepts of Southard and into the field of analytic psychiatry.

The most prophetic paper Dr. Karl published was "The Place of the Psychiatric Department in the General Hospital," which appeared in *The Modern Hospital* for July 1924. In this he expressed his discontent with state hospitals as being inadequate and overcrowded. In stating the minimum requirements for a psychiatric section in a general hospital, Dr. Karl went far beyond the maximum requirements of that day. "(1) Sufficient nurses constantly and alertly on duty to make it unnecessary to lock the doors. This needs no further discussion; the significance is obvious. (2) Nurses in charge must be of sufficient training and experience in the care of nervous persons. . . . (3) Good accommodations in the way of comfortable beds, comfortable chairs and attractive interior decoration are exceedingly important, much more so of course than in any other part of the hospital. (4) An unusual degree of quiet must be maintained. Visitors must not be permitted to trail through the halls, the clatter of dishes and movable furniture must be excluded, the odor of ether and other hospital horrors must not be detectable, and particularly the groans and screams of surgical and obstetrical patients must not be audible. (5) Hydrotherapy equipment is indispensable . . ."

Dr. Karl further stressed the need for directed group activity among the patients, and said that only treatable patients should share the ward, that there must be an aura of hope at all times. Even at that time Dr. Karl believed that the general hospital was the place for the mentally ill as well as the physically ill, and said that thus "All of the disadvantages of institutionalization, stigmata, crowding, isolation, inadequate nursing, etc., are avoided. The [psychiatric] department is merely a part of a hospital, designed for sick people, sick people of a certain kind, to be sure, but treated much the same as all other sick people, by doctors and nurses and not by superintendents and attendants."

Even as he wrote this article, Dr. Karl knew that the time was not far distant when he could no longer continue to keep mental patients in Christ's Hospital, even if he did bear the grandiose title of chief of the Neuropsychiatric Department of that institution. He gave time to the Topeka State Hospital, but he knew that he could not keep his private patients there if they were to have the care he required. Far too often he saw people who could afford private hospitalization wait in jail until some place, distant from home and family, was found for them. He and Dr. C.F. had often discussed this problem and knew that someday they would have to have their own hospital. At that moment, however, both were working overtime to support the type of medical practice they had chosen. It was impossible to make or save enough to open even a modest sanitarium. But even when the sanitarium was an impossibility they also talked about establishing a school for abnormal children, for which there was an equally great need.

iv

Although Dr. C.F. was studying psychiatry with Karl and seeing many psychiatric patients, the treatment of diabetics consumed most of his time, and from the time the clinic was established the diabetic patients had provided a steady and dependable income. While Dr. C.F. had made no spectacular contribution to the treatment of diabetics, he was certainly as successful in treating this disease as any doctor in America. Meticulous laboratory work, careful study of each individual patient, rigid diet, and something that resembled a psychotherapeutic regime brought results. New patients entering the hospital were introduced to older patients in various stages of recovery; the goals of treatment were illustrated, so to speak. Dr. Karl had learned from this and therefore wanted only treatable patients in his psychiatric ward.

In the early 1920s there was not much more Dr. C.F. could do to refine the treatment of his diabetic patients. Neurosurgery and the use of pancreatic extracts had failed; it seemed that research in the field had exhausted most possibilities. As far as diabetes was concerned not much was going on in the great medical centers. In 1920, however, a young Canadian orthopedic surgeon by the name of Banting was trying to start in private practice and to tide himself over he took a job as demonstrator of physiology at the medical school of the University of Western Ontario. One night he chanced on a paper on "Surgery, Gynecology and Obstetrics," and in reading it found an account of some experiments on dogs. It said that when the pancreatic duct was ligated it caused complete atrophy of the acinar tissue but no change in the Islets of Langerhans, the area that produced the secretion that had to do with the proper utilization of sugar in the body. Hundreds of physicians may have read this article, seeing nothing startling in it. Perhaps Banting was naïve enough about endocrinology to be able to see trees in the forest of pathology that had baffled specialists. What he read excited him. He made a note, "Ligate pancreatic ducts of dogs. Wait six or eight weeks for degeneration. Remove the residue and extract."

Selling his surgical instruments, Banting went to Toronto and, by sheer force of conviction rather than by virtue of his scientific background, obtained the use of a laboratory and a medical student as an assistant. Following the directions he had made in his note, he made an extract from the Islets of Langerhans. By removing the pancreases of other dogs he made them diabetic and treated them with the new extract. The extract was feeble, but the results were promising enough to make him hopeful. Before he had time to become discouraged he chanced on an obscure paper by Laguesse, which reported that the pancreas of newborn babies was rich in Islets of Langerhans but poor in digestive cells. Here was the hint at a possible source of a more potent extract, and at once Banting went to work in making an extract from the pancreases of newborn or unborn animals. He had used alcohol to kill whatever digestive potency these organs had, for it was the digestive juices that killed the potency of the essence he needed.

When this substance was injected into the diabetic dogs the result was dramatic. The blood sugar went down at once; the dogs lived far beyond the time they would have if untreated. The first human upon whom this extract, which he called insulin, was used was a diabetic physician. The result was even more dramatic than in the dogs; the doctor reported his sensations and the new feeling of well-being that surged through his body. In 1922 the discovery of insulin was announced and shortly thereafter the first insulin was released to carefully selected specialists in the treatment of diabetes. Dr. C.F. was the physician chosen for his part of the world. As he administered the first doses his excitement was great. If this substance really worked he would no longer have to subject his patients to the torturous regime of a near-starvation diet. When the insulin did work he felt as if he had at last reached the peak of a mountain that he had been climbing all his life. Beyond lay surcease from suffering for the people with whom he had toiled most. He was jubilant, then humble.

Insulin had wiped out Dr. C.F.'s specialty; from now on any general practitioner could treat diabetes and Charles's services would be required in the great experiment for only a short time more. He was grateful that the new psychiatry was absorbing him and he was preparing to devote himself to his son's specialty.

v

At the same time that insulin was being developed, another new element came into the Menninger medical practice. As a student and admirer of Ernest Southard, whose scope and impetuosity were so much like his own, Dr. Karl had been quite protected from the teachings of Freud. He had heard of him, of course, and had read a paper or two which had not especially attracted him to the man. But in the day-to-day problems of psychotherapy, Dr. Karl found himself pretty much on his own and realized that he had been taught very little that was of service to him now. He was a fine neurologist and he thoroughly understood the physical aspects of psychiatry as well as the social and family determinants. In Southard's hands psychiatry came close to becoming a social science. There had never been time for depth psychology in the treatment of individuals.

A patient came to Dr. Karl and in the course of treatment told him quite a lot about the previous treatment he had had from a psychoanalyst. Much of what the man told Karl made sense and the young doctor turned his attention to the works of Freud. When John Stone came home from Chicago with enthusiastic reports about psychoanalysis, Dr. Karl listened intently but a little dubiously, for it seemed that to become an analyst one had only to get oneself analyzed. Having thus learned the method as well as having reached a state of analyzed maturity, one then began to treat patients. No degree in medicine or psychology was needed, it seemed, and many of the practicing analysts were laymen. As Karl talked to his father about this, he found that the elder man liked this trend not at all. He had read some of Freud and had great respect for him, but not for the vogue he had created in America.

Karl continued to be interested in analysis, but he was far too busy to go away and get the training analysis he would need in order to practice as an analyst. He was, however, willing to make an experiment—in the form of John Stone. By dint of much arguing he got his father to agree that they should help finance Stone through an analysis. If what he learned was worth while, he could then practice from their office. Karl was sure that he knew John Stone well enough to be able to evaluate the effect analysis had on him. Stone was agreeable and went to Chicago and into analysis.

In the matter of psychoanalysis, Dr. C.F. had advantages that Karl could not have had. Psychiatry had come upon Karl full blown, so to speak. He had encountered his first mental patients as he treated neurosyphilis during his interneship; when he decided to study mental illness he came under the influence of Ernest Southard, a dynamic personality and an intellectual giant. It was difficult for those under his influence to evaluate his work and methods. He appeared to be doing something where nothing had been done before. His genius for research and inquiry disproved more than it proved, and this was a great contribution in a time when there was so much deadwood to be cleared away before psychiatry could even hope to become a science. Southard, as a man, was too impatient for a treatment process as slow and painstaking as that of Freud, especially where there was so little physical evidence of what was going on. For a time Southard and Karl were almost indivisible as personalities; the younger man was so much like the older that he could not help emulating him Dr. C.F., on the other hand, had not been deeply involved in psychiatry; he had watched its developments from the viewpoint of the general practitioner. He had shown his natural insight when he delivered the paper on *The Insanity of Hamlet,* and even before that he had noted the work of Charcot with hypnosis. Through his reading of German medical journals, the Freud controversy had reached him before it did most of his colleagues and had alerted him to the rare articles on Freud and analysis that appeared in American journals. He had more than an open mind; he had an alert curiosity about psychoanalysis and he could see its value both as a research method and as a treatment tool. He did, however, resent its use by laymen.

Dr. C.F., like most men of his day, could have been called a prude. In ordinary social and family life sex was not discussed or given recognition, except in a negative way. Where his patients were concerned, however, Dr. C.F. was not a prude. He saw the dominant role sexuality played in the lives of both children and grown-ups and he was especially aware of the consequent guilt. Rather than repelling him, the sexual element in Freud's work heartened him. Freud had courage in an area where prejudice had too often interfered with science. Dr. C.F. had always tried to cure venereal disease, not punish or hide it. Freud and venereal disease were both subjects the doctor could not and would not have discussed with Flo. But then he had never discussed any other part of his medical practice with her, other than to keep her informed of the health of their friends.

For Karl, psychoanalytic thought had a freshness that it could not have for Dr. C.F. The latter often used certain phases of Freud's work to reinforce convictions that had grown out of long medical practice, while Karl used his discovery to give himself new and better techniques of treating his patients. If Will had heard or read anything about Freud it had little impact on him.

He expressed an interest in the emotional side of physical illness but was not, at that time, interested in psychiatry. Nevertheless, something quite similar to dynamic psychiatry had begun to be adopted by the Menninger Clinic. Patients were learning that a neurosis might be deeper and older than they thought it to be. Topeka physicians were noticing that many of the Menninger patients were improving beyond all expectations. Requests for consultations increased, even if there was dark muttering whenever Dr. Karl gave a talk that touched upon the work of Freud.

vi

Something new and very important had come into the lives of Flo and Charles Menninger during the early 1920s. Ever since the children had gone away to school they had talked of having a country place where their home and their garden could be consolidated. Flo accepted the fact that a garden would always be an important part of the doctor's life, and although she could not get the same intense satisfaction from flowers that he could, and did not understand the delicate nuances in the various grafts and varieties of the same flower, she did enjoy their beauty. She also knew that the sale of flowers could help balance the budget and pay for Charles's extravagance in buying new plants and bulbs. Even the flowers produced on the lots showed a little profit in some years and as the buds matured she would pick them and hustle them into cold storage against the demand that would arise on Decoration Day. Thus it was that the doctor sometimes never saw the blooms upon which he had waited longest and doted most. In Flo's life, economics, not aesthetics, was always the determining factor. Dr. C.F. might use every sort of strategy and deception in order to preserve the blooms of a certain plant, but he had always acknowledged that Flo had the right of financial practicality on her side. By joining her in her quest for profit, he could enjoy the flowers while he picked them. The doctor also loved to give flowers and plants to his patients; his one vice was that he often did so without letting Flo know about it. With flowers selling at fifty cents a dozen, Flo could see only that he was giving away nickels.

The search for a country place that would give them the view and the garden they wanted was futile. A run-down farm would not do, and they could not afford an elaborate place. Then, in 1922, Mr. and Mrs. A. A. Goddard, old friends, invited them to visit their summer house north of the city. The Menningers did and were enthralled. The small house was on as much of a hill as you are likely to find in that part of Kansas, and it had an excellent view of Topeka. The hill would even lend itself to terraces for gardening. Flo and Charles implored the Goddards to sell them a bit of the land on this rise, but the Goddards were unwilling to sell. Finally, on a last desperate chance, Dr. C.F. asked Goddard to give him first chance at the house and land if he changed his mind. Goddard said that he would.

The doctor and Flo often talked of the Goddard place but had almost given up ever owning it when, in the summer of 1923, it was offered to them. They bought it at once and the old house on Topeka Avenue was put up for sale. In it a half dozen boys had been raised and educated; from these roots a half dozen new families had sprung. In a sense, the old house had been a sort of community center: Topeka's most important Bible classes had been started there, as had the Topeka boy scout movement, not to speak of myriad boys' clubs and similar ventures. On a sheet, hanging between the two great rooms, many Topekans had had, through projected pictures, their first experience of art, and there had been musical evenings for all who cared to come. The house had seen no scandal, and Edwin's injury had been as close as it had come to disaster. It was a difficult house to leave, even for a pastoral dream.

The move was made as painlessly as possible. Pearl Boam still owned her family's home, and the Menningers moved there with her as they waited to occupy the Goddard place. Then came a morning when the doctor went to his offices and Flo to her Bible classes and both returned to the place they had decided to call Oakwood. As they gazed out over the city lights they knew that they had found the place they wanted for their later years. When Flo looked out of the window in the morning the doctor was already at work on his garden as he was to be on every clement day that they lived there.

CHAPTER ELEVEN

i

KARL's tremendous expenditure of energy worried Dr.
C.F. Their practice was prospering, and their dream of a clinic
seemed to be coming true, if only in a small way—a way suited
to Topeka, a town that was likely to resent too much self-assurance
and too sudden success. But Karl was involved in everything and
as secretary to the staffs of two hospitals he was clashing with the
surgeons who had always dominated the hospitals. In his classes
at Washburn he had never hesitated to attack prejudice. As a boy
he had had the bluntness of his mother, and her sensitivity to
hurt; even now, he was shocked and injured when people did
not continue to like him in spite of the freedom with which he
expressed his views. These injuries seemed to spur him on to even
greater efforts.

The young man was a superb physician, sensitive to his patients'
needs and feelings, and alert to anything that might help them.
His integrity was absolute and he probably gave away as much or
more of his services than did any doctor in town. The patients
at the state hospital got just as much attention from him as did
private patients, and while he did charge substantial fees to those
who could afford it, his fees were no higher than those of any
specialist of equal caliber. But the large fees were what Topeka
noticed, not the services Karl gave without fee.

One local paper particularly enjoyed criticizing Karl, especially
after he had begun to use Freud as a basis for his lectures. This
paper never mentioned Karl by name; it didn't have to. Karl was
the only full-fledged psychatrist in private practice in Topeka.

BILL FROM MENTAL DOCTOR TO PATIENT WITH
DELUSIONS OF WEALTH ALMOST A CURE.

Local physicians are enjoying the recent experience of one of Topeka's mental hygiene experts. A patient was sent to him from one of the outlying precincts, a small town near Topeka. The doctor put him through everything and incidentally noted what the man said about his extensive farm holdings, the number of stocks and bonds he owned, and several bank accounts he carried, all for considerable amounts.

The mental doctor prescribed an extensive course of treatment, most of it at home, following a week in Topeka for observation. A cursory examination of the patient's resources as listed indicated that he was well off. In due time, a bill was rendered for $3000.

The better half of the patient protested that the bill was unreasonable, suggesting $25. The doctor wrote back, explaining that many poor persons were treated free, and to make up for that the bills were based on the patient's ability to pay. Followed a recital of the patient's resources, as related to the doctor.

"But those are the delusions of wealth we wanted you to cure him of," the head of the family wrote back.

This was a not very good anecdote that had been told a dozen times in a dozen cities, but in Topeka it was in the news columns and aimed at a particular man—Karl Menninger. Karl Menninger saw red and prepared to sue. The story was pure fabrication, but he had heard some of the many guffaws it had brought from the townspeople. He was as deeply hurt as he had been when he was rejected by the fraternity at Washburn. He labored to give Topeka the best and in return he got ridicule.

Occasionally Dr. Karl would mutter a threat to go elsewhere and practice, but Dr. C.F. had known his son too long to take this seriously. Even though practicing in Topeka was a little like being forced to work in an operating theater under the scrutiny of critical and antagonistic eyes, Karl would not have had it any other way. The boy who had been called feeble-minded by his friends in this very same city would grapple with the troubled minds of that city and set them right. He had nothing to hide and he knew, too, that he functioned best where most was demanded, that his only danger was in getting into a position where the demands on him were not constant and great. Rebuffs only drove him on.

Dr. Karl had thought that if he had a day to spare each week any Kansas City physician of standing and perception would be glad to lend him an office for consultations. When he finally got around to writing to a friendly doctor about this he got back this reply:

"Dear Karl: Regarding your move down here, think it over long and hard, considering all angles, then rent an office well equipped with good soft chairs and spend six days a week here and one in Topeka. You won't even get a good opinion of our town one day a week. The change will take courage and will not be void of disappointment. You can be a big town Doc spending one day a week in the country but the reverse is not true."

Within a month, Dr. Karl was spending one day a week in the office of Dr. Logan Clendening. Dr. Clendening was at that time the most famous physician in Kansas City and one of the best known in America. His book, *The Human Body,* published in 1927, was tremendously successful, and his syndicated medical column reached most American cities. Dr. Karl's association with Dr. Clendening continued as long as the doctor was in practice. He never converted Clendening to psychiatry, but some of his best hours were spent in trying. Dr. C.F., far from being jealous of this relationship, was proud of it and encouraged it. He and Clendening had been fellow teachers and respected each other.

The situation with regard to keeping patients in Christ's Hospital was growing more tense. Having to keep the patients hidden was not good for them either. Something had to be done, and neither father nor son could see a ready solution. Finally Dr. Karl mentioned the problem to T. N. Neese who, with his wife, Daisy, was an attendant at Topeka State Hospital. The Neeses were superior to the attendants of that day and were ambitious as well. Neese, who had some small savings, said that he and his wife would open a sanitarium and operate it for the Menningers, taking a profit from the charges for board, room, and their services. Dr. Karl jumped at the offer. Dr. C.F. was not quite so enthusiastic, but he did feel that any move away from the hospital would be a good idea. He made it clear to Karl that if the place was to bear their name they would have to control it, and that that could best be done by making an investment equal to or greater than the Neeses'.

It was early in 1925 that the Neeses set out to find a place. Downtown locations were out of the question because of zoning. Finally, on the western outskirts of the city, they came upon the

Christensen farm, which had a large residence, a double garage, barn, and some other outbuildings. There were twelve acres of grounds, and on these were many large trees. The moment he saw the place he wanted it.

Of course, the cost of the farm, not to speak of the equipment that would be needed, was far beyond the $5000 the Neeses had saved and were willing to invest. Indeed the cost and the backlog were beyond the Menninger savings and so there was only one thing to do, form a corporation and sell stock.

"You and I know that the kind of sanitarium we want to run will never be able to pay anything over token dividends," Dr. C.F. told Karl. "We can't go to people and offer them a great cash yield on their investment. But if we go to the people of Topeka and tell them the money is for something that is needed and convince them that the way we run it will pay them dividends in satisfaction, they'll subscribe to our stock."

Karl agreed that this was true, but he did have some doubts that the people of Topeka would subscribe to anything he offered. Corporation papers were drawn up, and it was decided that the Menningers would give a dinner for some of the leading physicians and businessmen of the town and put the matter before them. Dr. Karl would give the main talk of the evening, but his father would introduce him and then sum things up before they asked for subscriptions.

Thirty-five people were invited to the dinner and perhaps thirty came. Dr. C.F. had taken pains to let each know the purpose of the meeting so that they could decline the invitation if they were not interested. Few of the laymen had ever heard Karl speak, and perhaps that opportunity induced some of them to come.

Dr. C.F. introduced Karl not so much as a son, but as the man who had brought him a new understanding of mental illness and of the need for developing resources that would insure these suffering people better treatment. It was beneath the doctor to plead with people. He was simply telling them that Karl was a man worth listening to.

Dr. Karl went directly into the subject by describing the role mental illness played in Topeka and the facilities that were available for its treatment. He discussed mental illness historically, from the earliest medical records to the work of Pinel, and of three crusading laymen, William Tuke, Dorothea Lynde Dix, and Clifford Beers. He said that psychiatry was just becoming a science and was, in effect, an orphan. General hospitals did not want its patients and thus research facilities were denied those who needed them most. He described the things that were accomplished where research was made possible and showed how even a spinal puncture could seem like an expression of concern to a neglected patient. Finally, Karl informed his listeners that Topeka did not need a modern sanitarium in order to catch up with other cities, even Eastern cities. Few cities had any sanitariums at all. Topeka would be taking the lead. At the end he outlined the clinical service that he and his father had built up and stressed that it would be available to the patients at all times.

Karl was at his best, a scholar and a physician with a flashing mind and indubitable zeal. At such times he could be magnetic; he drew people toward him instead of repelling them, and gave them an indication of the warmth that each of his patients felt for him. As he stood beside his father, the man who had been physician to most of those present, they saw in the proud dignity of the older man a source of stability and respectability.

Sam E. Cobb, president of the Bank of Topeka and the future father-in-law of Alf Landon, was the first to offer to subscribe. Following him was David Neiswanger, a real estate agent, and J. D. M. Hamilton, an attorney. As the dinner broke up, the physicians, W. F. Bowen, J. A. Crabbe, and Arthur D. Gray came and made their pledge to Dr. C.F. Within the month a meeting was held and officers were elected. They were:

C. F. Menninger, President
Sam E. Cobb, Treasurer
J. A. Crabbe, M.D., Vice President
David Neiswanger, Secretary

The sanitarium corporation was entitled to issue $50,000 in stock, but even before half that amount was sold work was begun on the Christensen farm, and Dr. C.F. divided his gardening time between there and Oakwood. The Neeses were to have an apartment in the main residence, but all other rooms were set aside for patients, with arrangements for two or three patients to a room. As much as possible, the house was furnished like a residence;

the living room and dining room were pleasant and informal. Furniture from the old house on Topeka Avenue was used. As for occupational therapy. Dr. C.F. knew what most of that was going to be: the patients would help him with the grounds.

In September of 1925 the house was ready, and one evening while Dr. Karl was out of town Dr. C.F. moved six patients from Christ's Hospital to the Menninger Sanitarium. The nurses helped him, but he spent most of the night at the sanitarium making sure that the move had not been upsetting to the patients and that everyone knew just what he was to do in any emergency. The doctor was tired when he drove home.

It was just seventeen years since his visit to the Mayo Clinic. Perhaps twelve beds was a small start, but the doctor had seen a great deal happen in the six years since Karl had joined him. Will was coming, he hoped, and he would see a lot more. Though he had planned to stop taking night calls, he had an idea that the drive he was taking between Oakwood and the sanitarium was one he would be making on many nights. As he stood at the door of his house, he was glad that he could look out over his city. He had a warm feeling for it. It had given much to an awkward and half-educated young physician.

ii

Oakwood was as much the center of family life as the old place on Topeka Avenue had been. Grace, Karl's wife, was there almost every day and often stayed overnight when Karl was out of town. By staying for dinner she gave Dr. C.F. a chance to be with his grandchild. Karl usually drove past Oakwood before he went to his own home. He was closer to his mother now and understood her better. He did not discuss his practice or accomplishments with her, but he was always able to interest her in little things he picked up from his omnivorous reading. Karl's Bible classes were almost like her own project and he gave her reports on them.

Karl would go out into the garden, too, and work for a few minutes with his father. His father had little patience with these hit-and-run tactics, but that disturbed the young man not at all.

Dr. C.F.'s zeal was single-track; when he was gardening, he was gardening, and had forgotten that he was a physician, a corporation director, or even a husband and father. The flowers were everything and their moment the peak of accomplishment. To interrupt him at his gardening with talk of anything else—even medicine—was like profaning a prayer. A flower was something he related to God.

If he was called to see a patient that was another matter. Dr. C.F. would cease to be a gardener as he took off his work clothes, and he would become a physician as he put on his business suit. Now all he had learned of the art and science of healing was at the patient's command. There was only one difference: the patient could talk to him about flowers. He could teach the patient something about flowers, and to him teaching and healing were pretty much the same thing. Dr. C.F. would always look upon ignorance —especially ignorance of nature and its wonders—as a gaping wound.

But the elder doctor did like to have Karl come to see him and even come out into the garden. Karl had an instinct for plants that should be encouraged. But his mind sometimes frightened his father. It seemed that at times his son's talk was simply free association—ideas, recently acquired knowledge, bits of books, sayings of patients, plans and rejections of plans tossed out at random. Often there was nothing the listener could say, and Karl would appear hurt that he had received no particular response. But what awed the father was the way in which Karl would sometimes bring all this random material to bear on a central point and the fact that Karl's point was always psychiatry, the human mind, mental health. The discipline of medical school should have taught him to limit his field of investigation, but it was as if Karl had never undergone that discipline. At times it seemed that he was unable to distinguish between science and the humanities. Dr. C.F. knew that his son had the quality of genius, and that it made him uncomfortable, as it has all men in all times.

Dr. C.F. was looking forward to Will's coming home to join the practice. The boy had offers of good Eastern associations and had recently married Catharine Wright, a New Jersey girl, but Dr. C.F. felt sure that he would choose to come home. Aside from being a good physician, Will had qualities the clinic needed. He

was an independent thinker who would let no one make decisions for him. He would never compromise, and yet he was a
diplomat in that he could see that there were often two sides to a
question. Combine these qualities with his personableness and
you had a natural leader, one who could make you feel that you
were going along with him and that that was just the way you
would have it.

Edwin had moved to Stuart, Florida, and it had become clear
that he would make that his permanent home. His first marriage
had ended in divorce. His work as cable editor for the New York
Herald Tribune, with its night hours and its constant pressure,
had taken its toll of his health and he needed a warmer climate.
It is also doubtful if any son of Dr. C.F. could thrive for long in a
place where he could not have a garden and interest himself in
growing things. In Florida, Edwin found more than health and
a garden; he met a fine woman—a Christian Science practitioner
—who became his wife. She helped him with the weekly paper
and the job printing plant he had bought. Although his divorce
had come as a shock, especially to Flo, Edwin was happy, and
that was what counted. They had already agreed to educate Edwin, Jr., Edwin's son by his first marriage.

The thing that pleased Dr. C.F. most was Edwin's interest in
flowering trees, for very soon after his arrival in Florida Edwin
began to be regarded as an authority on that subject; he devoted
much of his time to the studying and planting of trees that bore
flowers. The doctor and Flo planned to visit him in Florida as
soon as possible. Nor had Edwin broken off contact with his
brothers; there was a constant exchange of letters, each carrying
some complex problem with which one hoped to defeat the other.

Oakwood had drawn the doctor and Flo more closely together.
With Karl in practice and Will coming home, she was less nervous
about money and the future. She had relaxed a little from her
former religious strictness about the little joys and habits of life.
When Karl had sneaked a few unlabeled bottles of beer into the
basement in the summer and Dr. C.F. had enjoyed one on a hot
evening, she chose to believe that it was ginger beer and carefully
refrained from asking for any, preferring her own iced tea. Pearl
could humor the doctor in such things as this, for it was she, being
in league with Karl, who served the beer. It was not that the beer

mattered so much. What mattered was that everyone was more relaxed in this new atmosphere of permissiveness.

iii

It is easy to say that the sanitarium was a success from the beginning, for it was not difficult to fill a place that had a capacity of only twelve patients when there was no other place within seventy miles where people who wanted private care could go. As long as the sanitarium accepted patients only from the Topeka area it would never have to be much bigger than that. But Dr. Karl's consultations were ranging out into a wider field, and there were patients from Kansas City who wanted to come to the sanitarium. Oklahoma was without private mental-hospital facilities, and Karl had enough calls from Tulsa to think of opening an office there. As more stock was sold, plans were made for a new building, a twenty-five-bed lodge-type structure where patients could have private rooms. Already a tool shed had been turned into a sort of craft shop. Dr. C.F. had filled the chicken sheds with chickens; three new cows and a horse were occupying the barn. He had transplanted flowers and shrubs from Oakwood, and the local press had commented that the sanitarium would soon be Topeka's show place.

At almost the same time that Dr. Will finished his interneship and some additional time as a resident in internal medicine at Bellevue Dr. C.F. and Karl found themselves swamped with work at home. Practice in the downtown office was growing. In 1925 there were 2121 laboratory procedures, 2060 office treatments, and 224 X rays. There were 333 new patients, some of whom were being treated by a psychotherapy that was based upon the Freudian dynamic as Dr. Karl was coming to understand it. Actually, there was no psychoanalysis, as such, but merely a tentative and improvised technique based upon Freud's theories. Soon there was not time enough to take care of all the demands, and Dr. C.F. wired for Will to hurry home.

On the day Will arrived Dr. Karl was out of town and Dr. C.F. was preparing to go to a meeting. It had been Will's idea to discuss a partnership with his father and brother before he went into partnership with them, but within a half hour after his arrival he was taking care of patients, and after a few brief directions he was put in charge of the sanitarium. It was only after several days had passed that he managed to find Karl and his father together and bring up the matter of partnership. Both men seemed astonished that he wanted to discuss it; they thought he was already their partner, as indeed he was. As for the terms, they would be worked out by the business manager. The public announcement of Dr. Will's entering the practice said that his work would be restricted to internal medicine and the emotional involvements of physical illness.

The clinic really needed an internist at this point. Dr. C.F. was devoting more and more time to neurology and psychiatry, and his practice in diabetics was now confined to teaching new patients the use of insulin. He felt that in the time he had been involved in psychiatry he had fallen behind on the new developments in internal medicine, and that his son, after his experience in the great Bellevue Hospital and teaching center would be a better internist than he himself was.

Even in his first busy weeks Dr. Will took time to acquaint himself with what was going on in scouting in Topeka and, because of experiences he had had at Woods Hole, Massachusetts, at summer school, decided to organize a troop of sea scouts. No one in the Menninger family thought that there was anything unusual about this. If one of their clan had not been zealously active in community life they would have thought something was wrong with him. The Menninger method of measuring each other's health was to observe the amount of zeal that was being expended, no matter what the direction. Unity of purpose was not necessary, but action was.

iv

In the early part of the century, and even into the twenties, the "rest cure" for mental illness was much in vogue. The "rest cure" had been introduced in the latter part of the nineteenth century by Dr. S. Weir Mitchell, a Philadelphia neurologist. The patient was kept in bed, allowed no visitors or diversions, and was fed as often as eight times a day. The term "nervous prostration," came from this cure, for the patient was indeed prostrate. Even Freud once saw some merit in this method and in 1895 wrote, "Moreover, I have made it a practice of applying the cathartic psychotherapy in acute cases with a Weir Mitchell rest cure. The advantage lies in the fact that on the one side I avoid the very disturbing intrusions of new psychic impressions which may be produced during psychotherapy; on the other hand, I exclude the monotony of the Weir Mitchell treatment during which the patient frequently merges into harmful reveries." Freud was later to revise his idea of rest. Depressions grew worse under such a permissive regime, and schizophrenics were helped in effecting their withdrawal from life. Dr. C.F. and Dr. Karl had already learned this from their own clinical experience; there had been a time in Christ's Hospital when they did encourage their patients to stay in bed and did feed them five times a day. It was a good tactic in a place where people had to be kept quiet, but that was all the method had to recommend it.

From the beginning the sanitarium began to function like an annex to the Menninger home, where idleness was in itself a form of illness. Those patients who were able to worked in the garden from dawn till dusk. Pearl Boam's brother, who had come to the sanitarium to help with the cows, chickens, and garden, was always glad of an extra hand or two. He knew as well as the Menningers did that to become interested in the earth, its plants and its animals, was to be interested in life again. To be waiting for the birth of a calf, the hatching of eggs, the blooming of a plant was to give oneself continuity of purpose. To help bring about these things was in a small way taking command of life. For patients who did not take to gardening and farming there were other activities—not basket weaving, or the similar purposeless occupations that were prescribed in most hospitals—but things that could become true hobbies. If a patient was well enough he was encouraged to take courses at Washburn. Karl gave them lists of the books he read each month; Dr. C.F. encouraged the study of nature; church and Bible class attendance was encouraged. Any patient's idleness became a matter of great concern.

Nor were the patients allowed to isolate themselves in solitary pursuits for the whole day, for in a house such as the Christensen residence they had to live together as a family. The rivalries, resentments, jealousies, and dependencies that inevitably developed became significant material in psychotherapy. When a neurotic trend was acted out, the therapist would get a report from the nurses and quickly show the patient what he was doing and, if possible, why.

For quite a while Dr. C.F. and Karl had been giving definite directions to the nurses about how they were to behave toward certain patients. "Show this patient that he is worthy of your affection and esteem," Dr. C.F. might tell a nurse. Or Karl might say, "Be kind but firm with this patient. He'll become more ill if you're too easy on him. Convince him that it isn't kind to let him get more ill even if he seems to want to." Dr. Will noted that what his father and brother were doing was prescribing attitudes. As he took over the directorship of the sanitarium he saw how verbal orders might mean one thing to one employee and another to a different employee. At the weekly staff meetings the prescribing of attitudes was formalized so that each staff member, physician and nurse, would know that there was a unified attitude toward each patient and the reason for it.

Since the clinic downtown and the sanitarium could not be completely separated, joint staff meetings were held. It was made clear that everyone contributed to each recovery and that any report on anything that would help a patient, or help the relationship of the staff, could not be inconsequential. Even the business meetings were thrown open to those who wished to attend. Always, Dr. C.F. stressed that the example of the workers in the sanitarium and clinic was all important, for often the clinic and sanitarium people would be the patient's only contact with the well world. That world must seem desirable and stable; moreover, the doctors and nurses had to be friends for whom the patients would want to get well.

To some Topekans it seemed that the patients at the Menninger Sanitarium were excessively happy and therefore must be living in some sort of sin. Tales of wild permissiveness spread from time to time. If a woman with a post-partum psychosis came to the sanitarium there were apt to be tales that her child had been conceived there, and that the Menningers encouraged promiscuity. Fortunately the doctors heard more about these rumors than did the patients, and the rumors were comparatively harmless. Taxi drivers who brought patients from the train to the clinic, and then took them shopping later, saw that people did get better, even crazy people. Tales of the Menninger prowess spread and some of them were as wild as the scandals. One thing was sure: Dr. Karl was earning the grudging respect of Topeka's doctors. When a man's skill was proven to them they could see and accept it, whatever their earlier prejudices had been. Dr. Will, who had patients in all the hospitals, was a man they respected tremendously. They wanted their sons to be in his scout troop, wanted him to participate in consultations, and invited him to join their clubs.

By 1927 it was imperative that construction begin on the building that was to be called East Lodge. The Menningers now had a waiting list of sanitarium patients, and inquiries were coming in from surrounding states. Twenty-five beds should be easy to fill. And it seemed that it might be a good idea to move the downtown offices into the residence when the patients were able to vacate it.

v

In the meantime something else had happened. With the sanitarium a reality, Dr. Karl was eager to start his school for abnormal children. When Dr. George Stevenson, of New York, referred Miss Stella Pearson to the Menningers with a child she was caring for and wanted to have examined, he also wrote Karl that Miss Pearson was a fine teacher of abnormal children and that he would be wise to employ her if he could. It turned out that Miss Pearson was anxious to work under the Menningers and that she had a sister, Mrs. Lulu Holcomb, who was also a skilled teacher. Karl saw no reason to wait any longer for his school and impetuously told Miss Pearson that arrangements would be made for her. With the pledge made, the Menningers could not withdraw it, nor did they wish to, though they would have preferred to wait a little longer. The money would now have to be put up by the downtown clinic.

In late 1925 a house at 1407 Buchanan Street was rented. The Menninger Clinic advanced all the money for the lease, the equipment, and the women's salaries, and in addition gave them an interest in the school. It was just before the New Year that South-ard School opened with ten children enrolled, most of them board-ers.

Very quickly the Menningers learned the sad lesson that no mat-ter how much care the children might require the families would not pay the price for their care and treatment that they would pay for adults. From the very beginning they knew that the school would be operated at a loss and that they would have to under-write it. Still they were determined to go on. There were few places where children with personality disorders could get treat-ment, and doctors who worked with such children would have a fruitful field of research. At the beginning it was necessary to take a few mentally retarded children, but the aim was eventually to take only children of normal or superior intelligence who were emotionally ill.

The school was to create many other problems. The first loca-tion had to be abandoned because of the complaints of neighbors, and so a larger residence and grounds was found in a more se-cluded neighborhood. Part of the aim in treating the children, many of whom would not be able to return to their homes for a long time, was to move them out of the school into foster and boarding homes. In order to do this it was necessary to find peo-ple who wanted such children and knew how to handle them. When the teachers or Dr. Karl went out to make inquiries among people who had answered an advertisement requesting homes for the children, they found that they were very often misunder-stood. If they said that the child would have to be treated with exceptional kindness and not criticized too much, some gossip would spread the story that Karl Menninger had said that he wanted a home where his school children could smoke, drink, and indulge themselves sexually.*

Actually, the school was just about as permissive as the Men-ninger home had been. From the beginning the main burden of caring for and treating the children at the school fell to Dr. C.F. He gave them complete medical care, and he spent at least an hour each week with every child. It was always a puzzle to him

* The writer encountered this rumor as far away as New Mexico as late as 1948.

that others could not manage these children as easily as he did. There was something about him that awed children and won their respect. He never had to threaten punishment; they seemed afraid of his displeasure just as his own children had been.

Other Topeka physicians were interested in Southard School, and Doctors Belknap, Weidling, and Lattimore all contributed time. John Stone was the school psychologist. The school was doing all the psychological testing for the Kansas Children's Service League, which placed children for adoption. Teachers who wanted to learn something about abnormal children could always visit the school and, if they wished to go further, join Dr. Karl's classes at Washburn. Even at the outset the school had a definite contribution to make to Topeka and to Kansas.

vi

When John Stone had come back to Topeka from his training analysis he had found that Dr. Karl was already practicing a type of psychotherapy that was very much like psychoanalysis. Moreover, he seemed to be quite expert in it from the beginning. Since he had not been trained to follow the classical Freudian precepts, as laid down by Freud's followers, his method had great flexibility. He was not shy about terminating or altering treatment at any given point, and he had adapted Freud's techniques to short-term therapy, in which a patient might be seen only a half dozen times. All Dr. Karl's knowledge and intuition were lent to the dynamic concept of personality development. His ability to relate the most diverse things gave him great scope in utilizing Freudian theories. He could adapt most of what he had learned under Southard to this concept. His exposition of Freudian theory, in talking or in writing, had a vibrant clarity. He was a missionary for the dynamic concept; he applied it to everything. When home life intruded on his thoughts, he retired to a room at the state hospital to read and write. The place had another virtue; at the state hospital his clinical material was as ready to his hand as his library. When he wrote lectures and papers they had the immediacy that comes from dealing with living material. Also, Dr. Karl relished words and apt references and he enjoyed writing. Even in his isolated room he had a sense of receiving a direct response from his audience.

Until 1928 he had no very clear idea of writing a book, but at that time Dr. William Alanson White, who recognized Karl's talent, asked him if he would write three chapters for a collection on mental health which he wanted to publish. White, a distinguished psychiatrist, was for many years Superintendent of St. Elizabeth's Hospital in Washington, D.C. He was not deterred by the fact that the man he was asking to write about analytic concepts was not a trained analyst. When Karl set to work on these chapters, he got out all his lectures at Washburn as well as all his published papers and case notes. Logan Clendening had already published his work, *The Human Body*. Why not, Karl thought, a *Human Mind?* Perhaps if he explained his cause and its principles he would be less of an oddity in Topeka and he would be helping psychiatrists everywhere. What was to have been three chapters became the idea for a book.

The book was to him what scouting was to Dr. Will, flowering plants to Edwin, gardening to his father, Bible classes to his mother. It was this and more. Karl's vocation was psychological medicine, and it was a true vocation. Writing, as he saw it, was but part of his practice, part of his teaching. He had not diminished his central drive by taking up an avocation; he had reinforced it.

This stanza of Robert Frost's *Two Tramps in Mud-Time* might well have been written for Karl:

> But yield who will to their separation,
> My object in life is to unite
> My avocation and my vocation
> As my two eyes make one in sight.
> Only where love and need are one,
> And the work is play for mortal stakes,
> Is the deed ever really done
> For Heaven and the future's sakes.

As the book grew, Karl became almost a stranger to his family. He was obsessed; it was as if the book and his practice were for his own salvation. He did not hesitate to call upon anyone who could help him. Nelson Antrim Crawford read and criticized the script as did John Stone. Then when the book went out there were rebuffs since publishers could not believe that materialistic

America was interested in the human mind. Perhaps they did not even bother to read the book, thinking that it would be filled with vague and metaphysical thinking or scientific jargon. But the book was alive.

In his preface Dr. Karl said: "I have rolled off pages of it in the cabooses of freight trains and in the lounge of the Twentieth Century. Parts of it were conceived in railroad depots and in the wards of the hospital. There are passages that still retain the flavour of the coal-oil lamp on the farmer's kitchen table.

"Then there have been so many interruptions. No one but doctors and mothers know what it means to have interruptions. Mrs. Jones has a headache, Mr. Smith has obsessions, Helen Thompson perplexes the dean, and George Hall has just been arrested. Telephone calls demand to know if mother may have some oranges, if daughter rested well last night, and if chiropractic is a cure for epilepsy. Interruptions by the assault of sticky little hands and the most imperative news about the neighbour's dog. All sorts of interruptions."

Finally Dr. Charles E. Rogers, of the School of Journalism at Kansas State Agricultural College, saw the manuscript and sent it to Mr. Carl van Doren. In 1930 *The Human Mind* was published and was a Literary Guild selection, which meant that it was an immediate best seller. It was as if a psychiatrist and his practice had been sent into many homes and the country—or at least the reading segment of the country—developed a new insight. Karl Menninger's name appeared widely in newspapers and magazines and in many minds that name and psychiatry became indivisible. Whether or not other psychiatrists liked it, they seemed to have found a spokesman. The Menninger family was no longer Topeka's, it was America's.

The Human Mind was one of the first books in which a psychiatrist openly and eloquently discussed the everyday problems that he met in his practice. Dr. Karl took the reader into his confidence and let him see how the world looked when viewed through a psychiatrist's eyes. In doing so, he gave the seemingly ordinary thought processes a new meaning as he revealed the emotional forces that lurked beneath the surface. Since Dr. Karl was greatly concerned with getting a new understanding for both the mentally ill and for his specialty, and had in mind an audience of medical students and general practitioners as well as laymen, he didn't "write down" or attempt to "popularize" the subject. The result was a book that was both optimistic and scientific and even though this was the pioneer work in its field it has remained something of a classic. In the years that have elapsed since it was first published there have been three revised and corrected editions running through numerous printings. The book can be looked upon as a sort of an atlas of the psyche, for in each edition previously unexplored areas of the mind have been opened up and described. There is little doubt that this book is one of the landmarks by which the progress of psychiatry in this century can best be measured.

CHAPTER TWELVE

i

ONE THING that set the Menninger Sanitarium apart from most other sanitariums in America was that it came into being as an adjunct to the general practice of medicine. Another difference was that from the beginning it was a part of the community, not a strange cloister in which a psychiatrist and his wealthier patients remained hidden. Local money was invested in it, and most of the employees were local people who went home at night and were friendly with their neighbors. There was nothing mysterious about Doctors C.F., Karl, and Will Menninger; they held Bible classes, promoted municipal rose gardens, ran scout troops that got national awards. Moreover, you didn't have to be mentally ill to go to see them as physicians. Dr. C.F. would lance a boil or treat your child's croup, and Dr. Will would treat your chest pains or asthma. There was no stigma attached to going into the Menninger offices.

To be sure, there was a certain amount of prejudice and simple ignorance among the people of Topeka, and a great deal of it was brought to bear on Dr. Karl, Southard School, the sanitarium, and what these people took to be the teachings of Freud. There was a good deal of malignant gossip and a certain amount of prying and peeping. In a sense, this was good for the sanitarium. It had to produce results or be ridiculed. Certainly no patient was ever cured because of this kind of pressure on his doctor, but the pressure undoubtedly added to his relentless drive. There is no doubt that it had spurred Dr. Karl toward public education in his book, *The Human Mind.*

When East Lodge was opened there was room for twenty-five

patients; during its first year, 1928, it had an average population of twenty. The opening had been attended by most of Topeka's physicians and the public had been invited. This was a modern building of which any institution might have been proud. Topeka papers spoke of the sanitarium as a new industry. Because most of the patients would be restricted to the grounds, Dr. C.F. had insisted on getting motion picture projection equipment. What he had in mind was educational films, but he wasn't averse to letting the patients have pure entertainment as well.

After the publication of Dr. Karl's book, prospective patients from many states applied for admission; so did physicians for training. There had to be some doubling up in the sanitarium rooms. There was an average of thirty patients, representing twelve states. People were beginning to come to Topeka for psychiatric evaluation and diagnosis. They would stay in hotels and boarding homes and see their doctor either at the downtown office or at the offices at the sanitarium.

From the very beginning, total medicine was brought to bear on each patient, for although the problem might be emotional, a psychiatric diagnosis was not enough. Complete physical studies were made, just as they would have been at Mayos' or any other large clinic. Consultants in every specialty had been appointed to the staff and were on call. Dr. C.F. supervised the diets, something in which he was a specialist, while Dr. Will was the hospital doctor and director, and Dr. Karl was the director of psychotherapy. There were frequent staff meetings, attended by all the employees whose work brought them into contact with patients. The recommendations of the nurses were considered seriously, and they worked more closely with the doctors than they ever could have in a general hospital. Word of this method spread, and many nurses requested training at the Menninger Sanitarium, but since the sanitarium was too new to be approved by the American Medical Association a nursing school could not yet be started.

In 1929 the West Lodge was built, a structure similar in architecture to the East Lodge, and having the same capacity. The growth of the sanitarium since 1925 indicated that it could easily be filled and it would have been, had it not been for the stock market crash and all that ensued. There was not enough money to equip the new building. Ben Boam, Pearl's brother, had to do the interior painting, and the building stood empty while an average of twenty-nine patients was crowded into the East Lodge.

During the early days of the great depression it was an exceptional institution that could hold its own, and rates of seventy-five dollars a week and up, such as were charged at Menningers', were far beyond the reach of most people. Dozens of applications were dropped from the waiting list. While the private practice of the clinic continued to increase, it was difficult to collect fees. The Menningers always welcomed a discussion of fees, but many people were too proud to reveal their true financial plight. "No Charge" was written on more and more charts. The sanitarium carried patients who were making progress and could no longer pay their bills. It did not go into the red, but its profit for the year of 1930 was only a little over $400.

Each year the Menningers had to underwrite a substantial loss at Southard School, out of their own pockets. When the new lodge building had to be built, and there were no buyers for the stock, all the Menningers took on additional shares. One thing was sure: the financing of every Menninger project came from the private practice of medicine, and there would have been no backers had it not been for the respect that Dr. C.F. commanded as a private practitioner. No one would have mistaken him for a businessman. It was because of their respect for him that Sam Cobb, David Neiswanger, and others contributed a business acumen that was of greater value than their cash investments.

Actually, the sons he had raised and educated, and the reputation he had established, represented Dr. C.F.'s total savings from thirty years of medical practice. And he was one of the most respected physicians in a fairly large city. Certainly he always had the best clothes and had driven good horses and cars; his home was comparable to that of the merchant of moderate means, but other physicians had lived as well and had still accumulated substantial savings. The difference was that Dr. C.F. had tried to conduct his business so that a medical bill would not be a greater burden to the patient than his illness had been. This practice reduced his income and much of his money had gone for new equipment and for trips East to study, as well as for books and periodicals. His investment in the treatment of diabetes was probably as great as or greater than Banting's. He and a good many physicians like him had enabled people to live until a Banting came along. They were medicine's great journeymen. When the techniques he had perfected during a lifetime of practice were made obsolete overnight it was a great victory for him, not a defeat.

The doctor had been waiting for many years for the opportunity to discuss the day-to-day problems of medical practice with his sons. These problems would always call for an improved practice, for the mastering of new skills and arts, and for more scientific methods. It was simply taken for granted that a new X-ray machine would be more important than a membership in the country club, and that a pledge of $10,000 to the Christ's Hospital building fund was more important than acquiring some shares of Standard Oil—a man put his money into those things that gave him satisfaction. It was Dr. C.F.'s view that every religious man was dedicated, no matter what his trade or profession might be, and he expected this dedication of everyone.

In many ways Dr. C.F. was naïve. As the clinic and sanitarium got more referrals it came to his attention that some of the referring physicians expected something like a splitting of the fee, a practice that was more general in that time of surgical ascendancy than is commonly recognized. In the case of a patient who had been referred to Topeka from some outlying town the routine practice would have been to call the referring physician in for a consultation and let him collect a sizable fee for the trip. The Topeka physician might have seen to it that the visiting physician was offered appropriate entertainment. Dr. C.F. was all for inviting referring doctors to Topeka and entertaining them, but with a difference. His idea of what they would enjoy was a clinic where cases would be presented from which they might learn something of psychiatry that could be applied in their own practice. It might also be that they would have some contribution to make, and if they had, they were invited to do so. Out of this idea grew the annual clinics for general practitioners and some of the earliest general conferences on psychosomatic medicine to be held in the Midwest. Some doctors were quite bitter about this innovation; others were enthusiastic.

ii

While Dr. Karl was writing *The Human Mind* Dr. Will was also writing. In the period between 1925 and 1930 he published twenty-eight papers in periodicals of the various medical specialties. One, in collaboration with Dr. Karl, was "The Wassermann Reaction in the Blood and Spinal Fluid of Paretic Neurosyphilis." Some of these papers were collaborations that grew out of his associations at Bellevue. The rest covered an incredible number of subjects: "The Frequency of Pupil Anomalies in General Medical and Surgical Cases"; "Wound Healing in Syphilis"; "Congenital Syphilis and the Thyroid Gland"; "Mechanical Factors in Chronic Appendicitis"; "Juvenile Dementia Paralytica" and "Ketosis Diet in the Treatment of Epilepsy," to mention only a few.

In 1927, Dr. Will had decided that his future lay in psychiatry, and he went to St. Elizabeth's Hospital, in Washington, for a residency in that specialty. Because of his earlier training and his work with Dr. Karl, only six months of resident training was required of him. This training was important since the Menningers hoped to get their own sanitarium approved as a training hospital, and to do so the brothers would have to be certified by the American Board of Psychiatry and Neurology.

The Karl Menningers now had three children: another daughter, Martha, and a son, Robert, had been born. Dr. Will was also supplying Dr. C.F. with grandchildren. Roy Wright was born to Catharine in 1926 and Philip in 1928, and another son, William Walter, was to be born in 1931. Dr. Will's wife, Catharine, had not neglected her own scholarship while she had her children; she had received her master's degree in religious education from Columbia in 1927. Her plans before marrying Dr. Will had been to become a missionary and during their courtship and the early days of their marriage Will had thought of becoming a medical missionary. During his internship in Bellevue, however, he decided that medicine in itself was a mission.

In most ways, Dr. Will was much more his father's son than was Dr. Karl. He had his father's calmness and his even temper and he was thorough and meticulously scientific. Where his father was inclined to be overly optimistic, however, Dr. Will merely kept an open mind. He didn't say that good things weren't going to happen, but on the other hand he didn't think that they had to happen. He was less adventurous than his father and believed in taking precautions. His cautiousness sometimes put him in the position of being the lone dissenter when a plan was being discussed. Dr. Karl would precipitously launch out into something new, his father would agree with modified enthusiasm, conjecturing that whatever it was would probably be for the best. Dr. Will, who had a great respect for and belief in his brother, knew that some of Karl's precipitousness was not as wild as it might seem to an ordinary person. Dr. Karl often came to a decision by a process that might be hidden even from those who were closest to him and if anyone challenged the idea he was answered with a mass of documentary evidence as to its validity. A mind that constantly collected every sort of knowledge from every available source was difficult to defeat and Dr. Will never sought to do that in these discussions; he made Dr. Karl think out loud and then analyzed his thoughts step by step. Very often Dr. Karl would find himself modifying his idea as he went along. Dr. Will's calm reasonableness asserted itself through his presence. Dr. C.F.'s role was to rephrase the idea and present it in a form that was acceptable to both his sons. Since his own attitude usually lay somewhere between the two, he was ideally suited to this role, and he knew just when to put the firmness of finality into his voice and seal the matter that was under consideration.

Dr. Will was by no means a conservative; it was only that nothing seemed radical once it had won his approval. It was beneath Dr. Will to approve of anything, or seem to, just to be amiable. His diplomacy ended whenever he was asked to commit himself to something, but anything that he accepted had his full backing, and that backing was so valuable that neither Dr. C.F. nor Dr. Karl wanted to enter upon any venture or innovation unless Dr. Will was with them. He was much less like his mother than Dr. Karl was, but when it came to protecting the Menninger interests and security he took his mother's place at the conference table.

Just as he knew how to get boys to work for and with him in his sea scout troops, so did he know how to get his patients to work for him as a psychiatrist. For example, Mary B., a patient

at the sanitarium, had a listless attitude toward her work at occupational therapy. Her depression had weakened her physically
and she was bedridden. Since she had always done sewing and
had enjoyed it in the past, the occupational therapist suggested
that she make a quilt. Mary was incapable of making decisions as
to designs and material until her therapist, Dr. Will, talked with
her. He liked ships, he told her, and he had never seen a quilt
that really carried out a nautical pattern in colors that represented
the sky and the sea. Sending a nurse for some drawing material,
he sat down on Mary's bed and drew some pictures of ships. As
she watched him draw, she began to believe in his interest. "You'll
have better ideas than mine," he said. "I'm only showing you what
I like." Soon Mary began to think of the quilt as a gift for her
doctor. In order to have the right materials she had to get out of
bed and find them and then she had to use a sewing machine,
and that was in a room where other women were working. They
became interested in what she was doing, and she became interested in explaining what she was doing and why. The quilt was
an artistic triumph. It stayed at the sanitarium; Mary did not.

At another time, Dr. Will put two men to work on a barbecue
oven. One was depressed and the other very much withdrawn.
But as they worked together their idea of what the oven should be
became more elaborate and required much discussion and planning. Dr. Will was in on every step of its construction and both
patients felt that his mouth was watering for the steak that would
eventually be broiled on the product of their labors. In later years
these men revisited the sanitarium often to have a barbecue on
the fireplace that bore their names.

Perhaps Dr. Will's own highly developed sense of organization
made him look upon a well-organized life as a goal for his patients.
As director of the hospital he saw to it that an ever widening circle
of opportunities for organization and activity was made available
to recovering patients. The staff never assumed that the hospital
had any patients who could not recover if their doctors were sensitive enough and alert to all opportunities. Paretics, people who
had suffered enough damage from syphilis to their central nervous
systems to make them lifetime custodial patients, might be treated
at the sanitarium until the disease was arrested, but they went
elsewhere for custodial care. Even when the sanitarium was in

financial difficulties Dr. Will saw to that. Menningers was always to be an active treatment center.

Maybe it was because paresis placed so many patients beyond all hope of recovery that Dr. Will adopted that subject as his own during the years from 1928 to 1935. Twenty published papers dealt with the subject of juvenile paresis and were finally published as a book, a standard work on that subject.

Whatever portion of Dr. Will's zeal was not absorbed by his medical practice, writing, and administration, went into his work with Topeka's sea scout troop. In a city that is equidistant from the coasts and has only a river, Dr. Will won national scouting awards time and again. He also wrote a handbook for sea scout leaders and held offices in the national organization. As a hobby he kept up the stamp collection he had started as a boy. His specialty was issues commemorating medical men and events.

In 1930, Dr. Karl went to Chicago and got his training analysis under the auspices of the Chicago Institute for Psychoanalysis, which Dr. Franz Alexander had just organized. (Dr. Alexander, who had practiced in Berlin, had been invited by the University of Chicago to become professor of psychoanalysis—probably the first time such a position had been established, in America or abroad.) Certificate No. 1 of that institute was issued to Dr. Karl. Dr. Karl was now officially an analyst, but he had always been that rare thing, an intuitive analyst.

As a student and emulator of Dr. Elmer Ernest Southard, Dr. Karl had been exposed to the teaching of Freud by a man who both fostered and ridiculed the Freudian theories. Dr. Southard sponsored analytically trained physicians in his hospital but never wholly accepted them. Thus it is probable that most of what Dr. Karl learned about Freud during this period had to do with the frailties of his theory as Dr. Southard saw them. When Dr. Karl finally turned to Freud's works he had a powerful prejudice to overcome, for he had admired Southard as he had no other man, and the acceptance of Freud was by the way of being a betrayal of his master. But Dr. Karl did accept Freud, and without turning against those teachings of Southard that had been valid for him. Under Southard, Dr. Karl had laid a groundwork of neuropathology, descriptive psychiatry, and a zest for research and experiment that was to stand him in good stead.

Just how long the dynamic principles of Freudian psychiatry had been incubating in Dr. Karl's mind is indicated by the vast mass of material he had available to illustrate those principles in *The Human Mind*. There are few parallels to his use of all types of literature and personal experience to bolster a psychiatric theory. Psychoanalysis was undoubtedly a living reality for him long before he was analyzed.

Case reports show an application of this belief, but members of his mother's Bible classes were shocked when he illustrated his text from Scripture. As an example of resistance he gave this: ". . . A man with an unclean spirit, who had his dwelling among the tombs; and no man could bind him, no, not with chains. . . . And always, night and day, he was in the mountains and in the tombs, crying, and cutting himself with stones. But when he saw Jesus afar off, he ran and worshipped Him, and cried with a loud voice, and said: 'What have I to do with Thee, Jesus . . . ? I adjure Thee by God, that Thou torment me not. . . .' And he besought Him much that He would not send them [the devils] away out of the country." Dr. Karl explored a number of religions, seeking, and often finding, the truth behind the ancient "spontaneous recoveries."

His studies impressed upon him the effectiveness of short-term therapy. Dr. Karl was not bound to the idea that only months on the couch could bring about cure or improvement.

Psychoanalysis in its classic form is the most time-absorbing and at times the most emotionally disturbing form of therapy. It is not unusual for a patient to be under analysis for at least two years, during which he sees his doctor for an hour a day five days each week. The attachment the patient develops for his therapist has been known as the transference neurosis, so great does his dependence upon the therapist become. At times this transference will appear in the form of love and at others in the form of hatred as the patient works through his deeply hidden conflicts and acts them out. In such therapy as this, one analyst can treat no more than eight patients at a time, presuming he works eight hours a day. Obviously, only a very small percentage of the mentally ill have the time and money for such treatment even if there were enough therapists, which there are not. Freud himself was given to looking upon psychoanalysis as a research method, or tool, and through its practice he and others were able to develop at least a workable anatomy of the personality. Armed with a knowledge of the Freudian theory and technique a psychoanalyst could also become what could be known as a dynamic psychiatrist, using the knowledge he had gained from classic analysis in a more direct and shorter-term treatment of certain cases of mental illness. At times the aim would be merely to relieve painful symptoms rather than to work with the total personality. Short-term therapy could mean a variety of things in a practice such as Dr. Karl had in Topeka—an unhappy young couple could need some simple marriage counseling or a perturbed student might need some vocational guidance. But in such cases it well could be that physical symptoms such as headaches, fainting spells, nausea, and the like would bring them to the doctor's office. Such people might be relieved in a half dozen office visits, for the aim in such therapy was to relieve discomfort and not produce a mature, serene personality that would be totally adjusted to all exigencies. The physician couldn't guarantee eternal mental health to these people any more than a general practitioner can guarantee complete immunity to disease to everyone he has cured of some passing disorder.

Long before he had become a member of the Chicago Institute, Dr. Karl had reported on the successful treatment of one woman by psychoanalysis. This was the case of Marie, a girl whose strong attachment for her father had disrupted her life. Her mother was her enemy, and as her father grew older and became critically aware that she was emotionally handicapped she felt betrayed by life. She had made a success of a department of her father's business, but now her discontent and misery spread and affected not only her own work but business as a whole. She had never been able to form a deep attachment to anyone but her father, but she had been a tease and had led many men on until they believed that they loved her because she loved them. Except in the case of an older man who was quite the opposite of her father and detested by him, she had never become deeply involved. This one involvement ended badly and left her bitter toward all men. She could see no future; her view of the past sickened her; she threatened suicide.

The story of this analysis is the story of resistance in all its varied forms. At the beginning there seemed to be a quite positive trans- ference—a strong emotional attachment to the analyst—but this was just the sort of thing she had given to other men before they tried to return affection. Where she had given material freely during the early sessions, she now became unable to talk to the analyst. Suddenly she could not afford treatment, she said, and when the financial block was cleared the possibility that analysis was a form of quackery began to bother her. When this was over- come she would be late for her session or not appear at all. Then there were days of silence and evasion. But she always came back. She had begun to value the doctor's patience and soon she was more deeply dependent on him. As she did things she thought he would like and reported on them, she discovered that she was acting in accordance with her own deep wishes. The restrictions that had made her a girl in flight and then a bitter recluse in her own home began to lift. In living for the doctor, she began to live for herself. She began to catch glimpses of him as what he was, a dispassionate witness.

As she worked through the last maze of knots that bound her to the ancient frustration of the daughter who has loved her father too well, she understood her hatred of her mother and her mother's jealousy of her. One day she saw that she no longer needed the hatred and jealousy that had become her reason for living. When at last the analyst told her that she no longer needed treatment, she thought that he was being cruel and was rejecting her. In a few days, however, she saw that her release from treatment was the best kind of acceptance. There were moments when this ac- ceptance frightened her and she wished to go back into treatment, but this feeling passed. Business and emotional success were easier than she had ever hoped they could be. She could visit her family, unafraid; she had grown up. Two years of analysis had accom- plished what thirty-five years of living had failed to do.

People who met Dr. Karl on the street or in any non-professional situation could not have believed that he was capable of such patience. He was so impetuous that his business and community ventures very often seemed to those involved like attacks. He wanted to do what he felt had to be done and this made it appear that he was taking charge of everything in which he became at all interested. If he had not had a father and brother like Dr. C.F.

and Dr. Will, he might have been more readily accepted as what he was, a busy, impatient man who thought on his feet and acted out his thoughts. But his father's great poise and solicitous quietness and Will's diplomacy and earnest desire to be helpful did Karl scant service. He stood out as the different one.

When a group of men would gather to discuss Karl's eccentricities and his most recent clash with the town there would always be one or two who would have little to say. They were the men who had gone to Dr. Karl as patients and who owed him more than they dared admit. They could never believe that the man they knew was the same one who was being discussed so heatedly. Had Karl been their surgeon or their banker they would have defended him to the last ditch.

Dr. Karl was continually being hurt by his home town. Often he threatened to leave, as he must have threatened to leave a family that may also have had difficulty at times in understanding him. But his loyalty to his family and to Topeka was greater than any transient burst of anger and disappointment. He loved the city, and he loved his state, and his clashes were always to be lover's quarrels. In these quarrels it was usually Dr. Karl who did the making up. When he went to Chicago for his analysis he took out an Illinois license and practiced there for a time, making more money than he could have in Topeka. But he knew that he was in exile and he felt it keenly.

With the exception of painting, Dr. Karl shared his parents' feeling for the arts. When he was in New York or Chicago, however, and went to plays, concerts, ballets, and operas, they only made him feel his exile more deeply. He was away from the land where there were no such diversions, the place where one could work longer, write more, and still have time to read and garden. In the great cities the emotional pressures that he felt in Topeka were gone. When Karl stepped out of the door of an office building or clinic he became a cipher among ciphers. No one cared whether he was a genius or feeble-minded. The mind Karl's struggles had perfected was like a machine without fuel in the city. Where thought had been there was torpor, and then agony. Once when Karl came home from the city he was ill and his father thought that he must have encephalitis, so slowed were his thoughts. Be-

fore a neurological examination could be made Karl was in action
again and driving himself harder than ever.

Even though the economic depression did cut down the number
of patients seen at the sanitarium, the quality of treatment improved each year. In 1931 the sanitarium won the approval of the
American Medical Association as well as that of the American
Hospital Association, and a nurses' training school was started, one
of the few in the country that offered graduate work in psychiatric nursing. Dr. C.F. had taught at Christ's Hospital for many
years and took over the courses in neurology. Karl lectured on
psychodynamics, and Dr. Will taught the use of "attitude therapy"
and general psychiatric hospital procedure. The school was popular from the start, and often there were more nurses working at
Menningers' than there were patients. For the time being, attendants had been replaced entirely.

Mr. and Mrs. Neese, being attendants, felt ill at ease because
of the preponderance of nurses and sold their interest in the
sanitarium. There were no hard feelings. The place had simply
outgrown them. They went on to operate successful rest homes
in other communities. Mildred Law, John Stone, and most of the
older employees stayed on. Though there were no profits in the
sanitarium to be shared, the clinic had a profit-sharing system,
sick leave, and paid vacations as early as 1921. As well as being
laboratory technician, Mildred Law had become an important
figure in clinic and sanitarium conferences and often helped to
set general policy. She had become a close friend of the Menninger
family and was loved by them all. Tuberculosis had taken her
away for three years, but her job was held open for her until she
returned.

John Stone continued to do psychological testing, but he had
very few patients as an analyst and he was concentrating on his
role of business manager when the Neeses left. From that point on
he was in almost complete charge. He was like one of the
Menningers in that he never gave a thought to the hours he
worked or the energy he expended. Although he continued to
make some show of being a non-conformist, he did everything he
could to train himself as a hospital administrator and even joined
the societies of that group.

Pearl Boam's brother, Ben, was in complete charge of the grounds and building maintenance, a job that required some genius in adapting old buildings to new uses. As the cows and chickens were dispensed with there was even talk of converting the barn into a recreational and cultural center. And patients were always suggesting new projects in building in which they needed his help. His greatest asset was that he and Dr. C.F. saw eye to eye on matters of keeping up the grounds and planting new flowers and trees. This was rare, for Dr. C.F.'s trust of human beings usually failed when they worked for him in the garden. The rare wrangles he got into were with laborers and gardeners who were hired by the day. He not only tended to drive a hard bargain with these people but he wanted to supervise them constantly. Karl and Will always tried to keep him away from new or extra help on the grounds, which was difficult to do since the doctor usually called on his plants as often as he did on his patients.

In a paper, "Therapeutic Methods in a Psychiatric Hospital," which was published in the *Journal of the American Medical Association* in 1932, Dr. Will described the kind of institutional treatment that was the Menninger ideal and practice. He said:

It is not wisdom to maintain the mentally sick patient in this individualized environment indefinitely. He must gradually win his way back until he is able to leave the artificially created atmosphere and re-enter the world of reality.

The emotional response which develops toward persons who provide this haven for him and minister with such understanding to his wishes, conscious and unconscious, is the chief factor in the process of recovery. The hospital building and all the material armamentarium are of little importance compared with the personality relationships that exist between patients and members of the staff. Every doctor is familiar with the part this confidence plays in the treatment of his patients and he is aware also of the influence, adverse and favorable, of relatives and friends upon his patients. This familiar principle must be capitalized and greatly reinforced by making it a matter of study and practice of every employee of the institution. Every member of the personnel must be interested not only in carrying out his particular routine function, but also in contributing something personal to this ruling principle.

This principle must be carried out in a systematic way, with special application to the needs of each patient. One way to assure this is to give each patient a schedule of assigned activities selected particularly for him at the beginning of the week. This not only informs him that he is being given individual consideration, but also maintains a continued plan of prescribed therapeutic attack with opportunity for successive personal contacts in occupational therapy, recreational therapy, physical therapy, reading, music and other creative activities, rest, psychotherapy, and study groups. The friendly relationships which the patient forms in the course of his schedule transform this daily plan from a progression from one unrelated unit of treatment to another into a continuous process of treatment facilitated by varied occupations.

Where in other sanitariums an hour of occupational therapy and an hour of recreation were called a "program," the Menningers had only their personal standards of what constituted activity; they kept their patients occupied from breakfast to bedtime. The average stay of a patient was less than four months, a third of that for public institutions. There was no waiting for therapeutic opportunities; they were created.

Dr. C.F. was impatient because there were not enough opportunities to train doctors in the techniques that were working so well. He knew that by teaching he and his sons would also be subjecting themselves to the responsibility for further growth and improvement. In 1933 the Menninger Sanitarium was approved for residencies in psychiatry by the Committee on Education of the American Medical Association. This meant that young physicians who had finished their medical interneships could come to Menningers for the additional training that would make them into psychiatrists. The doctors in training would have to be paid nominal salaries and there would have to be a significant number of patients with various disorders to study as they worked under and were taught by physicians who were certified in the specialty of psychiatry. Three young doctors, Robert Knight, Leon Stone, and Charles Tidd, were the first to join the Menningers.

With this new program of training, the sanitarium had six doctors available to its thirty in-patients as well as an additional twenty-eight nurses who were taking their graduate training. Already Menningers' was one of the better staffed private hospitals in America, and, as has already been noted, it had medical consultants in most specialties. Of course, these young doctors got much more clinical experience than would have been available in an ordinary sanitarium of that size. Southard School offered material in child psychiatry, and Dr. Karl was rapidly developing an out-patient clinic to take care of the many requests for evaluation and treatment that were coming in.

One thing that limited the Menningers in their efforts at this point was the lack of funds for research. Since the sanitarium had been incorporated as a profit-making organization it could not solicit such funds from the great foundations. Whatever research and writing was done had to be financed out of the physician's own pocket and carried on in his own time. To assist in this, since there were now three potential writers on the staff as well as three active ones, Jeanetta Lyle, an experienced editor, was hired. She also assisted John Stone and took care of public relations in general. As the fame of the sanitarium spread, more visitors came and the physicians could not always spare time to show them around. There was also a dream of starting some sort of bulletin as an outlet for the many good unpublished papers on psychiatry that the Menningers were always coming across. With little to work with, Miss Lyle was faced with an impressive future. The modest job she was hired for was full of possibilities she was supposed to bring into being and not the least thing that was asked of her was that she find out how one set up a non-profit foundation that could solicit funds for research.

Dr. Karl was a good friend of Dr. C. C. Burlingame, the director of the Hartford Retreat, in Connecticut, one of America's oldest mental hospitals. In the course of his travels he had visited this and a few other sanitariums, as had Dr. Will. These places were not competitors of Menningers' since most of them were in the East. Whatever was done at the Menninger Sanitarium was done purely for the good of the patient, not because the trade forced them to improve. As to the comparative merit of mental hospitals, it is doubtful that the Menningers had much idea of where they stood. They were doing the best they could with what they had to work with. Certainly the gymnasium, workshop, recreational office, and library that had been modeled out of the old barn could not compare with the fine buildings they had seen in the East, and even their new buildings were only adequate in comparison. Few of the staff had come to them with training from other places; most were trained on the job. In a sense, a very real sense, the Menningers functioned in isolation. Dr. C.F. always insisted on an application of the principles he had learned at Mayos', but that was the only instance in which they functioned in reference to anyone else.

For this reason it startled them when they heard that *Fortune* magazine, in preparing a comprehensive study on psychiatry and mental hospitals, had singled them out as the only example of a Western institution of worth. From his experience with the publicity resulting from his own book, Dr. Karl feared the results of such articles. The sanitarium had just reached a point of genuine effectiveness, and a great deal of it was due to the intimacy that grew out of its smallness and isolation. He did not want this spoiled and he was afraid of false growth. After a conference with his father and brother it was decided to send Miss Lyle East to try to prevent the complimentary but unwanted publicity *Fortune* was about to give them. If she could not convince the editors that such publicity was undesirable, she could at least impress them with the reality of their situation.

The *Fortune* editors had their piece already prepared when she reached New York. There was little she could do but verify the few facts they wanted to check, and she was not allowed to see the whole article. The rest of her trip was spent in investigating the possibilities of getting money for research. Here again she ran into a blank wall, for everywhere she was told that the thing for the sanitarium and clinic to do was to convert itself into a non-profit foundation. Finally she was referred to George Tomblyn and Son, an organization that raised money for schools and hospitals. He told her the same thing, "Form a non-profit foundation," but he offered his help if the Menningers should decide in favor of that.

When Miss Lyle got back to Topeka and made her report, Mr. Tomblyn was sent for and a conference was held which was attended by the heads of every department in the sanitarium, the Southard School, and the clinic. Everyone was against the Menningers giving up control of the sanitarium. Dr. Karl was afraid of bigness at that point and thought that it would be bad for the morale of the staff and that they would lose their sense of mission. Dr. Will seemed to agree with Dr. Karl, but Dr. C.F., alone, said that he was not afraid of losing control. He had lived long enough to know that control usually rested where it belonged.

Since Southard School was the problem child of the Menninger enterprises it was decided to turn it into a non-profit organization. The total investment in it had come from the Menningers; it was completely in their control and theirs to do with as they liked. The school was to be the testing ground of the non-profit principle. Actually, but not legally, the sanitarium had always been a non-profit corporation since it had never paid dividends.

In the April 1935 issue of *Fortune* magazine five American sanitariums for the mentally ill were singled out for special comment. They were: Bloomingdale Hospital at White Plains, New York, an endowed institution with a history reaching back to 1821; Craig House at Beacon, New York, founded in 1915 and catering to the very wealthy; the Austen Riggs Foundation at Stockbridge, Massachusetts; the Hartford Retreat in Connecticut; and the Menninger Sanitarium. Three of these institutions were opposed to analytic methods and all had more means at their disposal than did Menningers'. Menningers' was the only sanitarium west of the Alleghenies to be chosen.

"The Menninger therapy has three basic principles," said *Fortune*. "They are worth setting down. First is that synthesis of the medical-organic and psychological approach already noted. Second is the individualization of treatment . . . Treatment at Menninger may be anything from putting an introvert at second base in a ball game to force him into social contacts, to prescribing a chapter of *Moby Dick*. Third is what the Freudians call 'transference,' what Dr. Riggs calls 'reeducation' and what Dr. Menninger calls 'scientifically controlled friendship.' Every patient sees his doctor every day, and it is the doctor's business to give sympathetic understanding that the patient usually doesn't get at home.

"'Instead of supplying a uniform environment which seems comfortable to us healthy persons,' writes Dr. Menninger . . . 'the hospital furnishes each patient with an environment that he can accept with greater ease and comfort, because it allows him to express himself on a simpler level than that of the reality from which he has taken flight.'

"This is a good summary of the creed every sanitarium director professes. The Hartford Retreat and the Menninger Sanitarium are outstanding today because they have made a serious and intelligent effort to carry out this theory."

This article in *Fortune* might well have been the end of an unusual American success story. A small-town doctor had climaxed his career by gaining national recognition. Topeka had been given the hospital and clinic that had been promised one morning nearly thirty years before. Or had that promise been kept? The answer was to be found only in Dr. C.F. and his sons.

CHAPTER THIRTEEN

i

AT OAKWOOD, Dr. C.F. was able really to devote himself to gardening for the first time in his life. If he chose to leave the office for a while he knew that his sons could take his calls for him. He no longer had to watch over his diabetics so closely and he rarely took obstetrical cases. During the day Flo would be at her Bible classes and Pearl would be away teaching school. Edwin, Jr., was living at Oakwood, but he was never at home until late evening. The phone could ring as insistently as it wished and the doctor could not hear it out in the garden. His hearing had been failing slightly, and he had found that its failure could be quite selective in cutting out those things he didn't wish to hear. Even if he imagined that the phone was ringing, it was a luxury to ignore it. Telephones had commanded him during most of his adult life.

Where another man might have turned to more lurid vices Dr. C.F.'s clandestine life was centered around the purchase of bulbs and plants so expensive that Flo would have gone into a state of shock had she known the price he paid for some of them. He savored the secrecy involved in smuggling a forty-dollar bulb into the garden. Where someone else would have made a conspicuous event of such a purchase and would have had the neighborhood watching the development of his exotic plant, Dr. C.F. enjoyed startling people by letting them discover the rare bloom. When they wondered where he got it, he would be mysterious and then would delight in giving a lecture as he identified the bloom. He sold cuttings and bulbs, but never for anything like the price he had paid for the originals.

Only Karl, and occasionally Pearl, knew of the doctor's expensive vice, and they both enjoyed it with him. Pearl, as Flo's companion, knew that Flo wanted her husband to enjoy his new freedom. Where once Flo had wanted to know all the details of financial expenditures, she now avoided having them brought to her attention. She would have reacted as always to extravagance, but she wished to avoid the anxiety and depressions that such knowledge was apt to bring to her. There was no longer any great reason for fear of poverty. Leah and her brothers were all secure and safe and her mother had passed on in 1918. Her children and grandchildren had more than enough money by normal standards. She loved her daughters-in-law and found them to be just the sort of women she would have chosen for her sons. There were times, indeed, when she would even side with the daughters-in-law against her sons.

Flo and the doctor had a happiness that few people of their years ever attain. Both were busy; both had achieved a fair portion of their dreams. They had worked out their separate lives without working against each other. They were two people going their own ways, and neither was jealous or resentful of the other. There were times when the doctor was respected for being Flo's husband and times when she was respected for being his wife, but neither was dependent on the other for community standing. The doctor was always to accept Flo as being somewhat his superior, and he was proud of her.

Five hundred women, under sixteen teachers, studied thirty weeks a year for three years just to get a diploma from Flo Menninger's Bible classes. No other woman in Topeka wielded such power. Her advice and friendship were often sought, and she gave of them graciously and wisely. To a degree, she controlled the world she had once feared. Only in moments of severe depression did she see that to have power and success one must be somewhat isolated. Everyone wants to be on the receiving end of sympathy and friendship; there are times when even the strongest want to be humored and indulged, or at least allowed to be thoroughly human. When Flo had such feelings they filled her with fear, for her mother had once had love and affection and Flo had seen how she had suffered when it was taken away from her. That the suffering had taken place in poverty had made it even worse and had confused the issue for Flo, the girl. Love of her sons had always been safer than love of her husband.

At Oakwood, however, Flo worked in the garden with the doctor, and they both felt a great contentment. As before, she appreciated her husband's devotion to flowers rather than the flowers themselves. Since he did not understand her response he thought that she was coming to see what he did with flowers and he loved her for relenting from practicality and joining him. He never realized that to her beauty was a sentiment. She could respond more deeply to a verse or a story that told of beauty conquering the sordid than to beauty itself. On the back of an old wheeled seat that stood at the head of the garden the doctor had painted this verse:

> The kiss of the sun for pardon.
> The song of the birds for mirth;
> One is nearer God's heart in a garden
> Than anywhere else on earth

Flo loved this verse and looked upon the garden as a sort of illustration for it. But as Decoration Day neared the verse was forgotten. Wax-paper wrappers had been printed for the flowers, and Flo saw to it that no bloom came to maturity and faded before it was plucked, wrapped with a dozen others, and rushed into cold storage. Blooms were worth fifty cents a dozen, and that was the way Flo saw them. Each year, thinking to have some flowers to enjoy for a while, the doctor planted more and more until five whole acres were covered with them. This simply meant to Flo that she had to get in help for the harvest and get help she did. Every member of her family who was available would be called upon, men would be hired, and the doctor had to give up every thought of medical practice and stay home to protect his plants. He might lose the blooms but at least he could save the bushes and bulbs. It was a singlehanded battle, for Flo's enthusiasm caught everyone and they swept through the acres of flowers like an army. There was no bridge or plant where the doctor could play Horatius. If he stood off the invaders at one point, he would see a precious plant being devastated at another. He might shout, wave, and throw clods, but it was to no avail. The invaders thought the doctor was being eccentric. His only defense was to pick the flowers from the most precious plants and enlist the aid of someone to deliver them to Flo for wrapping.

When the harvest was over and he looked out on the almost denuded hillside upon which a few late and stray blooms were left him for his work, Flo was happily adding up her account books. In some years she had as much as a thousand dollars to show for the harvest, and there were still the grapes to look forward to. The doctor had planted those in hopes of taking them to friends and giving some to his sons for wine such as his father used to make. But Flo had found a market for those, too, and she looked with suspicion on the extra baskets Karl would take home with him. Strangely enough, she did not begrudge the doctor the "grape soda" Karl usually brought him during the summer, but she never wanted to taste it. That she should be so gracious about this made up in part for the rape of the flowers.

As the holidays neared, Flo's preparations would be as elaborate as ever. Grandchildren and their parents cracked nuts for the hundred or more pounds of candy that would be made. The knitting that had been going on all year was intensified as the number of mittens was counted and found to be insufficient. Clothes were made, and there were many extra trips to the grocery and butcher shop for piles of supplies the little electric car couldn't carry. Mildred Law chauffeured Flo on many of these trips. Finally baskets would be collected and filled with provender and clothes. Flo had a way of finding out who the poor were and where they lived, and during Christmas week she was continually busy delivering baskets. This was no enterprise of her Bible class, though she encouraged her students to be charitable. Her giving was her own personal business and was done without show. Each year a large part of the profits of the garden went to those who needed it most. And Flo Menninger did not confine her giving to Christmas; she could be called upon by the needy at any time of the year.

Dr. C.F. was happy in his home, and as the pressure on him relented he relaxed into what was his own idea of a householder. Edwin, Jr., gave him a chance to collect and enjoy music. A better phonograph was acquired, and with it the beginnings of a collection of good music. As he taught the boy about Bach, Beethoven, Brahms, Wagner, and other great composers he had an excuse for adding records to the collection. Sometimes there would be a concert before breakfast and there was always one in the evening. The doctor needed to teach as much as Flo did and he shared her belief that enjoyment had to be justified. But Dr. C.F. did not need moral stories to illustrate his text; the music was its own best explanation. He usually talked to the boy about the composer's life and the period in which he lived and he never talked while the music was playing. If Pearl and Flo talked during a concert, the doctor's deafness again became selective. He cut out their voices until they were like the sea, or the wind in the trees—eternal sounds, which indeed they were.

On winter evenings the doctor would sometimes read to the women, perhaps a translation of Goethe or one of Shakespeare's plays. If one of the natural sciences had engaged him especially he was apt to read excerpts from some book on that subject. There were occasions when the Bible seemed appropriate, and he would read from it. Only when he read books on medicine and psychiatry did he cut himself off from the others in the house.

Every year the doctor and Flo and Pearl went to the meetings at Chautauqua, New York. They would rent a cabin and prepare their own meals, each finding his or her own friends and attending the lectures, concerts, and exhibitions that met his individual interests. Thus all were left with instruction and description to share with the others. Since Dr. C.F. was a humble as well as a reticent man, few of the people he met knew whether his title was in medicine, divinity, or philosophy. Certainly he never sought to enjoy the prestige that might come from being known as the head of a famous clinic. Flo and her work were better known than were he and his work.

Trips to see Edwin and his family in Florida were usually timed to coincide with the cold wave in Kansas. These trips were Dr. C.F.'s special delight. Edwin's flowering trees had opened up a new realm for him and he explored it thoroughly. Letters written to Karl looked like horticultural catalogues. While in Florida, the doctor and everyone else pitched in and helped with the mailing of Edwin's newspaper. Flo had interested a small Florida college in acquiring the Bible art she had collected over the years, and she spent much time with the curator. On Sundays they all went to the Christian Science Church; there were no clashes over religious theory. Edwin was lending his share of the Menninger zeal to fund-raising for a new hospital in his locality.

On all the trips away from home Flo or the doctor wrote letters that were circulated among the entire family and contained special bits of news for each of them. If there was clinic or sanitarium business the doctor took care of it in separate and private letters. His other correspondence never showed that he missed his practice or worried over what was going on. That was something he considered a completely private affair.

ii

In spite of the depression, the article in *Fortune* magazine brought more patients to the Menninger Sanitarium. West Lodge was furnished, equipped, and soon filled. Fifty patients from twenty-two states and one territory were occupying beds in what had been designed and intended to be a small, regional mental hospital. More young doctors were applying for training than could be accommodated. Physicians from Europe came to see how the Menningers did things and the meetings of organizations in the field of psychological medicine were seldom complete unless a Menninger read a paper.

When Dr. Will took his training analysis at the Chicago Institute for Psychoanalysis he was probably better known than the men from whom he received his training, at least to the lay public. The one thing that impressed him most about his analysis was that it revealed that not even subconsciously did he harbor the slightest antagonism toward his father.

Doctors from Mayos' came to meetings at Menningers' and one, Dr. Henry Woltman, the chief neurologist, became a particular friend of Dr. C.F. Topeka was beginning to discover that it was no more famous for its meat, grain, and railroads than for the psychiatrists it produced and the institution they had founded.

All this went almost unnoticed by Flo Menninger. Here is something she wrote of that time:

"One of our very happiest days was January 15, 1935, our fiftieth wedding anniversary. It was scheduled to be a typical busy day— Bible class, Building and Loan Association meeting and a special meeting of The Horticultural Society. William Claire was to be in Chicago and Edwin, of course, in Florida. So I had not thought of the day as any different from the many other anniversaries that had preceded it.

"But Pearl and Grace and Catharine mentioned the anniversary several times and finally a few days before they said, 'Now, mother, what are we going to do about this? If we have a reception we must get the announcement in the papers.' I said, 'All right, do whatever you'd like to do.' Preparations started at once.

"Pearl suggested that I get down my 'old medal chest' and select from it something to give to each of the children on Monday evening, when we were to have dinner with Karl and Grace. On Saturday evening, we loaded the table with *old* things of all sorts, and Grace came over Sunday afternoon to see what use could be made of them. She selected various old pictures, gowns and keepsakes, and she took my grandmother's spinning wheel and reel to adorn the fireplace. After supper, Karl phoned that he was coming to visit with us for a little while, and he brought William Claire, who had just come from Chicago to be with us for the anniversary.

"On Monday morning everyone went to work as usual. I spent the forenoon studying Isaiah, and when Pearl came home from school she said we must all dress up just as if we were going to a big party. With my hair specially fixed, my new dress, and with Doctor in his dinner jacket and silk tophat, our arrival at Karl's house created a real sensation. The children had never seen their grandfather in that hat, and their jollity was a good beginning for the evening's pleasure. Grace at once decided she would put on her best dress; then the children urged Karl to change his clothes, which he did. All dressed up just to stay at home! It did not take long for the four youngsters to point out where our efforts were successful and where they had failed.

"Suddenly we heard the bang of a car door, three yells like a war cry, and the door burst open as three little boys, Roy, Philip and Walter, came racing in, each one trying to make the most noise. And close at their heels was Edwin—Edwin all the way from Florida. William Claire and Catharine had brought him over. Such a surprise was truly one of life's greatest moments. They said I shouted, and the children wanted me to do it all over again.

"We had a wonderful dinner. Grace knew what the boys liked

to eat when they were home together, and she had planned accordingly. There were golden yellow candles, yellow flowers, beautiful dishes—everything was perfect. We lingered around the table a long time reminiscing about all the things that had taken place in the fifty years. One of the boys read the story of our wedding fifty years ago as I had written it in this manuscript. Edwin remarked that it had been twenty-one years since all three brothers had been together, back in 1914 at Buffalo Park, Colorado, but it seemed to me as if they had never separated. The supreme moment of the day came when Doctor and the boys gathered around the piano and sang, sang the old songs just as they had around the old red piano at 1251. I have always loved to hear them sing.

"On Tuesday, January 15th, I taught my Bible class as usual, and at three o'clock I found Doctor waiting for me. We went home to a house very different than usual. There were folks in the kitchen whipping cream, fixing chicken, wiping plates. The front rooms had been turned into a bower of flowers and there were lights and beauty everywhere—but out of doors it was rather discouraging. For a week the weather had been cloudy, foggy and rainy by turns. In the morning it had grown colder and misty, and then it began to rain and it rained all day. About five o'clock it began to freeze, and the weather got thicker as the night came on. It was a rather discouraging outlook for a reception three miles out in the country.

"But at four o'clock friends began to arrive, and they continued to come until about six-thirty, when there was a lull. As traveling was so bad, we felt there would be no more, but after seven, other groups arrived until altogether more than two hundred persons had called in honor of the occasion.

"It was a great pleasure to see the friends who came to wish us well, pleasant to recall with them the things that had been a part of our lives in the old days. I hope that other couples who have the privilege of fifty years of life together will have the added blessing of loving children to make their golden wedding anniversary as happy as our children made ours."

As an afterthought, a summing up of seventy-two years of living, fifty of it spent in marriage and raising a family, Flo Menninger said, "Dreams are a common indulgence. Some dreams are futile and fantastic, but others are well founded and become sound ambitions. They urge us to follow our purpose with faith, in the belief that we can do whatever we want to do if we think we can. There are many obstacles to be overcome, and many of them we cannot understand, but holding fast to a purpose wins. We can do the thing we want to do if we are earnest enough to make it the first and greatest object of life. I have never found it hard to believe that there is a God who rules the universe, and that He is the power and strength that man can have if he believes and trusts in Him. But how to live according to this belief—that has been my daily problem. How well I have succeeded remains to be told by my own family and by those who have tried to think with me as we have studied our Bibles together. The whole New Testament tells us about a way of life that cannot fail to help anyone who accepts the pattern. 'I am come that ye might have life, through His name.' Those who have tried this believe it, and by their living help others to a happier life."

Flo's family paid her homage on the fiftieth wedding anniversary; it was her day, not the doctor's. There was never any doubt that she was the head of the family, no question that it should be any other way. The success of her husband and sons she took for granted. She had freed them in order that they might have it. Her anxieties had given them time for contemplation; her fears had guarded their future; her formless ambitions had given each a sense of destiny. The order of the day was given by example and was always, "Be zealous, never give less than your best to anything." She did not understand the clinic and sanitarium, nor did she have much of an inkling as to what psychiatry was all about. Her husband and sons were zealously engaged in their enterprises; that was what counted.

Once Flo had said despairingly to Charles Menninger, "Oh, if you only had my ambition and drive along with your intelligence and personality, there is nowhere we couldn't go." Perhaps, in her sons, she had given Charles the things she had not been able to give him before. At any rate, on her fiftieth wedding anniversary she was serenely sure that a Menninger could go any place he wanted to go.

iii

It was said at that time that American psychiatry had not yet come of age. But in Topeka it appeared that not only had it come of age but that it had a family. Psychiatrists were always considered as being such peculiar people that it was hard to believe that they came from the same stock as others. Foreign-sounding names predominated, and many people had a feeling that psychiatrists must have come out of test tubes in some Vienna laboratory. Accents were expected, and on stage and screen the psychiatrist was always presented as a much more disturbed person than his subject. Few Americans thought that psychiatry could be applied to everyday life, and except in certain circles in the East, no one ever admitted that he or any member of his family had gone near a psychiatrist. Most of the medical profession looked upon it as a specialty that didn't belong in medicine at all.

Psychiatry had had trouble in putting down roots; it was as if it were rejected by the earth. Even in the great medical centers it had been something of a parasite, attaching itself to neurology. For a time psychoanalysis was superimposed on psychiatry because of its tenuous liaison with medicine through neurology. A peculiar situation existed in the medical schools; while half the hospital beds in America were filled with mental cases, psychiatry and mental illness were often given less space in the curriculum than leprosy, for example, of which there were never more than 3000 cases in America. No student doctor was ever encouraged to specialize in psychiatry and it was taken for granted that medical failures would eventually wander into jobs in mental hospitals and be adequate for this work. By indirection all young doctors were taught that psychiatrists were physicians who couldn't make a go of it in general medical practice.

Fewer than 20 per cent of America's 3500 psychiatrists were in private practice; the rest were employed by state and federal mental hospitals. From this statistic it could be assumed that 80 per cent of the emotional illnesses would need institutional care, that only 20 per cent of the doctors were needed to treat those patients who could come to offices or would voluntarily submit to treatment in a private hospital. Hundreds of thousands of people struggled along with handicapping mental disorders rather than face going to a state hospital. Families were sundered, careers wrecked, and whole communities suffered just because there were not enough psychiatrists, or because people were afraid to consult what psychiatrists there were.

"Scientific medicine" was busily exposing its lack of recognition of the psychological factors in illness. X-ray and improved laboratory and general diagnostic techniques were demonstrating that a great many very sick people had nothing wrong with them that could be demonstrated physically. As medicine had become less an art and more a science there was no way of coping with these people. The healer of old had no way of knowing that something organic might not be wrong with these patients, and with sincere concern and compassion he could often enlist their faith and cure them. The new type of doctor was perplexed by these patients and at times angered by them. "It's all in your head," he would say. He rarely had any suggestion as to where the patient should go other than out of his office.

If one of these sufferers from psychosomatic ailments ever found his way to a psychiatrist it was more or less an accident. If he did, the psychiatrist had probably become so remote from the realities of general medical practice that he would refer the patient back to an internist. There was a very deep chasm between general medical practice and psychiatry, and neither group seemed willing to build a bridge. Only in three or four widely separated institutions which rarely shared their findings was anything like psychosomatic medicine being practiced.

Strangely enough, most psychiatric research had been on an organic level. Dr. Karl had participated in it when he was in Boston. Pathologists had worked overtime looking for a physical explanation of schizophrenia and manic-depressive psychosis. The discovery of neurosyphilis had given impetus to this sort of research, but state institutions did little research, even of this nature. While the Freudian dynamic provided a research structure, almost all analysts were restricted to private practice. The psychogenesis of mental illness was almost entirely disregarded.

The general public knew almost nothing about psychiatry, save for a few jokes and the memory of some funny bits in films and on the radio. If they acknowledged that there might be something to be said for psychiatry, they assumed that whatever it was, it was beyond ordinary comprehension. The old saw, "Once a nut always a nut," seemed to most people to have some validity. They could not distinguish insanity from feeble-mindedness, and there were always a few feeble-minded people lurking about in any town or city neighborhood. There was rarely any consistent attempt to educate the public to the fact that many mentally ill people did recover and of course those who had been mentally ill did not want it known. State hospital directors had no public to whom they could appeal for increased funds to run their institutions and they were subjected to automatically decreasing budgets—the reasoning being that if they had survived on a certain amount one year they could get by on less the next.

This public indifference and medical apathy created grievous conditions in many hospitals, and during the 1930s only three or four states spent more than a dollar a day per patient for care in a state mental hospital. In some states less than fifty cents a day was spent. Patients were crowded into buildings designed for half the number that occupied them. The quantity and quality of the help was so poor that brutality and indifference were routine. Instead of trying to make the public feel guilty about this situation most of the men who called themselves psychiatrists were so fear-ridden that they concealed it from the public. Families seldom wanted to expose their "disgrace" by protesting.

Dr. Karl's book, *The Human Mind,* had been one of the few intelligent attempts to educate the public in psychiatric matters. It had been followed by many popular but unrealistic self-help books by psychiatrists, popular psychologists, and often by laymen. These and the psychoanalytic thinking that was finding its way into novels further confused the issue, for in some of the latter, the psychiatrist was presented as something of a wizard. The old Indian rope trick with its secured levitation was as nothing compared with the psychiatric nirvanas that were promised. Psychiatry in these texts and stories was no longer the art and science of healing the mentally shattered; instead it became the road to eternal bliss. People sought a substitute for character in the legerdemain of the psychiatric self-help books, and an excuse for any sort of sexual conduct could be found in books that were at three misinterpretative removes from Freud.

There were serious, talented men, and even great men, who were trying to improve psychiatry and its status, but most of them were lost in the remoteness of great institutions or else were quietly practicing in comparative obscurity. Almost all were aloof from the public. Psychiatry had never before the Menningers been the product of a community's needs and of the desire on the part of one family to serve.

Psychiatry in Topeka was what we have come to know as "the grass roots" variety, a provincial product, or even a rural phenomenon, and it recognized none of the limitations that were put upon psychiatry elsewhere. The Menningers, and eventually Topeka, did not find it strange that psychiatrists should come from one of the city's prominent families and that they should occupy a very large place in community life. Washburn College had one of the earliest mental-hygiene programs in the country, but after a little early resistance it was accepted as a normal part of university life. There is no way of measuring what preventive psychiatry did for that campus. In Dr. Will's scout groups, and elsewhere, the same force was quietly at work. Dr. Karl could be called by criminal courts as an expert witness; Dr. C.F. had the confidence of the older families.

Psychosomatic medicine was not called by that name in Topeka, but a large part of the practice at the Menninger Clinic was in that field. In the clinic a knowledge of psychiatric techniques existed side by side with the latest scientific practice of internal medicine, added to Dr. C.F.'s forty-five years of experience in the art of healing. There was no doubt that an intuitive and sensitive older physician was better able to deal with psychosomatic ills than were the modern internists. In this area, as in others, the sons learned much from the father.

For example, in a case where a patient was having recurring spells of weakness and loss of energy without anything being discernible organically, Dr. C.F. asked the man about the animals he owned and learned that he was a small farmer. A house call was made, not to see the patient, but to take a look at his horses, cows, and hogs. The disease that did not show up in the man showed up in a cow. It was undulant fever, and the man was successfully treated for that disease. The Topeka "specialists" had reached the point where they could examine an apparent psychosomatic case and say, "It's all in your body."

The Menningers were also learning that the percentage of institutional and private-practice psychiatrists should be reversed; that institutionalization could be prevented in a large number of cases if the psychiatrist was called upon in time. Their experience with referred cases enabled them to judge that at least 60 per cent of the people who called on doctors were doing so for emotional reasons.

Of course the Menningers had never subscribed to the common superstition of "once insane, always insane." Patients who came to the sanitarium were often as psychotic as those who went to state hospitals. The average length of stay at the sanitarium was three and a half months and most patients recovered or improved. Since the Menningers became friends with most of their patients there was no difficulty in making follow-up studies.

One of the most important things in a science as new as psychiatry is to be able to know something about what happens to the patients who are discharged as recovered or improved. By such "follow-ups" the strengths and weaknesses of the type of therapy used can be studied and future treatment can be improved. Indeed there can be no worth-while research in psychiatry unless the careers and adjustments of many patients are studied. The Menningers were fortunate in this respect, for most of their patients remained their friends and often had a sort of family feeling which caused them to write and visit voluntarily. It was thus that most case histories were kept up to date. This interest in the former patient's life was in no way an intrusion on his privacy; it was of a piece with the sort of follow-up that every general practitioner uses when he meets his patients on the street and inquires about their health.

Dr. Karl had been asked to do a monthly mental-health column for the *Ladies' Home Journal* and for *Household Magazine*. As he read and answered the letters of troubled people and tried to refer them to physicians who could help them in their own communities, he became painfully aware of how little psychiatric help there was to be had. He was also made aware of how poorly grounded the average general practitioner was in psychiatry, even simple psychiatry. At this point, his sense of mission became national instead of local. He began to visit medical schools.

During the late thirties Dr. Karl talked to the students and faculties of every medical school that would give him time and in most cases he paid his own expenses. He had two points to make, and he felt that both were crucial. One was that more young men should enter the field of psychiatry; the other was that the medical school should devote more time to teaching psychiatry, and that it should obtain the best possible lecturers and demonstrators. Dr. Karl was already a famous man, a thing which in itself impressed students. But more than that he was a dynamic and magnetic figure when he was crusading, and his scholarship and grasp of the essentials of all the specialties of medicine were impressive. Students felt that they were meeting one of the great men of medicine. Many of them stayed after his lecture in order to talk to him and some of them wrote to him later and said that they had decided on psychiatry as a career. Where should they go for training?

And so Dr. Karl's journey ended back in Topeka, where with his father and brother he discussed ways and means by which they could take more doctors into their training program. The training program they had was costing them almost $3000 per year per doctor. With three to five residents in training, they would be carrying their limit and yet, before the discussions were over, they were talking about a Menninger school of psychological medicine. As a means of keeping their hand in at teaching, and at the same time extending their mission, they started summer institutes in psychiatry for general practitioners.

Feeling that he was lagging behind his sons because he had not had a training analysis, Dr. C.F. applied for this training under Dr. Smith Ely Jelliffe, who was then visiting the Menningers. Dr. Jelliffe was one of the best-known analysts in America and had worked in close collaboration with Dr. William Alanson White. In 1909 the two had begun the publication of the *Monographs on Nervous and Mental Disease,* and in 1913, they had founded *The Psychoanalytic Review,* the first psychoanalytic journal in English. Dr. Jelliffe had trained many doctors, but after talking to Dr. C.F. he had to tell him, "I could not undertake to analyze you and I doubt if you can find a good analyst in America who will.

You are that rare thing, a truly mature man. I don't mean that in age only. I would feel like a fool with you on my couch. There would be no gain for you and it might be a shattering experience for me." Dr. C.F. was to apply for analysis elsewhere and he always got the same answer. That this answer was a compliment did not lessen his disappointment. He was always to feel that an important part of his education as a doctor had been neglected.

CHAPTER FOURTEEN

i

FROM THE MID-1930s onward Dr. C.F. began to talk of a gradual retirement. More doctors were joining the sanitarium staff, and the offices of the clinic and sanitarium had been consolidated into the old residential building of the farm. The offices in the Mulvane Building were closed entirely since there was no longer any need to duplicate equipment and, as the practice became exclusively psychiatric, there was no drawback in having the offices on the outskirts of town; a bus line went past the sanitarium, and it was easily accessible by car. Southard School remained separate, but that would always be the case. A full-time physician was now employed by the school, and once it had been made a non-profit organization a few small research grants were obtained. Still, there were problems at the school that only Dr. C.F. seemed able to take care of.

Having been refused an analysis, and having entered psychiatry so late in life, Dr. C.F. had no illusions about the contribution he had to make to psychiatry as a clinician. For over forty years the doctor had taxed himself to keep up with the developments in general medicine. As he decreased his medical reading and attended fewer conferences and conventions, he felt that he was falling hopelessly behind. He recognized, too, that psychiatry was developing more rapidly than any other branch of medicine and he could scarcely keep up with the contributions his sons were making. His best role, as he saw it, was to function in such a way as to give his sons a maximum amount of freedom. He found, for example, that he was good with elderly people with depressions —people who had never prepared for retirement and found themselves lost in a desert of idleness. He knew how to be firm with such patients, how to make them try hobbies and studies until they really became interested. Some he sent back to the positions they had left. Most of these patients could not and would not have accepted the counsel of a younger doctor.

His experience with older people led Dr. C.F. into sharing his interests with younger people and if he saw that a younger patient was wasting his time, he considered it a challenge. On trips to Florida he had become interested in conchology, the science of sea shells, and now he was collecting and reading avidly in this field. A class in conchology was started at the sanitarium and was so successful that it was followed by a class in botany and another in mineralogy. These classes contributed as much to the doctor as they did to the patients, for he was happiest when he was teaching natural sciences. In this field he became an evangelist. "Only when you are able to look into the heart of nature will you discover that you are walking on holy ground. Until you can do that you are only in the waiting room of life," he told his classes. If the doctor was ever lacking in patience it was with those who had no interest in nature, but if a patient showed the least desire to learn, the doctor's patience was endless.

These classes were to have been part of his retirement, but since they brought him into contact with patients he continued in his role as physician. As Dr. Will became more absorbed in the psychiatric management of the hospital patients, Dr. C.F. became the sanitarium internist and he was what might be called a "relief man" as well. When Karl, Will, or Dr. Robert Knight, who had become director of psychotherapy when he had completed his residency and training analysis, were called out of town he took their place and where other members of the staff might have to attend only those conferences that concerned them and their patients, Dr. C.F. felt obliged to attend all the conferences he could get to.

The doctor's failing hearing was sharply and brutally brought to his attention by a letter from the board of directors of the building and loan association of which he was a charter member. This letter said that it was felt that Dr. C.F. should retire from the Board because of "the burden of the years" and his inability to grasp things as a younger man might. He resigned from the Board and at once bought a hearing aid—"a push-button censor," as he was to call it. Young doctors in training at the sanitarium who often felt that he had the aid shut off, so silent was he at most conferences, soon learned that he could not only grasp things as a younger man might but that he could remember their errors for weeks. But he would invariably correct the guilty so that only they and he knew of the error.

Neither Dr. Karl nor Dr. Will ever made a change in policy or started a new procedure without first consulting their father; he was the best test they could apply to any new idea. If they could not make it clear to him in an appropriately short time, then the idea needed revision and simplification. He could inject his suggestions into any plan by merely repeating the proposal and including any amendments he wished to make. When new projects were introduced he judged them on the basis of their over-all value rather than on the immediate cost. This was true in such instances as the issuing of *The Menninger Bulletin,* a bi-monthly psychiatric journal that was first published in 1936. There was a need for such a publication, and Dr. C.F. remembered the important role medical publications had played in his early medical career.

From 1935 on he seemed to accept as a foregone conclusion that the clinic and sanitarium would eventually become a part of a non-profit foundation. Dr. Karl's educational plans were directed toward that goal as were Dr. Will's plans for research and experiments in the social and preventive applications of psychiatry. No private institution could maintain, as it did, three separate graduate schools—one in psychiatry, one in social work, and another in occupational and adjunctive therapies. True, the faculty was made up of physicians on the staff of the sanitarium and clinic and they were paying their way through their private practice, but that staff was already larger than could be found at most comparable institutions. Whenever it seemed possible that a small margin of profit would be shown, another member would be added to the staff.

Both Karl and Will felt that well-trained and experienced psychiatrists with an ability to teach should be acquired at any cost. The patients benefited from the presence of such men, and the Menningers felt sure that they would eventually make better use of these doctors than could other institutions. Scatter them and the nucleus of a fine school of psychiatry would be lost, not only to Topeka but to America.

But the salaries of such a staff and the clinical material that would keep them busy were not the whole of the problem, for such men needed to do research and for that they needed facilities and money. All were imbued with the same sense of mission as were the Menningers, and all were willing to make do with little. But even that little was sometimes lacking and while the *Bulletin* gave them an outlet for their papers, unless research could be carried on more freely the papers would soon dwindle.

ii

Topeka, with its extremes of climate and its cultural aridity, made a direct contribution to the dedication of the doctors and psychologists of the clinic and sanitarium. There were no concerts, no theater, none of the distractions of a big city. The only break in the plains surrounding the city was a river that was interesting only as a menace in flood time. Kansas was a prohibition state and for a time had a law against cigarettes. Revival meetings were important events, and often they were eruptions of bigotry. Few of the doctors shared the Menninger interest in horticulture as a diversion, and as one of the young doctors said, "Topeka is the town that gave the act of surrender real meaning." A man really had to believe that he was serving a significant purpose if he came to Topeka and stayed. But those who did stay came to love the city.

Thus it was that men with upbringing very different from that of the Menningers, and accustomed to much more leisure, were surprised to see that they were becoming zealots. Psychiatry and psychiatric matters got their full and undivided attention and they had time for reading and study that they had never had before; they could devote more time to patients. The Topeka group published more than doctors elsewhere did and devised longer and more complicated research. No problem was too big to tackle. Time had ceased to be a confining element.

Young doctors who came to Topeka for their training and stayed on as staff members did so because their sense of mission had become greater than their desire for personal comfort. Well-trained psychiatrists were in demand; they could earn good incomes almost anywhere they chose to live. Association with the Menningers had already blessed them with a prestige as great as could be obtained in American psychiatry. It would embarrass those men to use their names here, but anyone who thinks that these young doctors stayed in Topeka because of emotional and economic security can easily learn that the directors of some of America's greatest clinics are the men who were in Topeka during the thirties and forties.

Dr. C.F. and his sons probably never gave a thought to why Topeka inspired such selfless dedication. Topeka wasn't strange to them; they believed that one could have a rich life there and they took it for granted that men who came to work with them or came to them for training would be dedicated. Dr. C.F. would often enlarge on the advantages of Topeka to candidates for jobs. The rose garden in Gage Park was his special pride, and, he could point out with justice, Topeka was a fine place to raise a family.

iii

When Dr. C.F. had told Flo, "There is no environment waiting for us; we'll have to make our own environment," he could scarcely have guessed just what that environment would become or how many lives it would touch. Certainly they had proven that one doesn't have to accept the limitations of a town or its mores and they had proven as well that neither revolt nor compromise is necessary. When Flo objected to the ways and means of obtaining an education in the Bible she had not attacked those whose ideas were different from hers, but with the doctor's backing and quiet counsel, she had gone her own way and her way had almost become the accepted way in Topeka. And so it was with her boys' social life. As a class mother she had organized their friends; clubs set up in the Menninger home became institutions to which other boys adapted. Flo had also demonstrated that the enjoyment of paintings and good music does not have to be a lonely experience in a community that considers such things effete and pretentious. She educated that portion of the community with which she wished to associate.

In his own quiet way Dr. C.F. had done the same thing with medicine. With unobtrusive dignity he had transcended the limitations that were placed upon him by a homeopathic medical education and even some of the limitations that were placed upon him by his own anxieties and by Flo's anxieties and her seeming narrowness. But Dr. C.F. found freedom in the very things that should have bound him and he was always able to tell the difference between the things he really wanted and the things that should in theory have been his. As long as he kept his central fort intact he could ignore the periphery, where the battles of most men are fought and lost.

The Menninger family never accepted the limitations that Topeka placed on them—for the very simple reason that they were not looking for limitations. It could have been taken as an accepted fact that a homeopathic physician would always practice within a small, isolated group of doubtful prestige. The stigma was upon such a physician; he could simply make the best of a bad situation. Dr. C.F. did not accept the fact that being trained as a homeopath was a limitation, nor did he accept the fact that other physicians were in a position to restrict him. He was naïve, but in the same way that a growing oak is naïve about the boulders that would seem certain to impede its growth. Time and again Dr. C.F. had had it proven to him that Topeka doctors were not going to co-operate in anything like the Mayo plan, and the idea that superior physicians from other places would wish to settle in a community like Topeka was ridiculous. When his eldest son chose analytic psychiatry as his specialty, that would have seemed to have put an end to the idea of a family clinic; anyone could tell you that psychiatry could flourish only near the centers of wealth and enlightenment—Boston, or New York, for example. A psychoanalyst would be laughed out of the average Midwestern town. These limitations were real, built into the land and the Menningers' place of birth. Could any place be less likely to become a Mecca for psychiatrists than Topeka? If Dr. C.F. and his sons had wished to look for it there was discouragement in abundance.

In most success stories the subject is pictured as being all too aware of obstacles and the opposition; it is his role to break through the former and conquer the latter. He is told that he cannot do what he sets out to do, and he makes a spectacle of showing people that it can be done. This is one of the oldest stories in the world, the story upon which dreams are built, but it is not the Menninger story.

At Mayos' Dr. C.F. had seen how medicine could best be practiced and, having seen it, he felt morally obligated to give his city the best. He did not believe that he, more than another, was the Lord's anointed. By making the most of his opportunities to learn, however, he felt that he had undertaken an equal responsibility for teaching and serving, and he passed this sense of responsibility on to his sons. He and they never stopped learning, even when they knew that to do so would only add to their obligations. Success such as they achieved meant only that more demands would be heaped upon them. For example, Dr. Karl, by becoming aware of the deficiencies in psychiatric educational programs and facilities, and setting out to do something about this problem by lecturing, had ended with the responsibility of setting an example of what psychiatric education could be. In the psychiatric community of America he was in the position his father had been in when he came to Topeka—he had to make his own environment, which is to say that he had to build up a system of psychiatry that could, if need be, function independently of the main body of psychiatry. Dr. C.F. and Dr. Will did not consider it unusual that Dr. Karl should be doing this; they accepted it as inevitable.

It would seem at times that they thought their family to be more important than most. When Flo wrote a story of her early years of hardship, poverty, and pioneering, Dr. Karl would not rest until she had made it into a book and that book was published. The story had interested him and the grandchildren it was read to. Naturally, he was proud of the woman who had survived the ordeal she recounted, and he would have liked to invite the neighborhood in to hear the story read. This impulse was what made him see his mother through the authorship of this book. The book, *Days of My Life,** deserves a place in a select group of American autobiographies, for besides being the story of an exceptionally heroic woman it offers a picture of a type of religious thought that was tremendously important to this country and which has almost dis-

* *Days of My Life*, Flo V. Menninger, Richard R. Smith, New York, 1940.

appeared. It is also the story of a woman who had no idea what her husband and sons were doing, other than that they were doing it with a zeal that made them seem healthy and effective to her. In order to write this book, Flo Menninger, then in her late seventies, learned to type.

iv

In 1938 when Dr. Karl published his second book, *Man against Himself,* the method used in *The Human Mind* had been sharpened and had been brought to bear on man's self-destructive impulses. "Whoever studies the behavior of human beings," Dr. Karl said, "cannot escape the conclusion that we must reckon with an enemy within the lines. It becomes increasingly evident that some of the destruction that curses the earth is *self-destruction;* the extraordinary propensity of the human being to join hands with external forces in an attack upon his own existence is one of the most remarkable of biological phenomena." If such a book could ever be topical this one was. Man's drive toward destruction and self-destruction had reached its historic peak in Europe; in our own country we were emerging from a decade where millions were hungry and cold in the midst of plenty. Dr. Karl's sense of mission was as strong in this book as it had been in his first. A leading magazine said of it, "This book will leave you with a jubilant conviction of reason beyond chaos and a sort of crusading determination to make your cousins and your children and your aunts share its wisdom. . . . It will shoot a beam into the dark corners of your own unexplored or unhappy experience."

Dr. Karl wrote this book because it needed to be written, but he also had made it a substitute for his life with his own family. Perhaps the ardor of his early years of practice had taken him too far away from his wife and children, and he had made the sad discovery that there was apparently no way back to them.

By 1939, Dr. Karl knew that he was faced with the gravest decision of his life. His marriage had become untenable. It was not a matter of either being right or wrong, or either having sinned against the other. When he discussed the matter with his father and mother and spoke of a divorce they were horrified—especially his mother. She simply could not see why he couldn't go on living with his family, no matter how impossible the situation had become.

A family that had never cared much about public opinion as long as they were doing what they themselves felt to be right became all too aware of public opinion. Dr. Karl was not only a local figure; he was also a national figure who represented psychiatry to a great many people. His divorce would be widely publicized and there would be many malicious remarks about the physician who could not heal himself. He was not leaving his wife for another woman, nor was he charging her with infidelity or any other breach of the marriage vows. Finally Dr. Karl prescribed for himself and decided to go to New York for further analysis. If there was any way to avoid a divorce he wanted to find it.

In the East, Dr. Karl was in demand both as a therapist and a lecturer. He was also able to develop his friendships with men in his specialty and learn more about the way they worked, and for the first time the clinic had a full-time representative in the East who could explore the possibilities of creating a foundation and raising money for it. In 1938 Doctors Karl and Will, with the approval of the national society, had helped to found the Topeka Psychoanalytic Society.

It is significant that Topeka's society was the sixth local group to be launched in America, and that such cities as Philadelphia, Detroit, San Francisco, and Los Angeles did not establish such groups until later. As president of the Topeka society Dr. Karl was able to find ways of perfecting its training program and techniques while he was in New York.

A psychoanalytic society is made up of a group of psychoanalysts who have organized a psychoanalytic training and teaching program that is acceptable to the national and international societies. Thus every psychoanalytic society is in effect a school of psychoanalysis which passes on the doctors accepted for training by any of its members and organizes seminars and a more or less formalized teaching program to which all members of the society contribute time. It is also authorized to issue certificates to those doctors who complete training and analysis and the subsequent controlled treatment of patients. This latter service enables the senior members of the institute to pass on the quality of the future analysts as well as protect patients from their lack of experience. The training programs within these institutes may be highly formalized, but these institutes seldom have their own hospitals. Psychoanalytic training is not to be confused with training in neuropsychiatry. A psychoanalyst can be an accredited member of his own society and yet not be eligible for membership in the American Psychiatric Association, which now requires three years of resident training in psychiatry in an accredited hospital. In Topeka, however, analytic training and psychiatric training can take place concurrently.

There were a half dozen good reasons for Karl to be in the East other than the one that brought him there and his zeal was in no way lessened by his trouble.

During this period away from home Dr. Karl wrote almost daily to his father and mother. His mother was praying for a reconciliation, and her letters left no doubt that she expected her prayers to be answered. Dr. C.F. adjured Karl to resort to prayer, but he did not tell him how he expected the prayer to be answered. He, better than anyone else, understood his son's turmoil, and he warned his son against letting anyone else make his decisions for him. His greatest fear was that Karl might decide not to return to Topeka. He knew very well that if there was a breach of family loyalty, and if Karl's family troubles were carried over into the clinic and sanitarium, the spirit behind their work would be broken. Dr. Karl's talent and reputation were such that he could probably go further in his career without his ties to Topeka; certainly he could make and keep more money. Aside from their stock in the sanitarium, the Menningers had kept very little of their earnings and Karl had given more than the others because of the earnings of his books and because he was in greater demand as a therapist. But even when Karl's letters seemed to express some doubts about the wisdom of returning to Topeka he would at the same time be making plans that included the sanitarium.

All through this period of conflict Dr. Karl was planning his third book, *Love against Hate*. In this book he dealt with both hatred and love in their broadest and their narrowest meanings. It would be presumptuous to try to imagine and re-create the conflicts of this physician in exile, but the conflict between personal and impersonal love is one that many physicians know. By giving greatly to the many who are their patients they seem to deprive the few, their families, and it is hard for their families to believe that what is given in such abundance elsewhere is not taken from them. For the physician's wife who because of the responsibilities of a growing family does not share his dedication, and identify herself with his mission, there can only be loneliness and a certain amount of jealousy. Her husband's success can become a personal betrayal; if he discusses the happenings of the day in his home it can seem that he is giving the details of his infidelity. Soon there is no basis of communication. This may not have been the case with Karl and Grace Menninger, but it could very well have been. In a situation such as this each person has an equal right to feel misunderstood.

In the case of Dr. C.F. and Flo, impersonal love could flow outward as from a fountain and they accepted each other as distinct personalities with distinct missions on earth. If they could not share the joys of intense personal love, neither could they be crucified by the jealousies and insecurities it sometimes creates. If there were frustrations, they only fed the fires of zeal. Dr. C.F. had a choice to make between tolerance and resentment. He had chosen tolerance, and with it forbearance. In return he was given a strength that could not have been his had he been alone. A religion that now seems strange and narrow sustained them and guided them. This religion could not be passed on completely to their children. The world had changed too much. And indeed their children could be in greater need of personal love precisely because of their parents' deprivation.

If Karl decided to get a divorce, he would, in a sense, be divorcing his mother. For one of the few times in her adult life she would not get just what she had prayed for and let everyone know she expected. She was an elderly woman, and it might have seemed cruel to go against her wishes and apparently shatter her beliefs. Probably Dr. Karl knew better than anyone else that to humor her and try to please her out of pity would be to show contempt for her strength. To make himself miserable over such pity would be to weaken his own fibers, for unless both could emerge strong there could be no dignity in his decision. He decided for divorce.

And then he came home and found that he and his mother had a new respect for each other.

Dr. C.F. embraced his son when he returned. "You were courageous," he said. "May that courage always sustain your convictions. There is no time for feelings of guilt. We have a lot of work to do."

v

The Menninger Foundation for Psychiatric Education and Research was set up in the early months of 1941. It did not encompass or in any way control the clinic, the sanitarium, or the Southard School, nor was it controlled by these institutions. The Menninger Foundation was a separate organization that could channel funds for research and education into any worthy institution, including those controlled by the Menningers, so long as no profit was made by the use of Foundation funds. The Menninger Sanitarium and Clinic now had a staff of between fifteen and twenty psychologists and physicians, as well as thirty-five specially trained nurses and adjunctive therapists. Should the Foundation sponsor a project that called for the time of any or all of the Menninger personnel, the cost of that time could be considered a gift from Menningers' to the Foundation. The Menninger private-practice plan would be giving much more to the Foundation than it took from it.

The Foundation could underwrite the cost of training a psychiatrist and, through a special fund, it could even loan him money for living expenses. This, of course, eased the load the Menningers had been carrying at great personal expense. *The Menninger Bulletin* could not be completely sponsored by the Foundation, but if there were special issues of national importance, such as an issue on military psychiatry, it could be sponsored. There was one special issue on military psychiatry that was distributed to 5000 psychiatrists and draft-board physicians. The Foundation also took over research projects that the clinic was already supporting, such as studies of *Education and Treatment of Neurotic Children; Occupational Therapy Research; Hypnosis Research,* and *Validation and Evaluation of Psychological Testing Techniques.*

During the first year of its existence the Foundation had no full-time employees. The total administration costs were $429.33, although the net worth of the Foundation was $36,363.50. Of this $15,500 was given by the Menninger Clinic, part of which went for the purchase of some adjoining property and a house that could accommodate the Foundation files as well as provide office and laboratory space. The next-largest gift was from Mrs. Lucy Stearns McLaughlin of Santa Fe, New Mexico. She gave more than $13,000 to be used for a building to house the Occupational Therapy Research Project. There were other gifts from Mrs. Blanchette Rockefeller and Mrs. Albert Lasker.

The first officers of the Foundation were: Karl A. Menninger, M.D., president; John R. Stone, vice president; William C. Menninger, M.D., secretary; Robert P. Knight, M.D., treasurer; Mildred Law, assistant secretary; Merle W. Hoover, assistant treasurer. Dr. C.F. felt that he should not hold office so long as he was president of both the clinic and the sanitarium. He was, however, a trustee. Other trustees were Winfred Overholser, M.D., the superintendent of St. Elizabeth's Hospital, where Dr. Will had trained; J. Roscoe Miller, M.D., the dean of Northwestern University Medical School, Chicago; John C. Whitehorn, director of the Department of Psychiatry at Johns Hopkins. Other eminent physicians were members of the Foundation. The lonely physician who had made a pilgrimage to the Mayo Clinic in 1908 was in company the Mayos would have been proud to keep, and that company had come to Topeka to attend a meeting at his own institution.

The only elaborate plan of the new Foundation was the number of research projects that were in reserve and waiting for sponsors. These would have required $236,000, of which the Foundation was prepared to spend only $2500 for administrative costs, hiring a part-time secretary, so jealously was it guarding its money for purely scientific and educational purposes.

One major problem limited the growth and development of the Foundation. That was the lack of clinical material. There were times when the sanitarium had only two and a half patients per doctor and when the out-patient load could not have been over ten patients per doctor. The sanitarium probably had the highest proportion of nurses and therapists per patient of any similar institution in the country. Menningers came near to being the depository of the best psychiatric talent in America. There was a large waiting list of young physicians who wanted training, and the Menningers could very well have provided their own student body. In the rest of the country there was a grievous shortage of psychiatrists; in Topeka there was a shortage of patients per doctor and of facilities to house those there were. Topeka State Hospital was under a new administration and wanted no interference from people such as the Menningers. Operating on a budget of only a little over fifty cents per day per patient it had secluded itself from the psychiatric and medical community.

But before the crisis in clinical material had reached its peak, a world crisis was to supervene. In late 1941 the Army Medical Corps gave Dr. Will an appointment as a lieutenant colonel. Five more of the clinic's and sanitarium's best doctors went into the service and almost all expected to go. For reasons of health, and because he was needed at home, Dr. Karl was not called, much as he wanted to be. There is no doubt but that the decision that he could serve best at home was made by people other than himself and inevitably he was a little envious as he watched his younger brother put on his uniform.

vi

Just before Dr. Will and so many of the staff went into the service, Dr. C.F. felt that he had reached the point where he could now speak of himself as retired. He spent six or eight hours a day at Southard School and the clinic; for him that was a part-time job. But now the patients needed him again. Many of the private-practice internists in Topeka who might have been used as consultants to the sanitarium had been called away. Some of the doctor's old patients needed him, too, and so, as he neared his eightieth birthday, he was back in active practice. With Dr. Will gone, he had to act as arbitrator between Dr. Karl and the staff. Dr. Karl was attuned to constant growth, and he expected it even as the staff and subsidiary personnel diminished in number. The war made some new research projects seem essential, and he wanted them carried out.

Dr. Will had managed the hospital end of the sanitarium, and in doing so had taken over the hiring and training of nurses and therapists. In his quiet way he had united them into a team that understood the orders that were passed through him. These people required a minimum of supervision, but Dr. Karl did not know this and had been thrown into the breach without preparation. In the past he had functioned as chief consultant, teacher, and therapist; details had been taken care of for him. Now he had to find out how his own institution worked, and staff meetings were held early and late. On the business side of the sanitarium, Dr. Karl was likely to attempt to balance the budget by increasing his load of patients rather than by cutting expenditures. Undoubtedly he had been left in command just at a time when the Menninger institutions most needed an administrative overhauling. Dr. Will had not been neglectful, but things had been happening rapidly and not all the Menninger gains had been consolidated into an over-all administrative plan.

No matter how great the reputation of the Menningers had become, and how ambitious their plans, both the clinic and the sanitarium were simply a part of a private practice in which father and sons hired some assistants. Although the sanitarium was a corporation it was set up so that its profit or loss depended largely on the efforts and contributions of the Menningers. Patients came because of the Menninger reputation, not because of the facilities that the stockholders in the sanitarium corporation had bought. The chances for profit were decreased by Menninger methods, which were expensive and required well-paid and well-trained personnel.

John Stone had done well as a business manager, but with the coming of the Foundation, the diffusing of interests, and the complex administration of projects, he could no longer restrict himself to dollar-and-cent problems. Merle Hoover had been hired as assistant treasurer and Mildred Law helped him. Dr. Knight had been largely responsible for establishing the fees for therapy; now that he was in the service this problem had fallen on lay shoulders. Dr. C.F. still thought of fees in terms of two dollars a call and had no understanding of psychiatric fees. This was but one of the problems.

During the war many sanitariums were forced to close because of a shortage of personnel. Menningers', requiring more personnel than most, was certainly faced with this problem even though it was a place where people wanted to work. It was dangerous to ruffle employees' feelings, and somewhat hazardous to expect new and temporary employees to feel the same sense of mission that had sustained Menningers' from the beginning.

Without seeming to take an active hand in the management of the clinic and sanitarium, Dr. C.F. quietly cared for patients' physical ills and found time to talk to each of the employees with whom he came in contact during any given day. So long as people were not handling his plants and flowers he was a tactful employer and, more than anything, he remained a good listener. People could come to him with their complaints and feel that he understood them. When it was necessary, he could take Karl to task for his impulsiveness and lack of tact and when a certain firmness came into his voice there was no doubt of who was in authority.

In the Army, Dr. Will was holding a high-level job in administrative psychiatry. Part of his job was to train doctors to act as combat psychiatrists. He also had to do missionary work and see to it that psychiatrists were placed where they would do the most good. The draft-board rejections for reasons of mental illness and neurosis were appallingly high, and even then a great many emotionally disturbed people were being accepted for the Army. The Army lacked a nosology, a classification of mental diseases, that would allow physicians to communicate meaningfully with each other. Psychoneurosis meant one thing in one hospital and another in still another hospital and a patient transferred through six hospitals might be given as many diagnoses. The American Psychiatric Association had a nosology, but it was admittedly incomplete, obsolete, and inadequate. Fortunately it was something that he and Dr. Karl had discussed many times. But while Dr. Will surveyed the impossible number and variety of tasks that confronted him in the Army, he was also bombarded with the problems of the sanitarium, the Foundation, the Southard School, and the clinic, and Dr. Karl was writing to him as often as once a day.

For a time it appeared that Dr. Will was a man with two wars on his hands. It seemed doubtful that he could do his military job well and be useful on the home front at the same time. When the crisis at the clinic was most acute, he was promoted to full colonel and made chief consultant on psychiatry to the Surgeon General.

CHAPTER FIFTEEN

i

As AN INNOVATOR and pioneer, Dr. Karl's role had been to put new ideas into action. None of his ideas was static; once they were instituted they were bound to grow. The health of that growth, and its direction, would always depend on the skill of those who worked with him. At the outset of his practice, his father had spared him administrative details; the hiring of John Stone had given him further assistance, and with the coming of Dr. Will to the clinic there was a creative and administrative accord. An administrator who worked with Dr. Karl had to be creative, as Dr. Will was. Dr. C.F., who was weak in administration, and in bringing new concepts of treatment into being, had something like a genius for selection. His great accumulation of clinical experience and his years of arduous study in search of better treatment methods had given him an encyclopedic grasp of medical literature. Since Dr. Karl was prolific with ideas this talent of Dr. C.F.'s for selectivity was helpful, but he too had left organization and administration to Dr. Will.

When Dr. Will left for the Army Dr. Karl inherited a smoothly operating organization—that is, it was operating smoothly for that stage of its development. But as new ideas were introduced something went wrong. Karl knew how they should be put into effect, and particularly what they would mean in terms of the patients' response, for he had an uncanny skill in putting himself in the place of the patient and in thinking from his point of view. Thus, if he gave an order from his office and then saw it miscarrying on the ward level, he was upset. He somehow expected his staff to act as his arms and fingers did when he commanded them. If, for example, he ordered a change in diet for the dining room, and it had not been put into effect at the next meal, he could not understand that the chain of command was a complex thing. It never occurred to him that the dieticians had ordered food without anticipation of change. He had to learn things like this by experience, and Karl Menninger was a man who was apt to have his experiences rather violently. Often he would feel impelled to make changes in procedure instead of making a thorough inquiry into the reasons for disruptions. The members of the staff admired him greatly and were disturbed when they displeased him.

In spite of misunderstandings Dr. Karl's sympathy for and empathy with the individual remained constant. Had any member of the staff come to him with his personal troubles, even if Dr. Karl was a part of that trouble, he would have received the warmest understanding. A man who has genius as a psychotherapist is bound to be so constituted. It would take a great deal of time, however, for such a man to learn just how much disturbance he can create among the people who work for and with him. Dr. Karl was starting his interneship in the administrative end of psychiatry in his middle years and he was learning that he had always assumed that he had taken much more responsibility for administration than he actually had. While he was learning, he could have very easily destroyed the very thing that all his years had gone into building. No one could know then that Dr. Karl was undergoing preparation for an even more difficult job.

After Dr. Karl had expressed his unhappiness and frustration in several letters, Dr. Will wrote a letter that seems to show that brothers can still be psychiatrists.

"I think short of being schizophrenic," Dr. Will wrote to Dr. Karl, "most of what one does is because he loves or hates someone and still has enough contact with the world to carry out his behavior in relation to these people. It seems to me that your own thesis of love and hate is on the basis of loyalty to a person, and not merely ideals or being a cog in an impersonal machine. It seems to me that this principle holds true whether the object be Hitler, Christ, or F.D.R. I regard it as a matter of leadership and I think your theory is correct that love is more effective than fear."

In this and other letters Dr. Will tactfully pointed out some of the administrative rules he had followed. Slowly Dr. Karl's creativity began to apply itself to organizational problems and it was not by accident that he became chairman of the Committee on Reorganization of the American Psychiatric Association, of which another Topekan, Dr. Karl Bowman, was president.

The stress and turmoil of the early war years are worth dwelling upon; out of such crises the brothers developed new skills and an even closer method of collaboration. Dr. Karl's advice to Dr. Will on clinical matters was unofficial, but it was certainly among the best he could have obtained. The nosology, or nomenclature, that Dr. Will compiled for the Army was an active collaboration of the brothers and gave Karl a chance to contribute ideas that had long been his. The brothers grew closer in every way and before the war ended they were writing to each other almost daily. The father shared their letters with growing satisfaction. He knew that by airing differences and solving them his sons had been forced to evaluate their constructive and destructive talents and learn to use them for a maximum effectiveness.

In any good relationship between brothers there should be some rivalry and when such brothers are among the outstanding men in their field such rivalry enables them to take the measure of their powers. Dr. Will must often have felt that as the younger brother of a famous man his talents were not always appreciated. He could even speak of himself as being "stolid and plodding" when such was not the case at all. Some of the best innovations at the sanitarium were his, but people had been accustomed to crediting Karl with such things and Karl's fame had brought patients to Menningers' when very often it was Dr. Will who treated those patients successfully. Dr. Karl was a man who could not help being spectacular; he was always giving his utmost, he always believed completely in what he was doing. Dr. Will was modest and almost shy, but once he set out to do anything he could follow it through to the end of time, and eventually would have almost everyone he knew working with him. At the clinic and sanitarium this quiet constancy had actually drawn attention away from him. Dr. Karl's zest for life and his relish of its phenomena drew constant attention to him and he had a talent for infecting those around him with enthusiasm. His displeasure, however, could be as great as his pleasure and it, too, affected people strongly. No one could work with Dr. Karl without being awed by his brilliance and his accomplishments. If Dr. Karl's exuberant behavior sometimes made people mistrust him, their mistrust was short-lived; rarely did a day go by in which his brilliance as a physician was not effectively demonstrated. Dr. Will's ability as a physician was probably as great as Karl's, but his successes attracted less attention for the simple reason that no one had ever doubted his eventual success.

Unquestionably the war made the rivalry between the brothers more acute. Their roles had been suddenly reversed. Dr. Will was placed in a position of national prominence, while Dr. Karl, for the first time, had to stay at home and take care of details. Certainly each must have had the impulse to demonstrate that he could do the other's job better.

In 1941 Dr. Karl married Jeanetta Lyle who had been with the clinic for almost ten years. She was no stranger to the family, and her competence in many fields other than her job of editing and public relations had won her a place in the top echelon of the clinic staff. Wherever she went she made friends for the Menningers, and although Topeka was not her home she had made a place for herself in community affairs. Often it was she who acted as hostess to visiting doctors, and many newcomers to Topeka found that she had paved the way for them. She had helped Dr. Karl with the editing of his books and papers. Quite suddenly he had found that she had grown indispensable to him. After their marriage he bought a place on the outskirts of Topeka where he could devote some of his time to his own horticultural projects. It was called Karlyle Woods.

ii

The job that confronted the army psychiatrist at the beginning of World War II was so vast and so complex that it was difficult to know where to begin. Although psychiatrists had written brilliantly about their experiences in World War I, no one in a position of command appears to have read their books since 1919. The psychiatrists in World War I had realized the stresses and strains of modern warfare created special problems in psychiatry, and that most psychiatric casualties were not psychotics, but borderline cases with emotional disturbances that could be treated in the field and often returned to duty. A combat psychiatrist could be as important as a combat surgeon.

The peacetime Army was either ignorant of or unimpressed with the report made on the experiences of the psychiatrists in World War I. In the entire Army Medical Corps there were only thirty-six physicians classed as psychiatrists, and only four of them were diplomates of the American Board of Psychiatry and Neurology. Even these few psychiatrists were not allowed to work exclusively within their specialty; they were often given general medical assignments. There was only one psychiatrist in the Surgeon General's office, and his job was not in administrative psychiatry. He reviewed retirement cases and did administrative odd jobs. Nor was there any pool of civilian psychiatrists in reserve. Out of the 180,000 physicians in practice in America, about 3000 were members of the American Psychiatric Association. Of these 70 per cent were state hospital doctors and had experience only in the care of psychotic patients. A very small percentage of psychiatrists had any experience in preventive psychiatry. As a whole, psychiatry was predominantly *descriptive:* it diagnosed, categorized, made vague prognoses, and administered care. If patients recovered under this care, which was chiefly custodial, they were considered as having been treated. The natural high recovery rate of the mentally ill gave these psychiatrists some standing, but they were certainly in no way prepared for the job that confronted them in the Army, if that job was to be at all creative. The Army, as if anticipating the sort of psychiatrist it was to get, arranged its hospitals so that the neuropsychiatric wards were locked and barred and prepared only for disturbed psychotics. These wards were also used as the disciplinary and prison wards of most hospitals.

On an administrative level matters were just as bad. Psychiatric classification was black and white; a man was either psychotic or he was fit for duty. That he might disrupt a company or, if he was an officer, a regiment or division was beside the point. There were instances where army regulations seemed to work toward the end of allowing the psychoneurotic misfit to do the greatest possible damage. There were no provisions for the treatment and reclassification of mental patients, and men who could have been returned to limited or special duty after some treatment had to be discharged. Thus the psychiatrists came to be considered a way out of the Army and had to cope with malingerers. Commanding officers sent men who were not mental patients, but disciplinary problems, to the neuropsychiatric service expecting them to be discharged, thus providing an incentive to misbehavior. The psychiatrists became the whipping boys for all the otherwise unsolvable problems that beset an Army that had grown from a quarter of a million to 5,000,000 almost overnight. To make matters worse, the psychiatrists were not even allowed to manage their own destiny. The neuropsychiatric wards were under the command of the chief of medical service. A psychiatrist who survived and succeeded in this atmosphere had to be a superb diplomat and tactician.

Draft boards had immediately recognized that psychiatric screening was necessary, and it was given much publicity, so much that everyone assumed that such screening was effective. In actual practice a psychiatrist, or a general practitioner acting as a psychiatrist, spent two or three minutes with each man. Even a cursory psychiatric examination requires three times as much time as a physical examination. Many people with deep-seated and handicapping neuroses make an excellent first impression; indeed, their specialty is to try to appear more normal than normal even if they don't realize that this is what they are doing. When psychoneurotics and even psychotics and feeble-minded persons began to appear in droves in the Army it could only seem that the Army was creating them, or that its psychiatrists were interfering incompetents who were creating illness where none had been before. No one knew or, apparently, cared that the psychiatric casualties of World War I were still filling the wards of veterans and state hospitals.

The average American was afraid of the psychiatrists; he thought these doctors were consulted only after one had become completely insane. To admit that you had seen one was to admit that you were addled; to be sent to one was to be accused of being incompetent. This was the way the public felt about any personal relationship with a psychiatrist—but on the impersonal level miracles were expected. Psychological warfare was coming into vogue, and to many people this meant that psychiatric wizards were sitting behind the scene plotting the enemy's mental downfall. One positive thing did happen. The magnitude of the psychiatric problem in the armed services frightened the people at home and they could see that there would have to be a great number of psychiatrists to take care of the casualties. The national shortage of psychiatrists was exposed to public view and like anything that is in short supply, the value of psychiatry was inflated by the public.

At the beginning of his army career Dr. Will was given general assignments in the field of psychiatry that allowed him to observe the situation from many angles. His quiet competence and great organizational ability won the respect of everyone he encountered. His fellow doctors in the Army forgot their prejudices against psychiatry when they worked with him, for from any point of view he was a physician's physician. Dr. Will won an influence that enabled him to carry forward his work on behalf of dynamic psychiatry. In the Navy Dr. Francis Braceland was doing the same thing. The two leading figures in naval and military psychiatry understood the structure of personality; they saw it as a whole, not as one or another classic group of symptoms about which nothing could be done. They could predict and demonstrate how men would react under certain sets of circumstances. Psychiatry had failed in World War I because such a concept had been lacking, and it would have failed in World War II had not the proper men been in a position to educate those around them. With the death of Colonel Roy C. Halloran, chief psychiatric consultant to the Surgeon General, Dr. Will stepped into that position, becoming director of psychiatry for the entire Army.

There was something a little ironic about this. It would have seemed natural for the position to go to one of the directors of a great state institutional system, instead of to the hospital director of a fifty-bed private sanitarium in Kansas. Soon Dr. Will was asking three of the greatest medical centers to help him give young doctors training that would make them capable combat psychiatrists. To a large extent he had to tell these institutions how he wanted men trained, and Menninger methods were put into effect where he least expected they would be. He must have felt a pang when he realized that some of these institutions lacked the faculty that he himself had back in Topeka. But Topeka was too far out of the way, and if he had used the sanitarium and clinic as a training center it would have seemed that he was furthering his personal interests. Of course, Dr. Karl demanded to know why their resources were not used, especially since the Army had constructed Winter Hospital in Topeka and it had a large neuropsychiatric section.

The education of psychiatrists was not the only problem. The 47,000 other physicians in the Army had to be given an understanding of psychiatric techniques; moreover, they had to be convinced that their prejudice against psychiatry was not justified. As much as possible, and it was possible to a high degree, Dr. Will made the young doctors under him feel that they were missionaries for psychiatry, and even that psychiatry would be judged by their personal conduct. This does not mean that he had an entirely dedicated group of men under him. The army system of assignments gave him many misfits. Any doctor who had ever worked in a state hospital was at once assigned to psychiatry. This included obstetricians who might have made a call or two at state hospitals to deliver a child. Often Dr. Will's job was that of reassigning people to positions where they could do the least damage. He had literally thousands of details to attend to and never enough assistants. Since he had no time to train assistants thoroughly, he learned that he could somehow communicate to these people his attitude toward medicine and psychiatry, and that once they had that, they would make decisions that were pretty much in accord with his own. Perhaps Dr. Will's greatest talent was for making people feel that he was assisting them in what they wanted to do, rather than that he was commanding them.

Dr. Will was never shy about asking for help, no matter what the source. In this he had some of his father's humbleness. While he and Dr. Karl did a great portion of the work on the army nomenclature, or nosology, it was revised fifteen times and passed through the hands of every major psychiatrist in the country who was willing to help. There are factions in psychiatry that are just as bitter against each other and just as prejudiced as were the factions of Dr. C.F.'s early days of practice. Like his father, Dr. Will was a sort of catalyst.

No matter how busy he was, Dr. Will always found time to keep his father informed as to what was going on, and he had extended an invitation to the elder Menninger to visit him in Washington at any time. As soon as he had been attached to the Surgeon General's office he had moved his family to Washington, and since he had to be absent so much on trips around the country and overseas he declined almost all social invitations and worked at home in the evenings. He was doing a great deal of writing now. Line officers as well as medical men had to be indoctrinated into the ways and means of psychiatry, and many pamphlets, bulletins, and directives had to be prepared.

At times Dr. Will needed reassurance from outside the family. It was helpful to find someone who would reaffirm his own beliefs and even reinforce them as did Dr. Alan Gregg, director of medical sciences for the Rockefeller Foundation. "What," Dr. Will asked of Dr. Gregg, "are the most important benefits psychiatry has to give?" Of course he was concerned about the benefits for the psychiatrist himself as well as for the patient. Here is Dr. Gregg's answer:

First, psychiatry along with the other natural sciences leads to a life of reason. It explains what must otherwise excite fear, disgust, superstition, anxiety, or frustration. It breaks the clinches we otherwise get into with life and all of the unnecessary, blind infighting.

In the second place, by showing us the rule, the uniform limitations, and liberties all human beings live under because they are human, psychiatry gives us a sort of oneness with others, a kind of an exquisite communion with all humanity, past, present and future. It is a kind of scientific humanism that frees us from dogma and the tyranny of the mind, a relief from the inhuman straight-jacket of rigid finality of thought.

Third, psychiatry makes possible a kind of sincere humility and naturalness I've never received from any other study or experience. Perhaps suffering accomplishes a similar miracle but too often suffering lessens one's delighted conviction in the liveableness of life—I don't know for I haven't known much suffering yet. But I know that psychiatry provides material for a quiet but extraordinarily tenacious kind of humility and a sympathy that is honest and eager.

And lastly, psychiatry makes it possible *to bring to others* these things I've mentioned: the light of reason, the oneness with others and an attitude of sympathetic humility, and understanding. Also it makes one able to receive these same gifts—and I would count him a poor physician who cannot receive as wisely and thankfully as he gives . . .

I am almost sure you will say, "But I don't mean that sort of thing. What specifically has psychiatry in the way of benefits?"

I didn't mention the rewards research offers to human curiosity.

Nor the satisfaction of being able to help poor, battered, dependent, frightened people and the justice of giving them the breaks just for once. Nor the immense economy of patching lives to the point of meeting life's demands. Nor the hope that we may understand what disease connotes as well as what it denotes. Nor the possibility that through psychiatric understanding our successors may be able to govern human politics and relationships more sagely.

It is letters like this that keep men in positions of power from feeling lonely. Dr. Gregg, one of the most articulate and humanistic physicians of our time, had said for the Menningers, and for every good psychiatrist, what they had not been able to say for themselves. It was developing and acting upon a philosophy such as this that had made Dr. C.F. the mature man that he was and his touch was in all of Dr. Will's work.

As Dr. Will worked quietly and tirelessly, aided by those men who made up the small group who had had experience in preventive psychiatry, military psychiatry began to change. Eight hundred and fifty thousand individual soldiers were hospitalized as neuropsychiatric cases. This demonstrated the relative accuracy of over-all civilian statistics that one out of every ten of our people will spend some time in a mental hospital. This was but 6 per cent of the total admitted to hospitals for all reasons, although this minority was publicized out of all proportion to its numbers. Of these casualties 60 per cent occurred in the United States and the other 40 per cent overseas, indicating that poor screening and not battle tension accounted for the majority of casualties. When treatment was instituted, from 40 to 60 per cent of the neuropsychiatric battle casualties were returned to full combat duty, and from 20 to 40 per cent to non-combatant duty. Seven out of ten of the patients with psychosis recovered enough to be sent home instead of to institutions.

Such relative success in treatment would have been impossible under a psychiatric system of the kind Dr. Will found when he entered the Surgeon General's office. As psychiatry proved itself it became a full separate division of the Surgeon General's Department, just as surgery was. Eventually 2404 physicians were assigned to neuropsychiatric service; there were 91 division psychiatrists; one psychiatrist to each Army as a consultant on morale and policy; combat teams of psychiatrists; counseling teams in

training camps doing preventive psychiatry, and 450 commis-
sioned clinical psychologists. There were training schools for psychiatric nurses and, where possible, enlisted personnel were given
special training. From an orphan service boarded out, as it were,
to the reluctant guardianship of medical services, neuropsychiatry
came into its own and acquired a prestige equal to that of any
medical specialty.

There were good reasons why Dr. Will came to hold the rank
of brigadier general, the highest rank ever attained by a psychiatrist. When Dr. C.F. and Flo went to Washington to visit Will they
found him unchanged, unimpressed by his new authority, and
eager to finish his job with the Army so that he could go home and
get on with his work there. Dr. C.F. could have attended high-
level meetings with the great medical men of the country, but he
found the horticultural wonders of Washington irresistible, and
devoted a large part of his time to them.

iii

Dr. Karl was busy in Topeka, but he did not restrict his
activities to Topeka alone. In 1943 he was elected president of
the American Psychoanalytic Association and he was active in the
American Psychiatric Association as well. The over-all standards
of state hospitals were bad and getting worse. When Dr. Karl and
a few others suggested that something be done about this situation they encountered stiff opposition. Dr. Karl and his friends,
however, were unimpressed by the group that was so reluctant to
change anything. Many of the young physicians in the Army and
Navy who were doing psychiatric work were asking for member-
ships in the APA and when they came home they would not be
satisfied with such training as was then being offered, nor would
they accept the conditions that prevailed in state hospitals.

Most state hospital superintendents were timid men with what
would seem to be thankless jobs. But those jobs did make them the
rulers of little empires, and many were jealous of their power.
They were isolated from the general medical community and protected from lay criticism by the superstition that the principles of
psychiatry could not be understood by ordinary men. These psy-

chiatrists habitually concealed the defects in their institutions, pitifully displaying baskets woven by the patients, and the one or two wards that would make a good impression. Since they had never taken the public into their confidence, they thought that to ask for money to make improvements, or even to bring the living conditions of their patients up to humane standards, would be an admission of past negligence. And so it was that the lot of the mentally ill was going from bad to worse as food costs went up and reliable personnel became scarce.

Dr. Karl and others tried to tell these men that they were actually showing contempt for the public when they refused to believe that the public would pay for decent care for its mentally ill. "Display before you are investigated," he told them. "Don't blame the public until you've given it a sense of responsibility."

There were all sorts of excuses for postponing any plan to improve hospitals during the war. There were those who said that it would be bad for the morale of the nation to expose the neglect of the mentally ill at this point and others who said that it would give our enemies a propaganda weapon. Since there could be no building during the war, and since overcrowding in institutions was a big problem, it was pointed out that it would be necessary to wait until after the war before any great change could be made. The thing that seemed incredible to Dr. Karl and to other enlightened psychiatrists was that the problem was rarely discussed in terms of patients. The political and personal convenience of many doctors seemed a much greater issue. The conscience of civilian psychiatry seemed, to say the least, defective.

Dr. Karl and other doctors who were in the public eye, and had the public's confidence, knew something of what was going on. Conscientious objectors had taken jobs as attendants in some state hospitals and were horrified at what they found. Some of them wrote to doctors like Dr. Karl. Mental patients were being kept like animals and were often treated worse than animals. The doctors in these backward institutions blinded themselves to what was going on. The reports that came in from some veterans hospitals were not much better, and these hospitals were receiving casualties of World War II, as were many of the state hospitals. This situation was not only victimizing patients, it was charged with danger to all of psychiatry. Honest and conscientious men who stood by helplessly while this situation existed would be disgraced along with the rest when the exposures came. To Dr. Karl and others whose interests did not rest with the state hospital group, it seemed that if they could not markedly alter the present they could at least prepare for the future.

As Dr. Karl got a firm grip on the administrative reins in Topeka, he initiated improvements. A canteen was added to the recreation center at the sanitarium, a small office building was built on Foundation property, plans for a service building were being drawn up. He was constantly in search of doctors and psychologists who could teach as well as do clinical work, and he somehow managed to maintain a medical staff superior to that of most institutions. He and his father were constantly discussing the school of psychiatry they wanted to have after the war. Perhaps they could train five or even ten psychiatrists at a time. At least $20,000 would be needed for that, and the means of raising the money were discussed. Dr. C.F. did everything he could to free the younger doctors for work at which they could most effectively increase the clinic's income.

One of Dr. Karl's chief sources of frustration was Winter General Hospital. Its psychiatric section was under a psychiatrist who had had some training at Menningers'; he badly needed and wanted the help Dr. Karl and his staff could give him. Psychiatry was still under medical services, but it seemed reasonable that the commanding officer would be grateful for some of the best civilian help that was available in the country. But just as Dr. Karl prepared to go to Winter, the commanding officer, bound perhaps by military regulations, issued an order that he could not do clinical work or even demonstrations. "You can watch a man have a convulsion if you wish," was the way he put it, "but you can't do anything about it." At the same time that Dr. Karl was being refused access to the wards, a Christian Science practitioner was allowed to enter the hospital and treat patients. Dr. Karl was furious, and his wrath could be heard in Washington. At that point there was little that Dr. Will could do about such things, and in any case the brothers were leaning over backward to avoid the appearance of using their power to further what might seem to be their personal gain.

Finally Dr. Karl was allowed to go into the hospital and help out. When he did, he found himself in much the same position he had been in during his early days in Topeka; he was in enemy territory and he had to make good. Suppressing his impatience with the Army, Dr. Karl taught by example and actually brought himself to cultivate and associate with the men who had opposed him. While he did this, those who knew Dr. Karl held their breaths and were amazed to see him remain moderately tactful. As he became familiar with the military mind his admiration for Dr. Will grew by the minute. One thing Dr. Karl could not adjust himself to was the waste inherent in having the nucleus of a fine school of psychiatry next door to a hospital with patients that needed treatment and doctors that needed training, and not using that school. Anticipating post-war needs, he wrote to General Hines, the head of the Veterans Administration, and suggested that Winter be converted to a V.A. hospital after the war, stating that he could supply it with a faculty and make it into a training hospital. General Hines, or someone in his office, dismissed the idea and even rejected his offer to act as a consultant to the V.A.

Dr. Karl did not know at that time that V.A. hospitals were often located where the political pressure was greatest, and that they had never been placed near medical centers unless by political accident. When he did learn of this, he went at once to the people of political importance in Topeka, but they too showed little enthusiasm. Dr. Karl knew how great the need for psychiatrists would be after the war, and, since he continued to visit medical schools, he knew that more and more young men were anxious to turn to psychiatry if they could get training that was comparable, say, to what they could get in internal medicine. Very little good training existed outside of Topeka. The four or five adequate training centers had a combined capacity of less than fifty men a year. Applications for training at the clinic were piling up, and young physicians who had worked under Dr. Will and Dr. Braceland, in the Navy, were already making their post-war plans.

Money continued to come into the Menninger Foundation, but it was never enough to carry on even the restricted research plans of wartime. The Menningers, and particularly Dr. C.F., could see the need of a small research hospital devoted to psychosomatic medicine, for there was no such institution in America. But raising money for this was impossible. This, among other things, demonstrated the need for linking the Menninger clinical facilities more closely with the Foundation. The obligation to show a profit or at least break even in the sanitarium was bound to determine the choice of clinical material. When an inordinate amount of time was spent on research cases the Menningers had to bear the expense.

The sanitarium itself was in a peculiar position. Those private sanitariums that were able to remain open during the war were in a very favorable position so far as profit-making was concerned and some were showing a 20 or 30 per cent return on their investment. Whenever the Menninger Sanitarium seemed to be on the point of making money some needed improvement would set it back until it was dangerously skirting the red margin. Dr. C.F. pointed out to Dr. Karl that they were operating a non-profit institution without having the legal advantages that should go with that. True, their life savings were in the sanitarium, but if they wished to grow in the direction of research, education, and still better treatment, they would have to give up those savings. Even though the Menningers were private-practice physicians they had long ago placed themselves on set budgets in order to support their favorite projects. Such things as *The Menninger Bulletin* were costly and brought them no conceivable gain. Ever since the *Fortune* article had appeared, the sanitarium had had a waiting list. They had their choice of consolidating the gains of the years, capitalizing on their reputation and growing rich, or going on with the mission that had inspired them and enabled them to grow.

Dr. Will had become a famous man and would undoubtedly be offered many fine positions after the war, positions where it might seem that he could realize his ideals more easily than at the clinic. Dr. Karl recognized that expanding their work together was the only thing that could keep Will and himself united and mutually effective. Dr. Will could not be at home to share in the planning and launching of a new Menninger Foundation, but Dr. Karl wanted him to know how important his role was even though he was fully occupied with other things. And so Dr. Karl wrote:

I'm not sure how to phrase it without sounding a little mushy but perhaps I can begin by recalling a motto that you have often quoted to me as we walked toward the dining room together. "Doctors may come and doctors may go, but you and I go on forever." You meant this to include father. We're probably not the best psychiatrists in the world—there might be one or two better! But we do have something that none of the rest of them have. We've got a working combination—there's nothing like it in the world—we've had strength here because following father's wise advice we began years ago to base our development on the theory of "united we stand." Now we don't stand united just because we admire one another's abilities or because we believe intellectually that team work is an advantage. We've been united because of our real affection for each other, and this has made our work a real enthusiasm.

Now, I don't think that anything can ever change the primacy of this bond of affection between us, a thing that is so rare in this world —or for that matter between almost any two people—and which is always so effective when it exists. It is no accident that the Mayo Clinic was built up by two brothers who worked together, or that the Cleveland Transportation Center was built by two brothers who worked together, or that aviation science was developed by two brothers who worked together. Two brothers working together are enormously powerful and we've got it—and I think we must keep it and treasure it and use it and enjoy it.

Dr. Karl further pointed out that they need no longer compete with each other for fame, that he would often be "Dr. Will's brother" now just as Dr. Will had been "Dr. Karl's brother" in the past. With this, it seemed to him that the last possible breach in their relationship had been sealed. And Dr. Karl had learned the hard way just what Dr. Will's task had been before fame came to him.

iv

In the late summer of 1944, Dr. C.F. felt that he was really experiencing the fulfillment of his dream. He had been disappointed that Southard School, the sanitarium, the clinic, and the Foundation had been forced to operate as somewhat separate enterprises. Something had been lost that way; there had been too much waste, too many opportunities to bicker about little things. As he and his sons decided to turn over all of their stock to the Foundation, as well as their prestige, all were relinquishing their life savings. But what had they saved for if not to give Topeka the best clinic possible? From Dr. C.F.'s point of view, he was not giving anything; he was receiving a gift from God. He had the sons he had prayed for, and they had more than fulfilled his hopes.

Now, just as he had gone out to sell stock in the sanitarium, he went out to ask the men who had bought it to give it to the Foundation. Somehow he found this job easier than the other. Most of the men he went to were proud to make a gift to the institution that had grown out of their original investment. These men knew that the Menningers as majority stockholders had not only given something like a quarter of a million dollars in holdings but that they were dedicating their lives to the Foundation as well. Control of their enterprises would no longer remain in the Menningers' hands unless they were worthy of holding that control. They had staked their lives and their fortunes on what they had to give to Topeka and the nation.

CHAPTER SIXTEEN

i

DURING THE WAR YEARS life at Oakwood went on much the same as before. More flowers were given away, and Dr. C.F. did more of the work in the garden because of the shortage of help. There might be difficulties at the clinic, but trouble and its consequent worry never followed the doctor as he went out among his plants and flowers; he was always serene when he returned from the garden. It is little wonder that he spoke of this work as being "the embrace of God."

He also found that troubled times were those in which one could best set about improving oneself. An advanced course in plant paleontology was offered at Washburn, and he enrolled in it. His study of conchology was becoming more elaborate. On winter evenings he catalogued and arranged his specimens in special cabinets or caught up with the correspondence this new hobby had created. Even if he had only four or five students in the classes in mineralogy, botany, or conchology, which were now a regular feature at the sanitarium, he prepared his lectures meticulously. As he saw elderly patients who were depressed by what they thought was their growing ineffectiveness, he could explain to them that aging men did not become ineffective, but perhaps only a little sated with the things that had so occupied their active years when ambition had been their driving force. What was needed was to try one's effectiveness in new areas, areas that were dominated by eternal values. There was one reward—serenity—and Dr. C.F. had attained that to a high degree. It sometimes puzzled his sons that he could seem more pleased by a new type of sea shell than by the progress made by the Foundation.

Another thing that gave him as great satisfaction as anything at the Foundation was the work Edwin was doing in Florida where he was now known as the "Flowering Tree Man." He had become an outstanding authority on flowering trees and, like every Menninger, he was a missionary for his specialty. He was preparing a book on flowering trees, and he had plans for beautifying the whole state. He had his own nursery, but it was more than a money-making venture; it was part of his plan. Dr. C.F. was in his full glory when he could work with Edwin in Florida during his winter holiday. The scope of the task Edwin had set for himself in his book on flowering trees, and the thoroughness with which he set about it, were just what the doctor expected of a Menninger. There were to be 3000 separate examples of flowering trees in the book, and Edwin proposed to raise each variety from seed so that he could describe it accurately. Karl, too, had become actively interested in flowers, and he and Edwin carried on a correspondence in this field.

In spite of the fact that she was doing much more than most active younger women, Flo Menninger often complained that she was slowing down. Since Pearl was no longer teaching school full time and was at home most of the day, she took the burden of housework off Flo's shoulders, but the extra correspondence Flo had developed because of her book and her new out-of-town Bible classes more than absorbed that extra time. The war created special problems with the Bible classes; transportation had to be shared, and of course it fell to Flo to organize it. Some nights she was very tired and complained of a pain in her chest, but by the next morning she would be up and busy with her many chores and projects. The annual trips to Chautauqua were kept up in spite of the inconveniences and hazards of wartime travel. Three grandchildren were in the Army, and packages had to be prepared for them. Bob, Karl's son, had been drafted just as he was ready to enter medical school. When he married, that meant to Flo that there was another Menninger to look after. Julia, Karl's daughter, had married a young doctor who was in the service.

Although Dr. C.F. had some qualms about giving their life savings to the Foundation, he was prepared to override any protest Flo made. There was no protest.

"I know you've taken this problem to God and got your answer," she said. "It's His will that you make this gift to Him. He will look out for us. We don't need much so long as the children are taken care of."

Dr. C.F., not wishing to take any advantage of the gift he and his sons had made the Foundation, had asked that he be put on a half-time salary. He was now chairman of the Board of Directors, but he was much more active than that title implies. He would not think of missing any major staff conference while he was in Topeka and he personally signed every Foundation check.

The elder Menningers had always been proud of Karl, but somehow it had always been accepted that he would be in the limelight. It was extremely important to them that Dr. Will should also have recognition. His advancement from lieutenant colonel to colonel and finally to brigadier general was a great fulfillment. He was also to win the Lasker Award "for distinguished service in the field of mental hygiene." Dr. Will became the most quoted and written-about doctor in the armed services, and the Menningers were proud that the public was at last seeing what they had always seen. As busy as he was, Dr. Will always found time to write long and detailed letters to his family. These letters were logs of his travels and were pecked out on his portable typewriter in planes crossing the Atlantic, in tents at field hospitals, and at theater of war headquarters between conferences. Generally limited by the requirements of security he wrote somewhat boyish descriptions of places he had visited, but there could be no doubt of the love that went into the writing of them. These letters were retyped and shared with everyone at the clinic and with many people in the Bible classes. Topeka was proud of Dr. Will too. He was *their* general, someone they were proud to have represent them.

In early February of 1945, Flo was more seriously indisposed than usual. Her chest pain was accompanied by some shortness of breath, and Dr. Karl had the clinic internist go out to Oakwood to see her. This doctor wisely judged that Flo was a woman who would not be invalided; all he could do was tell her to limit her activities for a few days. Dr. C.F. took a grave view of the situation, and asked Pearl to accompany Flo wherever she went and to spare her exertion whenever possible.

On the evening of the eighth of February Dr. Karl called on his father and mother, as he did every evening. Flo had been reading about the town Mr. Hershey, the chocolate king, had built near her birthplace in Pennsylvania, and since Dr. Karl had recently attended a medical convention there she asked a great many questions about the place. The success stories of this sort were always of great interest to her, and she derived a great deal of pleasure from them. That her family had a success story of its own never occurred to her. She told Karl that she planned to write Mr. Hershey a congratulatory letter the next morning.

The letter was never written. Before nine the next morning, Flo Menninger's valiant heart had given out. One of the few times she had ever called for help in her life was when she fell as she got out of bed that morning.

She had been active to the end. She had left letters that had not yet been posted to the twenty-four Bible classes she had founded in three states and sixteen cities and she had prepared revisions in last year's teaching that would become effective in next year's lessons. Her newspaper Bible lessons would still be appearing in 1955. The zeal bred of her anxiety and enterprise was to influence markedly America's thinking about the human mind. The girl who *had* to teach was with her husband and sons as they founded a great teaching institution. It was all but impossible for her family to imagine going on without her.

The Bible classes held a special service for her, separate from the funeral; a choir represented the Negro churches of the community, and seven representative members of the community stood on a platform holding unlighted candles. As each lit his candle he spoke of what it stood for—Purpose, Courage, Loyalty and Love of Home, Faith, Teaching, The Bible Classes, All that is Beautiful. With appropriate background music, a reader read poetry and Biblical verses that had been favorites of Flo Menninger. This was just the sort of service she would have planned for someone else.

Needless to say, Dr. C.F. went on with his work. He missed not one day at the office, nor did he give up a class. Pearl kept house for him. Knowing that his father received best by giving, Karl went to him each evening for consolation and reassurance. That people were concerned for him made Dr. C.F. impatient.

"In a little while I'll be able to do my spring planting," he told

Dr. Karl, and then added wistfully, "But I wonder who we'll get to take care of the harvest."

ii

In 1945, shortly after his mother's death, Dr. Karl was appointed to a commission of outstanding civilian psychiatrists to go to the European Theater of War and do a study of morale and psychiatry. The other doctors on this commission were Lawrence S. Kubie, Leo H. Bartemeier, John Romano, and J. C. Whitehorn. It meant a great deal to Dr. Karl to get into the uniform of an army doctor even though he was without formal rank, but it meant a great deal more to be allowed to participate in something he had had to view from the side lines, or in a menial and restricted role at Winter General Hospital. He was indefatigable, and people who took the trip with him still shudder when the name of Karl Menninger is mentioned.

The commission was supposed to follow a prescribed itinerary, but Dr. Karl abided by it only during official hours. In the evenings he called on the smaller hospitals or the camps that had not been included in the itinerary. He found his way into disciplinary barracks, or compared the recreational facilities of officers with those of enlisted men. When he had talked with soldiers at Winter he had paid special attention to their complaints and now he wanted to see what foundation they had. Dr. Karl would not be rushed through wards with the pomp and circumstance that usually attend a medical dignitary; he stopped and talked with the individual patients, giving ward doctors and commanding officers some uncomfortable minutes as he demonstrated his uncanny knack of getting the confidence of even the most befuddled patients. The younger doctors he met liked his way of puncturing stuffed shirts, and, in watching him with patients, they saw how a really skilled psychiatrist works. He seldom left a hospital without having one or two of these young men apply to him for training.

Incredibly enough, he also found time to meet civilian psychiatrists in the countries he visited. There were many refugee analysts, and he assured several of them that places were waiting for them in Topeka. It would seem impossible that one man could accomplish all the things Dr. Karl accomplished on that trip. He made more friends—and more enemies—than the ordinary man does in a lifetime. Since he was a man who lived through action the trip refreshed him. He came home with increased fervor; something had to be done about post-war psychiatry and he would do it singlehanded if he must.

Dr. Karl was not content simply to make an official report; he felt that the public should know what the problem was, as well as its responsibility for solving it. In a talk he was to repeat many times he said:

"There are limits to human endurance. If heat becomes too great we burn; if we become too cold we freeze; the human body can take heavy blows but it cannot withstand a slug of metal propelled by gunpowder. Flesh yields and bones break.

"Thus the wounded soldiers of the war gradually fill numerous hospitals scattered over the country and behind the lines in Europe and the Orient. A third of our physicians and surgeons, plus many from our allied countries, are working day and night on the firing lines of medicine and surgery in these far flung colonies of mercy.

"But it is not only flesh and blood that have their limits of tolerance. The human spirit can break also and does. The shock of induction into the military service, the burden of routine, the exhaustion of forced duty, the fatigue and horror of the foxhole, the constant threat of pain and death, the loss of comrades, the loneliness, the homesickness, the despair—these take their toll along with shells and bombs and bacteria. The mental faculties fail; fear and depression supplant courage; obsessions and delusions replace logical thinking.

"These are the casualties of the World War which in chronicity and in seriousness outrank all others. There are already about 500,-000 of them with more coming back every day—30,000 a month, 1000 every day! And what do they come back to?"

Dr. Karl knew very well what the veterans were coming back to, and he did not neglect to tell his civilian audience what it was. The public hospitals were a disgrace, and even if the public improved them who would staff them? Dr. Karl's estimate was that 10,000 psychiatrists must eventually be trained, that they must have 1000 clinics, and that 5000 psychiatric social workers and an equal number of specialized nurses must also be trained. It was the public's responsibility to see that the necessary money was made available.

People listened to Dr. Karl politely and applauded appropriately, but he was still having difficulty in raising the $20,000 that would be needed if the Foundation was to be able to train even five doctors a year in the first post-war years. In spite of this he had visions of training twenty-five or thirty doctors if the Veterans Administration would take over Winter General Hospital and let Menningers' supply a faculty, even if at their own expense. Further letters to the Veterans Administrator were of no avail, and so Dr. Karl asked the civic organizations and the leaders of both political parties to intercede for him. There seemed to be little that they could or would do.

After his return from Europe, Dr. Karl had been more active at Winter Hospital. Since he was wearing a uniform when he returned he was allowed to function almost as a staff member. At once he began to give lectures and clinical demonstrations for the psychiatrists in the hospital, and arranged for other Menninger psychiatrists to give seminars. On some of his trips to the hospital he took his father along so that he could see what the situation was in military medicine and also survey the plant that his son wanted so badly to have.

In his letters to Dr. Will, Dr. Karl often expressed his unhappiness over the treatment he saw men getting. After he had attended a Certificate of Disability Discharge Board he wrote, "We had one corporal this morning who had 33 months overseas and 23 months of combat, then had a transient psychosis. He had a row of battle stars clear across his chest, and not a damned word of praise or anything else was said to this fellow and it wasn't due to coldness on their [the doctors'] part. It was simply that they don't realize as I do what it means. I thought it was one of the most remarkable cases I had ever seen but they just routined it through until I made them stop and talked to the boy for quite a while and I'm sure that he left the service with the feeling that somebody understood that he had done a hell of a big job and wasn't 'just a crazy guy' the Army wanted to get rid of. . . . There isn't the right kind of rapport between patients and doctors and it is *not* because the doctors are officers. It's because the doctors don't really understand the patients and the patients know it." Dr. Karl didn't blame these doctors; he blamed the forces that kept them from getting the proper training.

iii

As more World War II veterans were discharged into V.A. hospitals for further treatment, the inadequacies of the old Veterans Administration became more and more obvious. In the Army, with all its shortcomings and red tape, the servicemen had been under the care of the finest physicians from civilian practice. In the V.A., the doctors had only to meet certain civil service requirements, and these requirements were all too low. When the practice of medicine became a civil service job it lost its freedom and dignity. Political appointees could dictate procedures; service organizations could bring pressure to bear. The official book of *Rules and Procedures* was scripture, and clinical medicine was secondary to it.

The story of the Veterans Administration is one of the most incredible in American history. The Teapot Dome Scandal and other cases of corruption in government were chiefly matters of political conniving for financial gain. No one was injured but the always-injured taxpayer. In the case of the Veterans Administration there was no great financial gain, but job-holding and patients suffered. A hospital might be built in the wilderness to pay off some political debt. Indeed, one of the neuropsychiatric hospitals closest to Topeka was at Fort Lyon, Colorado. It was hundreds of miles from the closest medical school and, for that matter, the nearest large city. It was central to nothing and exceedingly hard to staff, and patients' families could visit it only at the greatest inconvenience. It was but one of several hospitals so located.

In 1945 the disgrace of the Veterans Administration broke into the open. In a series of articles first published in *Cosmpolitan* magazine and reprinted in *Reader's Digest*, Albert Q. Maisel gave the public a glimpse of the care the veterans were getting. Second- and third-rate medical treatment was routine. Since the V.A. medical staffs sometimes had pensions to offer they expected respect, something they did not usually earn on any other ground. Most nurses, orderlies, and attendants were old civil service job-holders more concerned with living comfortably within the rules than with caring for the patients. The new case load was an inconvenience that irked them. In neuropsychiatric facilities they had a way of showing their displeasure with patients by the judicious use of boot therapy. Indifference was the rule and when a V.A. employee began to show personal concern for the patients he was rightly thought to be dangerous to the system.

The V.A. had the excuse of not having been able to get adequate personnel during the war and of not being able to build new facilities, but this did not explain away brutality that had existed long before the war nor the lack of anything that resembled adequate planning for the post-war period. Maisel's reports were too well documented to be doubted by the public or by the officials who read them. Medical and surgical patients were ready to bear witness against the men who had neglected and tormented them. There were too many neuropsychiatric patients who had recovered spontaneously and who could name the men who had beaten them in specific hospitals on specific dates. These were not just scattered cases; there were hundreds of them, from V.A. facilities all over the country.

The stories of what was happening to the veterans horrified the public; a change in Veterans Administrators was demanded immediately. The truth of the things that Dr. Karl and others had been saying for a long time began to be accepted.

General Omar Bradley was appointed Veterans Administrator, and as a former field commander of the invasion of the continent, he had everyone's confidence. His chief surgeon for the European Theater had been Major General Paul Ramsey Hawley, a man who had done a miraculous job in setting up medical services for the invasion forces. Never in the history of war had an army been so well served medically. General Hawley was appointed chief medical director of the V.A. and he went into that service taking the key members of his staff with him.

General Hawley was a physician in the great tradition; he knew that good medical treatment and medical education could never be separated. His first act was to establish what he called a Deans' Committee. On this the deans of all the great medical schools were represented; they, rather than politicians, would dictate the new V.A.'s medical destiny. The first step taken was to remove V.A. doctors from civil service and place them in a Department of Medicine and Surgery where the competence of these physicians would be passed upon by the Deans' Committee. The next step was to place V.A. hospitals near major medical schools so that they could have the facilities of first-class training centers and thus attract and hold the better younger physicians. Where there were army hospitals near the medical schools they could be taken over by the V.A. until such time as it could build permanent hospitals.

Bradley and Hawley were ideal choices for their jobs. They were military men whom both doctors and enlisted men would choose to serve under in civilian life and so they would never have trouble in enlisting personnel. Both were capable of generating great enthusiasm. They were sure of adequate backing, too, at least during the early post-war period when sentiment was strongly on the side of the veteran.

One of the biggest problems that faced the new administration was that of locating a training and treatment center in neuropsychiatry. None of the major medical schools had adequate psychiatric faculties for a major training center and since none of the members of the Deans' Committee were psychiatrists they, too, were at a loss for suggestions. Topeka was occasionally mentioned, but it seemed such an unlikely place geographically that it was never given serious consideration. At the same time a psychiatric training program was considered the most important single problem that faced the Department of Medicine and Surgery of the V.A. and it appeared that the V.A. might have to start its own school. But there was no facility of the old V.A. that had even the nucleus of a teaching staff.

iv

Dr. Will was too busy with the problems of the evacuation of troops and the disposition of neuropsychiatric casualties to be able to pay much attention to what was going on in the V.A. He had once called the training potential in Topeka to General Hawley's attention; there was not much more he could do. Dr. Karl was thoroughly discouraged about Winter Hospital. The commanding officer had it on good authority that it would be closed and abandoned in early 1946. Since it was a sprawling, one-story, cantonment-type hospital with small wards giving off miles of ramps, it would require more personnel than the ordinary hospital and would be much more expensive to operate. In any case it was the type of hospital that the Army routinely closed. Dr. Karl had not been called upon by General Hawley even though he assumed that the offers he had made to Hines had been passed on to the general. His congressman and a Kansas senator both assured him that they were bringing pressure to bear. In order to increase this pressure Dr. Karl continued to work with civic organizations, trying to interest them in financing the education of at least one or two residents in psychiatry. Over a hundred applications for training were on his desk.

In October 1945, just when things were at their darkest, Dr. Karl received a courtesy phone call from Colonel Arthur Marshall. He said that he was from General Hawley's office, that he and Dr. Karl had friends in common, and that he would like to drop by for a chat. Dr. Karl asked Colonel Marshall to come right over. He had heard that Marshall's job was that of surveying and closing hospitals and that he had been to Winter the day before and had as much as said the hospital was condemned.

Colonel Marshall and Dr. Karl became friends almost as soon as they met. Marshall had been the man who had formed base hospitals in England that could rapidly be transferred as the invasion force advanced on the continent. It had been a job that had to be accomplished in a very short time and had needed a man of action who could cut through the routine red tape of procurement. It had called for inventiveness and a willingness to improvise. Dr. Karl wanted to know all about how this work had been accomplished and soon the colonel and he were chortling over stories of how Marshall had helped the Army outwit itself.

"You know," said Dr. Karl, "I can't understand how a man like you can close Winter Hospital."

"Why?" asked the colonel. "It's deadwood clear out here in the Plains."

"Then you already have a neuropsychiatric training center in mind?" Dr. Karl asked. "I was going to tell you I could make that hospital into a neuropsychiatric training center and supply the faculty to train twenty-five psychiatrists."

"Only twenty-five!" Colonel Marshall exclaimed. "Make it fifty and I'll have the hospital transferred to the V.A. as quickly as we can get the Army out of it."

"Get them out by the first of the year," Dr. Karl said euphorically, "and I'll make it seventy-five."

"Hell," Colonel Marshall responded, "let's make it an even number—100. The V.A. has to have a pilot training hospital. We can get all the backing we want. There's nothing worse than a modest start. Now tell me about your faculty and how you'll set up the school. Whatever you haven't got we'll get." *

So far as the two doctors were concerned, the new V.A. pilot training center was an established fact. In a matter of minutes Dr. Karl had two secretaries taking down memoranda. Dr. C.F. was called in and given the good news, as was a startled Dr. Knight. Now clinical director of the Foundation, Dr. Knight had good reason to be apprehensive when he could see his entire staff being called away for a teaching job so monumental that it was hard to comprehend. There had never been a school of psychiatry in America that could enroll more than fifteen students a year. That was all that Bellevue and the combined faculties of two great medical schools were capable of handling. Dr. Will was even more astonished when he heard the news over the phone. "Now wait a minute, Karl," he admonished.

"There isn't anything to wait for," Dr. Karl said jubilantly. "It's settled, finished, done, an established fact."

For a few moments after he hung up Dr. Karl was silent and then he turned to Colonel Marshall and said, "Art, maybe we ought to call Washington and tell them what we've done."

"They're apt to get in our way," Marshall said, "but I'll call them."

Within ten minutes Bradley and Hawley were as enthusiastic as Marshall and Menninger. When Dr. Karl got on the phone and talked with his new superiors in Washington, he was at his persuasive best. He agreed that he wanted Winter V. A. Hospital to be the pilot neuropsychiatric training center for the V.A., but he

* This is one version of a story that has been told many times in many different ways. Another version is that Dr. Karl and Colonel Marshall settled on a figure of fifty psychiatrists in training and that Dr. Daniel Blain, head of the Department of Psychiatry of the V.A., raised the figure to 100. In actual practice the greatest number to be in training at Winter at one time was 125.

did not agree that it could be this if it were set up as a hospital that treated neuropsychiatric cases exclusively. In his opinion it should be a general hospital with all the services of a general hospital. Certainly it would lean heavily toward neuropsychiatric treatment and training, but there could be no adequate treatment or training in a hospital in which one specialty isolated itself.

Before the phone conference was over it was fairly well established that Dr. Karl would be the manager of Winter Hospital. The details of how Winter Hospital and the Menninger Foundation were to function in relation to each other were to be settled between Colonel Marshall and Dr. Karl. It was difficult for Dr. Karl to keep from announcing his triumph to the press, but he had been warned against that by Washington. By the time the hospital opened almost every politician and pressure group in the Midwest was to take credit for its founding, and Dr. Karl would have learned that it was good diplomacy to thank them all and let them think so.

v

Colonel Marshall had been on a scheduled field trip when he stopped over in Topeka, but after his meeting with Dr. Karl the rest of that trip was canceled. On flying trips to Washington he stirred up enthusiasm or quelled doubt, as the need might be, in order to expedite matters in Topeka. Although the V.A. had a new administrator, none of its basic rules had changed. If routine procedure were followed in transferring Winter from the Army to the V.A. and getting the needed equipment, the whole project would pass out of his and Dr. Karl's hands into the hands of the V. A. Engineering Department. Even with the establishment of the new Department of Medicine and Surgery, the engineers could still decide when and where an operating room was needed. They could open and close wards at whim. And so it was with the Procurement Division. Colonel Marshall and Dr. Karl had first met in late October of 1945 and they had scheduled the opening of Winter for January of 1946. There was no time to be wasted.

The number of legal corners that were cut can be judged from the fact that Winter V. A. Hospital did not have a completely legal existence as a V.A. facility until several years after its opening. At no other time in history could such shortcuts have been taken. The public's disgust with the discredited administration made the original personnel who were retained in most departments lean over backward to please the new administrator. Two extremely popular men were at the head of the V.A. and both had the blessing of the large service organizations. Even the most ardent budget balancers in the government were looking away from the V.A. for a change and were momentarily happy to see that it got any sum it asked for. If anyone seemed dubious about any request made by Colonel Marshall or Dr. Karl he was at once referred to General Hawley or to General Bradley.

In one instance, Colonel Marshall was in Washington when Dr. Karl said that he would like to have an adequate number of dictaphones, that keeping good case histories was a very important part of training. At that time Colonel Marshall had devised a method whereby Dr. Karl could order things he wanted by telephone, and so he said, "When you phone in your order be sure to ask for enough and never back down."

"How many would enough be?" Dr. Karl asked.

"Twice as many as you need and we can bargain from there on," Marshall said, having a vision of Dr. Karl asking for something like twenty-five dictaphones. Ten would normally have been considered a good supply for a hospital like Winter.

Since Colonel Marshall always listened on an extension when Dr. Karl placed his orders, he felt that he could increase the order if need be. As always, Dr. Karl was reading from a list slowly and in an even voice as the procurement agent took down the things needed. The orders were routine, a mimeographing machine, some medical equipment, and then Dr. Karl said calmly, "And ninety-nine dictaphones."

"Did you say nine dictaphones?" asked the startled procurement man.

"I did not," thundered Dr. Karl, "I said ninety-nine dictaphones and I want every one of them."

"I don't think even the company can supply that many offhand," the procurement man said.

"They'd better," Dr. Karl said ominously. "I could have asked for a hundred, you know."

The order was filled. Dr. Karl had followed Marshall's orders never to back down on a request.

Many military hospitals in the Midwest were being closed at that time. Although Colonel Marshall was attached to the V.A. he was still on active status in the Army Medical Corps, and his administrative assignment was concerned with medical administration and the closing of hospitals. Thus he and Dr. Karl were able to requisition trucks and liberate supplies according to their needs. Dr. Karl wanted an occupational-therapy and industrial-training unit at Winter that would be second to none in the nation. He also wanted to be sure that medical and surgical equipment were of the best and in good supply. And so the two doctors foraged far afield, and the army officials who were still at Winter became almost hysterical as the supplies rolled in. It appeared that Dr. Karl was getting ready for a state of siege.

Not all the foraging was restricted to medical installations. At one point Dr. Karl found a small locomotive and a half mile of railroad track that could be laid along the back of the grounds at Winter. He felt that it might be a fine thing for some patients to be allowed to drive something so powerful as a locomotive. As he admitted, it was something he had always wanted to do. But this railroad venture was a little bit beyond even Colonel Marshall's exuberance.

The zest and fervor that went into this part of the founding of Winter Hospital is important because it greatly enhanced the hospital's spirit. It also contributed stories to an already growing Karl Menninger legend. Men in the wards were to hear and repeat some of these stories; they gave Dr. Karl a special human touch and made him one of the most beloved of hospital directors. Echoes of this enthusiasm were to reverberate for a long time.

There are those who would use this period as an example of Karl Menninger's opportunism. Certainly he made the most of an opportunity, but it was an opportunity that had been created by his work, and the work of his father and brother. It could just as easily be said that the V.A. and the American people were the opportunists. When Dr. C.F. surveyed the new territory that was coming under Menninger jurisdiction he was humble about what was given them, but he would be the last to say that he and his sons had not prepared for it.

As things worked out, with Winter Hospital becoming the pilot training center for the V.A., it was almost as if Dr. Will and Dr. Karl ran in relay. One saw psychiatry through a war, the other

picked it up as it and its patients returned to civilian life. Dr. Karl
had learned a lot about the administrative end of things while Dr.
Will was away and he was prepared for the job ahead of him. But
still Dr. Karl's greatest function was that of the innovator. By taking on Winter Hospital, and promising the V.A. to train as many
men as he had, he had got the Foundation into sublime trouble.
It was faced with a crisis of a magnitude never imagined before.

The Menninger Foundation had the nucleus of a good school
of psychiatry, but as the plans for Winter grew it could be seen
how inadequate this faculty was in number. Previously, the Menninger doctors had supported themselves through the clinical work
they did. But now it appeared that even if the entire staff taught
full time there wouldn't be enough of them. Of course, there are
many sub-specialties within any specialty, and some of these are
purely academic and produce no income. For example, a full-time
anthropologist was needed, as was a specialist in education. There
had to be at least thirty senior psychiatrists and neurologists. They
would have to practice at the Foundation part of the time, and
there was not enough office space for them. They had to be recruited, too, and that was a problem.

This last problem was partly solved by the many contacts Dr.
Will and Dr. Karl had made on their excursions about the world.
Dr. Karl knew, for example, that his chief of neurosurgery would
be Dr. Leon Bernstein, an American who had been trained in
Scotland and had served with the British Army. He was not only a
fine surgeon; he was also research-minded and had a talent for
teaching. Bert Booth, a professor of humanities, had worked with
Dr. Will in the Army, and seemed to be just the man to organize
the Department of Education of the Menninger Foundation. Dr.
George Devereaux, the anthropologist, had already done some
work for the Menningers. In this way men were selected for the
faculty. The difficulty was that they had to be selected and ready
to begin work in a matter of a month or two.

Some extra office space had been added to the clinic and sanitarium facilities when the Foundation property had been bought.
A small office building had already been erected and a service
building that was under construction on the sanitarium grounds
would free some of the other offices. In the meantime offices were
being set up in an old garage and in a pump house. The telephone

switchboard had been moved to what had formerly been a road-side hot-dog stand. Money had to be raised for more buildings.

Then there was another problem. With the announcement that the Menningers were going to direct the V.A. training program at Winter Hospital some six hundred applications for training came in. Only one in six could be selected for the first classes. How to make that selection? What made a good psychiatrist? Had anyone ever done research in the field? No. This meant that not only did selection criterions have to be established and selection teams appointed, but that a chance for some very worth-while research would slip by unless a research project was set up at once. Luckily, former staff members were returning from the Army and before they began to get patients for treatment they could do interviewing. The Department of Clinical Psychology would have to devote full time to the applicants.

Dr. Will was needed at home as never before, but the Army needed him too, and he could not conscientiously leave his post until his job was completed. As Dr. C.F. helped where he could, he often wished that Flo were with him to see what was happening. And then he realized that it would have meant very little to her; that this was the sort of thing she took for granted. And so, to a degree, did he. He had felt that his dream had gone a little astray when the hospital and clinic had become exclusively psychiatric, and there were times when he felt that psychiatry's concept of total medicine was largely a matter of lip service. When Karl insisted that Winter be a general hospital he knew that his influence was at work. Karl had been impetuous in taking it on, but the doctor was accustomed to Karl's impetuosity and less afraid of it than he once had been. One thing Dr. C.F. was not afraid of, and that was the clinical practicality of any school or training program Dr. Karl directed. Even in the turmoil of organizing Winter Hospital he was still seeing patients for consultations and therapy, both at the Foundation and at Winter General Hospital. The best thing a doctor father can say of a doctor son is, "He is a physician," and Dr. C.F. could always say that of Dr. Karl.

By the end of 1945 doctors from all over the world were converging on Topeka. In one area at least, the V.A.'s disgrace was obliterated. Now it remained to be seen if the Menningers could live up to their reputation and promises.

CHAPTER SEVENTEEN

i

"THERE IS NOTHING more expressive of a barbarous and stupid lack of culture than the half-unconscious attitude so many of us slip into, of taking for granted, when we see weak, neurotic, helpless, drifting, unhappy people, that it is by reason of some special merit in us or by reason of some special favour towards us that the gods have given us advantages over such persons. The more deeply sophisticated our culture is the more fully are we aware that these lamentable differences in good and bad fortune spring entirely from luck.

"It is luck: luck in our heredity, luck in our environment (luck above all in our bringing up), that makes the difference; and moreover at any moment fortune's erratic wheel may turn completely round and we ourselves may be hit by some totally unforeseen catastrophe. It is luck, too, springing from some fortunate encounter, some incredible love affair, some fragment of oracular wisdom in word or writing that has come our way, that launched us on the secret road to health and on the stubborn resolution to be happy under all upshots and issues, which has been so vast a resource to us in fortifying our embattled spirit. At any moment we are liable, the toughest and strongest among us, to be sent howling to a suicidal collapse. It is all a matter of luck; and the more culture we have, the more deeply do we resolve that in our relations with all the human failures and abjects and ne'er-do-wells of our world, we shall feel nothing but plain, simple, humble reverence before the mystery of misfortune."

This is a quotation from John Cowper Powys that Dr. Karl Menninger read into his acceptance address when he became manager of Winter General Hospital on January 11, 1946. "This," he said as he finished the reading, "is the spirit in which we intend to conduct the hospital." His audience was made up in the main of lay citizens of Topeka who had come out in a storm to be present at the ceremony. He had also read a statement of Plato that eloquently presented the Menningers' medical point of view. It was: ". . . . So neither ought you attempt to cure the body without the soul; and this is the reason that the cure of many diseases is unknown to the physicians of Hellas, because they are ignorant of the whole, which ought to be studied also; for the part can never be well unless the whole is well . . . that is the great error of our day in the treatment of the human body, that physicians separate the soul from the body."

Dr. C.F. was in the audience and was somewhat puzzled that the townspeople should be congratulating him, for few knew of the pledge he had made to his city. Certainly he had never dreamed or intended that the hospitals in the Menninger orbit would have a payroll that was potentially as great as that of any other industry in Topeka. When Winter got into full swing it would have nearly 1000 employees, independent of the Foundation. The city was grateful for this economic boon.

The job Dr. Karl was taking on was in reality two jobs that were quite distinct from each other. He had to assist in organizing and directing a Department of Education at the Menninger Foundation which would operate schools and special courses that would offer varying degrees of psychiatric education to 1393 people. Only 119 of these would be physicians; the other training programs were an adjunct to the School of Psychiatry itself. The second job was to organize and operate a hospital with a capacity of 1500 patients. The Army had left the hospital fully equipped and with the beds made up. What happened from then on was up to Karl Menninger. Traditionally, V.A. hospital managers had been captives in a cage of mediocrity, the bars of which were rules and regulations.

The view Dr. Karl took of being appointed manager of Winter Hospital was that he was a private-practice physician called in to treat or supervise the treatment of a certain number of patients. He expected his prescriptions and orders having to do with the welfare of those patients to be honored. This was General Hawley's view, too. Medicine that had taken its orders from the government had proven itself to be totally unreliable.

Twenty-seven young physicians arrived at Winter on January 2 and enrolled in the first class of the Menninger School of Psychiatry. Each quarter thereafter twenty-five more physicians would be enrolled until the quota of one hundred had been reached. The course of training would last three years. Since these doctors would be treating patients as they learned, they would draw a salary of $3300 a year from the V.A. The V.A. would also pay their tuition in the School of Psychiatry, a sum which would compensate the Menninger Foundation for providing a faculty and certain facilities for the school. The resident physicians, or students, from Winter would also rotate through the various clinical facilities of the Foundation—Southard School, the clinic, the outpatient clinic, the guidance center, etc., and would thus get much more rounded experience than could be available within the confines of a V.A. hospital. Training analysis would be available to them through the Topeka Institute, but at extra cost. Since their psychiatric training was taking place in a general hospital, a broad study of psychosomatic medicine would be available and there would be more clinical opportunities in neurology. Residencies were available in internal medicine, general surgery, neurosurgery, and otolaryngology. Closely related to the School of Psychiatry was the Department of Clinical Psychology, in which there were to be nineteen residents. A School of Social Work and another of Occupational Therapy would share some of the classes of the other schools. One hundred and twenty-five cadet nurses inherited from the Army would also complete their training at Winter. The Menninger School of Psychiatry was teaching people how to work together as they acquired education in their various specialties.

Since there had never been a School of Psychiatry of such scope and size there were no precedents to go by, no curriculum to borrow from. Psychiatric teaching on such a scale had never been formalized. Within a short period of years psychiatric residencies had been increased from six months to a year and then to two years and finally three. Every teacher from the Foundation sat up nights working on the curricular problems in his special province. Even before the hospital was open Dr. Karl had written to the outstanding psychiatrists in the East and West, inviting them to lecture or conduct seminars. The students were encouraged to organize their own curriculum committee, since they were the real pioneers in a new type of medical education.

The residents themselves were the cream of the crop of over 600 applicants. Most had been in the upper half or quarter of their classes in medical school. Almost all were veterans and had distinguished themselves in the service. Some had been in private practice before the war and one resident was the former dean of a medical school and a board member in another specialty. Colonel Arthur Marshall had become too deeply involved in Winter to leave it, and he also enrolled as a student in psychiatry. These were people who were apt to be critical and articulate if the teaching fell below a certain standard; they had enrolled at Menningers' because they had expected the best teaching in the world. These doctors were making definite sacrifices in order to get this training. Although most were married and had started families—2.9 children per psychiatrist at one point—they were turning their backs on private practices that would assure them of a minimum income of $10,000 per year. Most had to borrow money to supplement the salaries they were getting. They were working for something they believed in, and they were willing to make a sacrifice for it. The sacrifices they made gave the Menningers an added responsibility.

ii

The relish and zest with which Dr. Karl attacked his job was infectious. When he pulled his old red convertible up to the curb before the office there was usually a burning of rubber. He would extend warm greetings and issue firm orders while the car was still shuddering. As he walked down the corridors of the hospital he gathered people as a snowball gathers snow, and he managed to talk to them and convey what he meant to each. Sometimes he would have a bag of apples with him and distribute them as he went along, or as he passed a Coke machine his extra change would go into it and two or three people would be startled to find Coke bottles placed in their hands. If he had no orders to give he had something to learn; there would be an exchange of some sort with every person he passed on his way to the office.

His desk was huge; on it was a battery of telephones and beside it some of his famous dictaphones. There was a keyboard of buttons with which he could call his secretaries and assistants and he played on this as on a piano. He always had some use for whoever answered a bell. On one end of the desk was an avocado crate. Into this he emptied newspaper and magazine clippings, letters, and bulletins which he found of interest in one way or another. If a secretary was standing by he would dictate and attach memoranda to some of these items as his mind routed and catalogued every item that went into the crate.

The office was long. There were chairs along the walls and over them were pictures of Freud, and of Dr. C.F. and Dr. Will. In front of his desk was a long conference table, and on this were piled magazines and books he wanted the staff to read. Six or seven times a day the chairs would be pulled up to the table and conferences with various committees would be held. Rarely did Dr. Karl see one person at a time. As he listened intently to one he would rummage in drawers and baskets and pass things to another person to read and comment on later. Every visitor, however, felt that he had Dr. Karl's full attention.

Dr. Karl was allowed to fill V.A. staff positions with men who could teach and control treatment. They would supplement the Foundation staff and be the backbone of the hospital. General Hawley had also seen to it that some superior men from the old V.A. were assigned to Winter. They were able to help Dr. Karl and the residents master some of the forms and formalities without which no government agency could exist. Questions of pensions and of the eligibility of veterans required a lot of paper work, as did the employment of new personnel, all of whom, aside from the physicians and psychologists, would be under civil service. Dr. Karl usually had an experienced V.A. man in his office, and as he made decisions and gave orders he would watch the face of the V.A. authority in order to gauge the sort of administrative weather he was running into. If there was real alarm in the face of his auditor he would demand, "Well! Can they put me in jail for that?"

Since most of the residents and staff had just come out of the service, their greatest fear was that Winter might degenerate into a repetition of the regulation-ridden life they had just left. They knew, too, that not all the employees of the former administration had been weeded out by the new administration, and that they were awaiting their day. There were even a few around Winter who said as much. All the doctors had accepted the V.A. as a necessary evil if they wanted Menninger training. From the beginning the V.A. reputation constituted a danger to morale, and there was reason to doubt that Dr. Karl or anyone else could beat the system.

As attendants and nurses were hired and patients began to fill the wards, V.A. red tape began to make itself felt. A doctor would give an order and have it countermanded by a lay functionary who had been sent from Washington to administer a department. A class would be scheduled for a certain room and the Engineering Department would say that the room was not to be used for that purpose. Dr. Karl called a meeting of the doctors, the supervising nurses and attendants, and the V.A. administrative officers. When asked why they had countermanded the orders of Dr. Karl's staff the V.A. administrative officer always referred to "R & P" number such and such.

"What," Dr. Karl asked loftily, "is R & P?"

"It's the official code of *Rules and Procedures*," said a V.A. man. "Its laws govern the administration of every hospital, even this one."

"Then there'll be no more R & P," Dr. Karl said briskly. "We'll dispense with that problem, expunge it from our memories. If anyone mentions R & P again I want it reported to me immediately. We're running a pilot hospital; it's supposed to set an example and not live within the laws of failure."

This, as it turned out, was not simply a dramatic gesture. Doctors saw their orders carried out, and classes were held where it was most practical and convenient. Dr. Karl did not openly flaunt the rules unless they happened to be especially ridiculous, but when they were he missed no opportunity. Once when he was showing a reporter through the hospital he stopped and exchanged greetings with a porter, asked him about his family, and gave him some encouragement. As soon as he was out of the hearing of the porter he said, ominously, "I could be put in jail for what I just did." "What did you just do?" asked the startled reporter. Dr. Karl pulled from his pocket a bulletin announcing a new order that forbade members of the Department of Medicine and Surgery to concern themselves with problems of personnel morale during working hours. Dr. Karl's attitude toward such regulations cheered the staff at Winter. He became the hero of every man who had ever endured red tape.

No one was better aware than Dr. Karl that attendants or "psychiatric aides," as he chose to call them, could make or break any treatment program. It was they who controlled the patients' environment for the greater part of the day and night. He knew also that people have a tendency to work against any program in which they do not play an active part. Through all available public media he let it be known just how important he considered attendants to be, and that he wanted the best. He said he believed that many men who had been in the Medical Corps in the service might want to follow that work in civilian life. He was right; many did. So a special training program for psychiatric aides was set up. He addressed each class that enrolled, using the normal reactions of those in the room to illustrate just what patients were suffering from. This half-hour talk of his was one of the most effective introductions to the study of mental illness ever given. Resident physicians were encouraged to teach in the Aide School for he wanted these two groups to be familiar with each other's problems. In lecturing to both groups, he stressed the essential importance of democracy in a hospital. Patients who were recovering from illnesses incurred while in the Army and Navy would have every right to suspect a staff that was set up along the caste lines of the services.

The problem of segregation came up very early in the history of the hospital. Topeka still advocated segregation, and there were some fairly strong feelings about it in the community. Dr. Karl had not considered it a problem since there had never been segregation in the clinic, sanitarium, or foundation, and Dr. C.F. had had a Negro receptionist for years. Negro physicians had been accepted for residencies at Winter, but there was some objection when Dr. Karl gave the order that Negroes were also to be hired as nurses and attendants. The old V.A. men said it was against policy, something that impressed Dr. Karl not at all. When some nurses and attendants objected to working with Negroes they were asked to leave or apply for treatment. Dr. Karl's view was that prejudice was a form of mental illness and Dr. Will had said the same thing many times. Negro patients and employees were placed without regard to their color.

From the day the hospital opened, Dr. Karl had asked that volunteer groups from various organizations come into the hospital and help out. He had seen what happened to V.A. and state hospitals when citizens had not been encouraged to participate. He did think, however, that the citizens who came into the hospital to help out with patients, some of whom had emotional problems, should have indoctrination and training. So there were regular classes for volunteer workers and Dr. Karl talked to each one. One of these was made up of a group of society women of the town. Dr. Karl began to talk to them and suddenly stopped. "I don't see any Negro women in your group," he said. "Couldn't they come today?"

"We don't admit Negroes to our organization," one of the women said haughtily.

"I'm sorry for you," Dr. Karl replied, "but your organization can't come into this hospital. There will be Negro veterans in each of the wards you visit and they are going to feel excluded when none of their race is included among you."

The group returned with Negro members. As incident after incident of this sort occurred, the morale at Winter soared. Dr. Karl made employees feel that working at Winter gave them distinction, and they became missionaries to the community. Even the diehard segment of Topeka had a new respect for Dr. Karl since he had brought a new and important "industry" to town.

Dr. Karl saw his father every evening, and his father often called on him at Winter. The elder man emphasized to Dr. Karl the importance of demonstrating that all the medical departments of a general hospital could be integrated best under psychiatry. Quite literally the psychiatrist was the only medical man who was not a specialist. Even the general practitioner restricted himself to the body. At Winter as nowhere else, the whole of the patient could be considered.

Surgeons and internists who had had their doubts about placing themselves under the direction of a psychiatrist began to change their minds. Dr. Karl knew much more about their specialties than they had imagined possible, and he had written at least one or two papers in each of their fields. He told them that it was up to them to instruct the residents in the problems that were peculiar to each of their specialties. A resident referring a patient to the medical ward was supposed to follow up and find out what happened, step by step. If the patient was then referred to surgery the resident might even find himself assisting in the operation and gaining a new respect for surgeons and surgery. On the other hand, the surgeons and internists began to absorb some of the principles of psychiatry. Hypnosis was soon being utilized in surgery; the medical wards became the psychosomatic wards Dr. Karl had wanted for the Foundation.

Although the twenty-five-bed wards made Winter Hospital an awkward place to staff, they turned out to be ideal for training and treatment. At least one resident, and sometimes two, was assigned to each ward and given full control, subject of course to the supervision of section chiefs, who were senior staff men. These young ward chiefs had daily conferences with their ward personnel. Nurses and psychiatric aides reported on and discussed the progress of their patients, and attitudes were prescribed just as they were at the sanitarium. Even when patients were presented to the senior staff, nurses and aides attended the meetings and contributed to the presentation. Dr. Karl was apt to appear unannounced on any ward at any time, a habit previously unheard of in a V.A. hospital manager. He had a way of finding out quickly whether nurses and aides had full participation in the ward team. If they didn't, he wanted to know why not.

Of course what was important in all this was how the patients responded to the setup Dr. Karl had created. Most patients came from service hospitals where they were accustomed to efficient but impersonal and often brusque treatment from men of higher rank. The enlisted man could rarely forget that the doctor was also an officer. In his first contact with Winter, the patient was met by a doctor who had gladly forgotten that he ever held rank. The problem was always to get the new patient to a ward as quickly as possible and into the hands of the doctor who would be his as long as he was in the hospital. Dr. Karl had made it a rule that when a resident accepted a patient in his ward he was becoming that man's physician in the largest sense. No matter how many times the patient might be transferred this doctor was to remain responsible for the patient, representing him in disputes, smoothing his way into new environments, and explaining all new treatments and examinations. Dr. Karl had a firm belief that where possible the doctor should explain all treatments and examinations to the patient. In every case the doctor-patient relationship was to be at least as close as it is in the ideal private-practice situation.

Not even during the earliest days of Winter was a patient allowed to vegetate in the ward. A regimen similar to that which governed the Menninger household was the rule. Patients, even many of those who were bedridden, were kept busy at a therapeutically productive schedule. Doctors were supposed to learn the patients' aptitudes and prescribe occupational therapy, recreational therapy, and shop training accordingly. There were classes of all sorts; all the arts and crafts were represented, even up to and including a complete machine shop. Patients were made to feel that the hospital needed what they could produce. Pictures were needed for the walls, furniture improved the wards, and there was sewing to be done for the women's section, which also had its own beauty parlor with specially trained operators. If a man liked fishing, he should be making fly rods against the day he would get out. If he wanted to learn to play a musical instrument, instruments and instructors were available.

There was a large canteen with a soda fountain and coffee shop. Patients, nurses, attendants, and doctors mingled there and no tables were set aside for special groups. Even though outsiders often visited the canteen a patient did not need to feel self-conscious because he had been classified as being emotionally ill. He was in a general hospital, and he might be there for any reason— there was no stigma.

Roaming as he did about the hospital, Dr. Karl managed to talk to almost every patient at least once, and each patient somehow felt that he had a special interest in him. When anyone felt wronged he could go to Dr. Karl and be sure of a champion. Few had to go to him since the schedule left very little time to imagine slights and injuries and brood about them. Somehow each patient felt it his obligation to get well *for* his doctor and Karl Menninger. "The atmosphere of people getting well" prevailed and it was a point of pride with the patients that people were coming from all over the world to see the way they were treated.

Four months after Winter was opened, General Hawley was

able to say, "This hospital typifies what we would like to have in every Veterans' Administration hospital in the United States. In none of the other hospitals have I found the real, full thoroughness that exists here, and I do not mean only in medical care, but in the management, relations with patients' families, and the integration of all the aspects of a general hospital."

Almost boyishly, Dr. Karl passed on to the staff every compliment that came to him. Although people were *supposed* to get well, an event was made of every recovery that came to Dr. Karl's attention. And the residents were learning what his avocado crate was for. Although most of the residents thought that he knew very little about their personal lives and interests, he found some interest that was special to each person, and when any article or bulletin relating to it came his way, into the crate it would go, to be forwarded later. Dr. Karl came to the hospital on Sundays to take care of such things.

The crate had still another purpose. On Saturdays Dr. Karl gave what he called a colloquium. The technique of this talk was something similar to free association, with various items in the collection as starting points. In his desire to awaken people's interests in all possible aspects of the world around them he was very much his father's son. At these times psychiatry, as such, was apparently forgotten. Sometimes a heavy book would be hoisted from the crate and Dr. Karl would read a poem or two, or a passage from Dostoievsky, or Thomas Wolfe, or some other author. At first the residents were startled by the content of these talks and made uncomfortable. There had never been time for such things in medical school. There was something disorderly about such talks, they were unscientific. Then slowly they began to realize that the humanities and natural sciences did have a place in their world.

Residents had reason to wonder when Dr. Karl had time to do any reading or even skim magazines, for he was at the hospital at eight every morning and usually started the day with a conference of some sort. This would be followed by routine administrative duties interspersed with trips to various sections of the hospital where a talk had to be given to some group during almost any working day. Going and coming from the wards, Dr. Karl would conduct business in transit. A week seldom went by without his appearing in each section for a case presentation and sometimes doing a demonstration interview. An official demonstration with a patient was done each week in a one-way-vision room. Here the residents could see how a psychiatrist of Dr. Karl's caliber worked. Two days a week he had classes in psychiatric theory and psychiatric diagnosis and at least two or three patient consultations would arise out of them. One night a week he also conducted a case seminar for the psychoanalytic institute. He always had one or two patients in therapy at the clinic, and there were important conferences at the Foundation that demanded his attention. There was rarely a lunch hour when he was not entertaining some visitor and on many evenings a week he and Jean were entertaining newcomers at dinner. He seemed tireless, and the energy and enthusiasm he displayed even late in the evening made some of the younger men feel feeble. They didn't know that he had been on a schedule like this since early childhood.

Dr. Karl was a father figure to many of the residents; they tried to emulate him, even in energy. Besides attending classes, lectures, and seminars, they had to keep up the treatment schedule in their wards. Hard work and long hours seemed to enhance the spirit of the hospital rather than lessen it since each doctor felt that he was making history, and to a degree he was. Winter Hospital during its early years probably represents institutional medicine at the peak of effectiveness and its influence on American psychiatry cannot be measured. At a time when institutional psychiatry was clinically and morally bankrupt Winter Hospital set an example that was to give psychiatry a future and a direction.

iii

Pearl Boam stayed on with Dr. C.F. after Flo's death and kept house for him. His sons did not want him to go on long trips unaccompanied, and so when he went to Washington to visit Dr. Will, who was still in the Army, or to Florida to visit Edwin, Pearl went with him. She had been in the family for over twenty-five years and perhaps understood the doctor better than anyone else did. She was an almost perfect companion. Since she had no outside interests that made great demands on her she could devote herself completely to the doctor. She was genuinely interested in everything he did. It was not a matter of taking Flo's place; Pearl had always had her own place in the family, and, being twenty years younger than the elder Menningers, she had been able to make their latter years easier than they otherwise might have been.

Except where to do so might interfere with his medical practice, Dr. C.F. had always deferred to Flo. He had not felt put upon as he did this; it was a small exchange for the great gifts Flo had given and the sacrifices she had made. He would have liked to invite visiting doctors to his home more often, but they and Flo would have had little in common. He could not have served them drinks, and they would have been made to feel ill at ease about smoking. He would have felt badly, too, if the talk had turned to medicine and excluded Flo. Pearl encouraged him to entertain the physicians who came to Topeka from all parts of the world. She saw to it that drinks were properly served and never made him feel that she was bored if he and the visitors talked shop. After all, her own father had been a doctor, and it was a depression caused by his death that had brought her into the Menninger family.

Dr. C.F. could now have a drink before dinner, and wine and beer when he chose to. It made him feel closer to his sons to have a drink with them occasionally. Now he had the smoking jacket he had dreamed of on the winter nights of his horse-and-buggy days and, moreover, he smoked in this jacket. He had always liked the smell of tobacco, and there was no reason why he should not enjoy it in his old age. He found that there was something to be said for changing your habits late in life; whatever he did was a matter of mature choice and he need retain only those habits that he enjoyed. He knew that it pleased his sons to think that he could expand a little. At eighty-four he had the appearance of a man in his late sixties or early seventies.

For a while it amused Pearl and the doctor when people they met on their travels thought she was Mrs. Menninger. He had always looked upon her as being so much younger that she could pass for his daughter. Soon they were to discover that it was not only their traveling companions who looked upon them as natural mates. Dr. C.F. had never been one to discuss his personal life, and he was a little irked when people began to show curiosity about his relationship with Pearl. When the idea came into his mind that in order to protect Pearl the relationship would have to be altered, the doctor realized how much he needed Pearl and how much she had come to mean to him. He could only wonder if she needed him as much as he did her. For the second time in his life he proposed and he was a surprised and jubilant man when he was accepted.

The ordeal of facing his sons and telling them of his engagement was one he dreaded. But the dread was wasted; his sons were relieved and pleased. The wedding was simple and quiet. Since Oakwood had become too much for a man of the doctor's years to manage, and because he could not afford to hire help, it was sold, and a small house near the Foundation was bought. Ironically, the Motor Vehicle Department had refused the doctor a driver's license in the same year he remarried, and he now had to be within walking distance of his office. His sons had offered to have someone drive him, but Dr. C.F. found that a half-mile walk was just what he needed to limber him up. As he often said, he had started his practice without transportation and there was no reason why he couldn't finish it the same way.

iv

In 1890 it had been a matter of monumental concern when Dr. C.F. had to hire a receptionist at a salary of five dollars a week. In 1946 meeting the payroll was still a matter of concern but it had grown to over $55,000 per month. Dr. C.F., who signed every check in his fine, Spencerian hand, knew there was no turning back. The Foundation would have to raise more money each year than he and his family had given in their initial gift. Tuition and reimbursement for the time the Foundation doctors gave to Winter produced only $119,121.30 per year. Unless contributions were forthcoming everything else had to be paid for out of the income produced by the various Foundation medical services—the sanitarium, the Out-patient Department, the South-ard School, the Department of Clinical Psychology, and the like. The fame attained by Winter Hospital made it a little easier to raise funds, but in nothing like the amounts that were needed.

The sanitarium, with a staff of 51, was filled to its capacity of 55 patients and had a long waiting list. The Out-patient Department, with a staff of 12 physicians, gave consultation or treatment to 790 patients during the year, and Southard School with a staff of 43 had 19 boarders and had seen 146 out-patients. The Psychological Division gave 3339 tests. All this was in addition to the work done by the Divisions of Clinical Medicine, Neurology, and Social Work. Almost all of the professional staff were teaching in addition to doing this income-producing clinical work. Dr. Robert Knight directed all clinical services and did a masterful job.

Dr. Will was needed more than ever. He had just won the Distinguished Service Medal for the tremendous administrative job he had done in the Army, and it appeared that he would deserve another when he returned and took over the reins of the Foundation. In emergencies small hospitals and adjoining public buildings have taken care of a disaster load of patients for a week or two. Topeka was in a similar position; the disaster of American institutional psychiatry and the unpreparedness of psychiatric training facilities had made Topeka the world center of psychiatry overnight. An institution that had been treating perhaps 500 people a year and training four or five doctors would now supervise the treatment of 8000 patients in a year and train specialists numbered in the hundreds. There had never been expansion like this in the history of medicine. Not even the Mayos had been faced with a comparable situation. And this was no short-term emergency.

There were not enough offices to keep all the doctors in contact with patients, and there was not enough space where the patients could sit and wait. A remodeled two-car garage, for example, housed nine doctors, a social worker, and two secretaries. Four doctors prepared their case histories and even saw some patients as they shared one long table. The other five doctors had small cubbyholes; and when one was vacant while the doctor visited the hospital, or taught at Winter, it would be taken at once by one of the doctors at the table. There was one phone for five people. In a remodeled three-room cottage, eight more doctors shared offices and carried a patient load of 148. A doctor seldom kept an appointment in the same office twice in the same day. He studied the other doctors' teaching schedules, made appointments for the offices that would be vacant at any given hour, and lived in a state of emergency. The offices were just as much in demand in the evening as they were in the daytime and that was often the only time the doctors could schedule patients.

In spite of this turmoil seven major research projects were in progress and four others were completed during the 1945–46 period. Somehow or other, members of the staff also found time to write and there were sixty-one publications by Menninger professional people during the year. No one thought it odd that in the midst of this Dr. Karl should put a notice in the daily bulletin asking for chess opponents.

In all the lectures that were given by the staff during this period it is impossible to find one that had to do with medical ethics, dedication, or selflessness.

CHAPTER EIGHTEEN

i

IN THE SUMMER of 1946 the state hospital scandal that Dr. Karl and a few other doctors had predicted broke into the open. *Life* magazine, *Cosmopolitan*, *Reader's Digest*, and many other magazines ran well-documented articles on the neglect of the mentally ill in even the most progressive states. These were not simply stories of overcrowded institutions operating on low budgets; there was nothing that could explain away medical neglect that went so far as to allow brutality to patients to become widespread. Pictures of emaciated, cowed, and half-dressed patients living out their lives in filthy, dilapidated buildings spoke more eloquently than words. A year later Mary Jane Ward's *Snake Pit*, a story of a woman's life in one of these institutions, became a best seller. There were other stories, equally shocking and believable. The nation was not only shocked; it was filled with shame and disgust.

A story that did not appear in print or in pictures was more damning. Doctors who called themselves psychiatrists appeared to be not only accomplices in the state hospital debacle but at times active participants in these crimes against helpless people. Public confidence in psychiatrists was badly shaken. The laymen who had written the exposés had often met with open resistance from doctors while they were trying to bring the truth to the public. True, state hospital superintendents were seldom real psychiatrists, but very often they had belonged to the associations of the profession and had dominated national psychiatric policy. Some even belonged to the National Committee for Mental Hygiene, a reputable organization that had been founded by Clifford Beers

almost forty years before. In his book *A Mind That Found Itself,*
Mr. Beers had depicted the same conditions that were now being
exposed in an even more sordid form. This organization had been
dedicated to seeing that such things never happened again.

In their own defense, these organizations could point out that
they had always prescribed that hospitals be adequately staffed
with a certain number of doctors and nurses per patient and they
had also set certain other standards for care. But the public had
never been made aware of these standards or told how poorly
they were maintained in their states. Until the criminal treatment
of the mentally ill had been exposed it had never been clearly
pointed out that there were not enough well-trained professional
people in the United States to staff adequately the institutions of
two major states. The crux of the whole problem was a shortage
of psychiatrists, but it was made to appear that America had
reached a crisis in mental health and had not had time to prepare
for it. There were dark mumblings on the part of some lay writers,
and even medical writers who were not psychiatrists, that psychiatry with its ardor for diagnosing peculiarities as insanities had
created an expensive public problem.

But the problem was not new, and insanity in the United
States was not increasing. A hundred years before the present
crisis Dorothea Lynde Dix, a schoolteacher who had gone into
jails and almshouses as a religious worker, had found mentally
ill people bound in chains, mistreated by drunken keepers, and
kept out in the cold—"because they can't feel anything." She had
started a crusade that resulted in the building of many of the state
hospitals in America. This campaign was carried into most states
of the union as well as into Canada and England. When she had
informed the public of its responsibility toward these ill people
the public had responded and people everywhere accepted
her thesis that "the indigent mentally ill are the wards of the
State." Most states were too poor to act on this thesis, so she went
a step further. Land grants were being made to educational
institutions by the federal government; why not land grants for
mental hospitals? There was no reason that Miss Dix could see.
It took several arduous years but she finally succeeded in getting
before Congress a bill granting 10,000,000 acres of land for the
support of institutions for the mentally ill and 2,225,000 acres

for the care of deaf mutes. President Franklin Pierce vetoed this bill even though there was a precedent for the making of such grants. The recurrent disasters created by a lack of money for mental health are a grim memorial to an almost forgotten president.

Miss Dix gave the mentally ill a place in the conscience of the public that has been re-established each time the neglect of these people had been brought to their attention. The strange thing is that this neglect has always been brought to public attention by lay people. American psychiatry is as old as the first state hospital; its first national association—older than the American Medical Association—was an organization of state hospital superintendents. Yet very few are the instances in American institutional psychiatry where one of its doctors has spoken up for his wards. That they had a right and a responsibility to speak up and demand money for a type of ancillary help equal to that in general hospitals never seems to have occurred to them. The attitude has been that they ought to be so grateful for any type of gain made for the mentally ill that they must reciprocate with a grateful economy that in most cases obliterates the gain. The first state hospitals were staffed with the very keepers from the jails and almshouses who had mistreated the mentally ill. Politicians capitalized on this tendency; when a budget had to be balanced they always knew that the least protest would come from the asylum keepers. They also knew that people who used roads would be articulate if those roads were neglected, but that the mentally ill could not speak up for themselves and their shame-ridden families would not. Mental hospitals were never a political issue, unless someone was trying to sell land for one or get a contract to build it.

Whatever individual hospital superintendents have done from time to time in raising the institutional standards of their states, and in providing decent care for their patients, a conscience cannot be said to be a traditional aspect of the body of American institutional psychiatry. It had usually resisted outside interference and moved forward only when there was such interference; there had been a few outstanding clinicians but never a crusader. In 1946 institutional psychiatry needed a conscience and a crusader as it never had before. If it was to regain the public's confidence it had to rise above this disaster.

Fortunately, psychiatry did not have to seek far. Dr. C. F. Menninger's sons, Karl and Will, had possessed all the necessary resources long before psychiatry made its demands on them. As the horrors of the state hospitals were being depicted in the press, Dr. Karl's work at Winter Hospital was being widely written about and people were seeing what psychiatry could be at its best as well as at its worst. General William C. Menninger had been one of the most articulate and proficient medical officers the Army had ever had, and he had operated without a scandal the largest psychiatric organization the world had ever known. Moreover, he had given the rest of medicine an understanding of and a respect for psychiatry. For once, psychiatry had its own crusade in action; it would not have to leave its destiny in the hands of laymen. Even the American psychiatrists, and they were not a few, who disliked and resented the Menningers had reason to be grateful for them now.

One hundred and fifty of the younger psychiatrists, along with the more progressive of the older group, had already rallied around Dr. Karl and Dr. Will. They appointed Dr. Will their chairman and called themselves the Group for the Advancement of Psychiatry. They began at once to do something about the state hospital situation. The press was invited to their meetings and even asked to sit in on committees. Among other things, they offered a consultation service to state hospitals that wanted help in reorganizing. To a man, they were sick of doctors who protected each other at the expense of their patients. As they became vocal about their feelings, there was no doubt of the strength they would have when the American Psychiatric Association, the parent body of American psychiatry, held its next meeting. It was virtually certain that Dr. Will would be the next president and that the reorganizational plans that had been initiated by Dr. Karl and the committee on reorganization would be put into effect.

And so it was that when Dr. Will came out of the Army in the fall of 1946 he was faced not only with the administrative and other problems of the Foundation but with the problems of national psychiatry as well. By 1947 he was president-elect of the American Psychiatric Association, the American Psychoanalytic Association, and the Central Neuropsychiatric Association, as well as chairman of the Group for the Advancement of Psychiatry.

Psychiatry could have had no better leader than Dr. Will, for not only had he won the respect of the nation with his wartime service but he represented an institution that was setting an example of what the new psychiatry could do.

Dr. Will's personal charm had grown during the war years and in his forty-ninth year he retained the energy and eagerness of a much younger man. People who came to disagree with him left finding instead they had agreed with him and had gained thereby. He had a quick mind for other people's problems and always led into any discussion by quickly restating them in terms that related to the matter at hand and his own point of view. There was no trickery in this; Dr. Will liked people and he made them want to be liked by him. He gave of himself unstintingly during those post-war years without ever dramatizing the personal sacrifices he was making; indeed he seemed to refresh himself by meeting demands that would have exhausted another man. He was at home less than three months out of the entire year of 1947.

Between the many conferences and talks he held and gave as president and chairman of the various groups, he had another mission to accomplish; the Foundation was running in the red at the rate of almost a half-million dollars a year and by 1954 was to need $700,000 in contributions in order to maintain its program. The chief burden of raising these funds naturally fell upon Dr. Will's shoulders. In every spare minute he was talking to groups that might have contributions to make, visiting the heads of great Foundations that might be prevailed upon to make grants for research and education, or convincing industrial leaders that psychiatry needed their help. There was always a deadline to make and he always made it, sometimes just in the nick of time.

This opportunity to travel in America and meet more and more people also enabled Dr. Will to do missionary work in his own special field, which had become the social application of psychiatry. He could always indicate the role psychiatry was to play in education, industry, national defense, and in the war against prejudice that was costing our economy millions upon millions of wasted dollars through the needless duplication of institutions and services. As he talked he also wrote, organizing his ideas and experiences into such books as *You and Psychiatry, Psychiatry,* and the massive *Psychiatry in a Troubled World,* a work in which he related his military experiences to the problems confronting society as a whole.

As Winter's fame and the general improvement of all V.A. hospitals had again given the V.A. some status, and when sentiment for our returning veterans was declining, a drive was immediately begun to cut the budget of the V.A. Winter, which required more staff because of its awkward structure and had been allowed a third more personnel than other hospitals because of its large training program, would have been first to feel the cut. There were wards that had never been opened because of lack of personnel, and other wards would have had to be closed. Dr. Karl had anticipated some such move as this and was ready for it.

From the beginning Dr. Karl had encouraged citizens' groups to visit Winter and interest themselves in the place and he had also established an excellent relationship with the press, his old enemy. Inviting the press and citizens' committees to visit the hospitals, he had doctors demonstrate just what a cut in the budget would mean in terms of treatment for the patients. An unopened ward that had been planned for neurosurgical patients and could not be equipped or staffed because of lack of funds meant that the neurological service was operating at one third capacity. The press and the citizens met patients who were being forced to wait. Dr. Karl did not have to brief the patients as to what they should say about the threatened cuts; the patients were quite eloquent about the matter.

By the time Dr. Karl had protested to Washington, the wire services had already picked up the story of his demonstrations at Winter. In his letter to General Bradley he said, "We all realize that this is not your idea, but that your hand is being forced and that certain members of Congress think this is just a political item. But they should know that there are many of us who are not politicians and not disposed to submit to political maneuvers. I came into this program because I saw the possibility of developing a great thing for the veterans and for the nation . . . but I, and many others like me, will drop it like a hotcake if penny wise and pound foolish policies are forced upon it. I am not willing to be connected with something shoddy or second rate, or something for which I must apologize." He further pointed out that the government had had to call in private practitioners like himself just because a politically subservient type of state medicine had failed. Dr. Karl left no doubt as to who would be responsible for another failure, should there be one. No cut in the budget for Winter Hospital was made at that time and the new wards were opened.

When the threat of cuts in funds continued, badly endangering morale at Winter and other V.A. hospitals, Dr. Karl called the employees together and told them that even if funds were cut he would not fire them. He had been called in as the doctor for 1500 patients and the welfare of those patients was his responsibility. When the government hired him as a manager they had contracted to fill his prescriptions. The government would either have to pay the bills he ran up or tell him to get out. As for anyone collecting anything from him, all he had was an old car and an equity in a house. When some of his colleagues tried to get him to compromise, saying that he was jeopardizing the training program, Dr. Karl pointed out that he wanted no responsibility for a training program that existed at the expense of even one patient's welfare.

"Cheap medical care is like unsupported insurance," Dr. Karl told the press. "In the long run, you just throw all of your money away unless you invest enough to do it right. You might just as well talk about saving money on your automobile by removing one wheel."

The stand Dr. Karl took was logical, and it was the sort of thing that people expect of a conscientious physician of the first order. Unfortunately, what he was doing had never before been done by a psychiatrist of stature and against the dreary background of institutional psychiatry his stand can be seen as what it is—the introduction of personal responsibility into institutional psychiatry. Dr. Karl was not being particularly heroic; he was only doing what came naturally to a Menninger. Many small-town private practitioners would have spoken up in a like vein had they been put in his position. He was acting within a tradition, and his father was a strong part of that tradition.

There were those in the medical profession who deeply resented the emergence of Dr. Karl and Dr. Will into positions of power that made them public figures. Some protested to medical organizations that a matter of medical ethics was involved, that even though the Menninger Foundation was a non-profit organization it did compete with private practitioners and private institutions and was using an unfair means of attracting patients. The cult of mediocrity that made such protests is always strong and articulate in every medical organization, and such people have been able quite often to make cowards of otherwise brave men. Actually, what the Menningers did reflected credit and glory on every private-practice psychiatrist and physician. That they had been able to develop such a great thing out of a small, private sanitarium actually lent prestige to private sanitariums. Many new ones were opening and those that were in existence thrived. As for the Menningers, fame was costly to them, for if you are a conscientious physician it can cost you time and money to attract patients you cannot possibly treat. There is a great mass of mail to answer, and ethical referrals have to be made. If people throw themselves upon your mercy they have to be taken care of until other arrangements can be made. Doctors Karl and Will had little time to spend with their families, and both were working for incomes much lower than those of the physicians who resented their methods. A segment of medicine was living up to another of its traditions—that all advance shall be resisted.

ii

Topeka had become one of the most psychiatric-minded communities in America. Almost every citizen could tell you that physicians from seventeen different countries were studying at the Menninger Foundation and that the physicians of thirty countries had visited Topeka during the last year. Almost every family had at least one relative working at Winter or the Foundation. Residents from Winter followed the Menninger tradition and taught in Sunday-school classes. Winter Wives—the name describes the organization—were civic-minded and had founded their own nursery school, a school that had become a model for the community. Dr. Will encouraged the young psychiatrists to interest themselves in the schools their children had to attend. Soon courses in psychodynamics were being given for schoolteachers. A speakers' bureau at the Foundation would supply speakers for almost any occasion, and there were Menninger psychiatrists in the membership of most service clubs. Dr. Will was an active member of the chamber of commerce which his father had helped found.

As the reputation of the Foundation grew, more people came for evaluations and out-patient treatment. Menninger patients were preferred clients of the hotels. The prejudice against mental illness had so diminished that there was actually some prestige attached to being a Menninger patient. When celebrities came to town, and they often did, the townspeople respected their privacy. At least one movie star was annoyed because no one asked for his autograph when he went downtown. Another, who took a hotel to pieces, found that the police and the injured parties understood his plight and only adjured him to take his treatment at Menningers' more seriously.

Patients who were in Topeka for prolonged stays needed places to live and, in some cases, quite a bit of psychological support from the people they lived with. Over the years an increasing number of Topekans took in boarders from the Foundation. Even people who did not need the money found satisfaction in being helpful to these patients who were making a readjustment to life. Patients from the great cultural centers of the East found that the stories of rigid, Midwestern narrowness were largely myths, and that Topekans had a tendency to be tolerant of their snobbishness. People who have had to make an adjustment to Topeka have often found it to be an important part of the therapeutic process and there are many who have stayed on to work or enter into business.

Gheel, Belgium, is a city that has been a haven for the mentally ill for centuries. It has proven that they can be productive or semi-productive citizens and take care of each other. The town exists by, and its economy is based upon, the care of the mentally ill. Topeka is not, however, the Gheel of America. It is a normal, small, Midwestern city with the added distinction of being a state capital. Its prejudices were once as rigid as those of other Midwestern cities. The Santa Fe Railroad, meat packing, tire manufacturing, and its position as a supply center for a rich farming country, supported the city's basic economy so that it thrived and grew long before it became a mental-health center. The wealthier farmers came to Topeka to live when they retired, and they were firm conservatives. It was a city that had issued an injunction in order to keep mental patients out of a general hospital; it had subjected Dr. Karl to a campaign of slander. One thing is sure, no outsider could ever have introduced psychiatry to Topeka—its least desire was to become a Gheel.

Only a couple like Dr. Charles and Flo Menninger could have sponsored psychiatry in Topeka successfully. To do so they had to command a respect that was without blemish. When you spoke of the doctor and his wife you were paying homage to every conventional virtue. They were the key that opened the door and let psychiatry in. Could the members of Flo's Bible classes condemn her sons? Hardly. Or could the patients of Dr. C.F. believe that he would sanction a doctor—even a son—who was not the best possible physician? Scarcely. But there was always a chance that the old folks had been taken in by their children's enthusiasm; the town would be wary of that. That wariness put the sons on their mettle. They had to demonstrate results, and those results had to stand the acid test of an ingrained fundamentalist conservatism and cynicism. Scripture was the weapon that was always used against anything new and unusual. Scripture, in Topeka, was almost under the exclusive jurisdiction of Flo Menninger, and her sons had learned two verses of the Bible every day of their youth.

It was not by accident that Dr. Karl could appropriately answer a famous clergyman who had charged psychiatry with being ungodly. "Consider, for a moment, what the daily work of the psychiatrist is," Dr. Karl wrote. "Consider his ministry of care to the most miserable, the most unloved, the most pitiable, and at times the most offensive and even dangerous of human beings. Consider the psychiatrist's role, properly conceived, as that of the friend, the guide, the protector, the helper, the lover of these unhappy people: '. . . passing through the valley of Baca, the rain also filleth the pools.' (Psalm 84)

"Consider what you call his tolerance, his forbearance, his patience with stubbornness, anger, spitefulness, silliness, sulkiness, belligerency, desperateness, unreasonableness, maliciousness—all the manifestations of hate. These he meets, if he is a good psychiatrist, with an attitude he is not ashamed to call love. We can live, he tells them, if we can love. . . . Does it sound ungodly?

And if it is misunderstood and criticized as wasteful, or as immorally permissive, the psychiatrist may comfort himself with the example of One who said, 'Neither do I condemn thee,' and at another time, 'For . . . she hath poured this ointment on my body.' —By the Grace of God, he [the psychiatrist] is *usually* rewarded with success—not his success, but the patient's! *Most* psychiatric patients get well. Hence it is that the chief prayer of every psychiatrist should be, " 'Keep back Thy servant also from presumptuous sins; let them not have dominion over me.' "

Topeka, in a sense, was the nation. If the town offered a resistance to psychiatry it also offered it a place where, once it was accepted, it could sink its roots deep into the American earth. It had nourished those roots when it gave money for the sanitarium; when the Menningers needed more money during the early days of the Foundation much of it came from Topekans. Psychiatry had to have a place and a family before it could become really established in America and in Topeka it found both the place and the family. The attitude Topeka shows toward the mentally ill will one day be the attitude of America.

As the Menninger School of Psychiatry became the largest and most important in the world it was natural that it should be wanted elsewhere. Dr. Will was offered the presidency of a great institution of learning and another old and famous medical educational center offered the Menningers almost endless funds if they would move their school to this institution. There the problems of year-to-year money raising would be over; the Menningers would be able to relax a little and spend a few evenings at home. When Dr. C.F. was told of this offer he simply asked, "Do we have to discuss it?" The answer was, "No." The Menningers' loyalty to Topeka was as staunch as their loyalty within the family.

Taxi drivers in Topeka are probably the only ones in the country who can excuse a small tip on the grounds of faulty early training, or where one chambermaid may say to another, "Room 566 is easy to take care of; he's a compulsive character," but that is only part of the story. Topeka has a little more civic maturity than most cities.

Psychiatrically speaking, Topeka had only one thing to be ashamed of. That was Topeka State Hospital, which was barely a half mile away from the Menninger Foundation and on the same street. This seventy-five-year-old institution, with its ancient, gray stone buildings, had been adequate in its day, but that day had long since passed. Dr. Karl had been allowed to work there under one director, but it had been many years since a Menninger had been encouraged to enter its grounds. Like so many state hospitals, the place had isolated itself and it never invited the citizens to see what was going on, as Winter did. It had refused to allow residents from the Menninger Sanitarium even to contribute time. There was no doubt that Topekans wanted to do something about this hospital, but they could see no way to go about it. The place had the aspect of a fortress.

iii

After serving two years as the manager of Winter Hospital Dr. Karl was forced to resign. Generals Bradley and Hawley were on their way out, and the strong sentiments about "caring for our boys" diminished. Major General Carl Gray, Jr., took Bradley's place. Gray was a railroad man of some repute, but the reasons why he was made Veterans Administrator are not very clear. Dr. Paul Magnuson, one of the nation's foremost orthopedic surgeons, and a man who would fight for his patients, was made medical director. When Gray, who apparently had some difficulty in understanding the medical services, asked, "Paul, why are you forever tussling with me? After all, you're working for me," Magnuson replied, "The hell I am. I'm working for the patients." In spite of this stand, Dr. Magnuson could not protect his patients. There had been cuts in the V.A. budget for the medical department in 1947 and these were increased in 1948. The medical department had to close 3000 beds because of a shortage of personnel and 4800 more personnel were affected by the new cuts.

Inspection teams from Washington, often made up of inspectors who were holdovers from the Hines administration, were frequent visitors at Winter Hospital. They were inspecting the many breaches that had been made in R & P and were ready to prefer formal charges. The fact that Winter Hospital was making medical history and in its first eighteen months of existence had treated 12,000 patients, as well as setting a medical example that was being followed throughout the V.A., meant nothing if a rule had been broken. Since Dr. Karl was emotionally and constitutionally incapable of living within rules that went against good medical procedure and simple human decency, he could, as manager, have placed the hospital in jeopardy. As chairman of the Deans' Committee and a consultant to V.A.'s central office, he could control the training program which was also the treatment program and in these roles he would not be subjected to the political control that affected managers. In short, he would no longer be governed by an administration that gave every indication of again becoming "shoddy and second rate." The morale of the school was dependent on his ability to take a firm stand in clinical matters, and he retained that ability.

When he angrily called Washington, he could now preface his blast by saying, "This is citizen Karl Menninger speaking."

The training program at Winter remained unchanged and with it the quality of medical care that was given the patients. The residents' attitude toward the V.A., however, had undergone a change; when Dr. Karl had been able to fight off Washington some 60 per cent of the residents were willing to continue working under the V.A. after they had completed training, but in 1948 that number had shrunk to 5 per cent. Many of these young men did, however, express a desire to continue in institutional psychiatry, especially in teaching positions.

Dr. Will and the Group for the Advancement of Psychiatry had pointed out that the solution to the problem of state mental hospitals lay in the establishment of training programs such as had saved the V.A. The graduates of Winter and other training centers could supply a teaching staff that would attract young doctors to state institutions. It was easy to demonstrate the effectiveness of such a plan for there were from three to four times more recoveries in hospitals like Winter than in the non-training hospitals. The cost per patient per diem might be twice as much, but in the long run the training hospitals gave more for the money.

Released from full-time duties at Winter Hospital, Dr. Karl had a chance to look around and see what was going on elsewhere in Topeka. One of the first things he saw was Topeka State Hospital. For years it had been a mediocre custodial institution. Then a new superintendent, apparently more economy-minded than the last,

upset the applecart. A staff that could put up with custodial
inertia had at least some standards beneath which they would not
sink and so there was a mass of resignations. Whatever the trouble,
and it may have been caused by the traditional economy rather
than by personalities, Topeka State Hospital had reached a dead
end. At this point Dr. Karl visited the hospital. He did not like
what he saw and he said so. Reporters were visiting the hospital,
too, and John McCormally, of the Emporia *Gazette,* did a masterful job of reporting their findings. An acting superintendent was
appointed—Dr. William F. Blair. Governor Carlson then appointed a special investigating committee made up of Dr. Blair;
Dr. Franklin Murphy, head of the University of Kansas Medical
School; State Representative Paul Shanahan; Dr. Haddon Peck,
an outstanding Kansas physician, and Dr. Karl Menninger.

McCormally wrote: "Some people don't like Karl Menninger.
His friends say that's partly because he is a success: partly because
he writes letters like the one he sent to his boss when he learned
Congress was cutting Winter's budget. He is a busy, nervous man,
in a hurry to reach a goal men have plodded toward for centuries.
He is, for instance, disturbed about the situation at Topeka State
Hospital about which most Kansans have been little disturbed for
seventy-five years. He isn't diplomatic. He said what any sensitive
person would say after looking in on F Ward in the old stone
building: 'This is abominable, medieval, criminal!' and he said it
loudly.

"'I shall keep on saying it,' he said. . . . 'And there is no one
who can honestly defend those conditions. The State is criminal
because when it takes the job of providing care for its citizens and
then fails to do so that's a crime. As a psychiatrist I can't conscientiously keep quiet about it. . . .'"

In effect, the state said, "Put up or shut up." The Menningers
were given the job of rehabilitating Topeka State Hospital. Doctors Will and Karl had talked of good state hospital psychiatry and
now they were asked to administrate. They would get none of the
lavish backing that Dr. Karl had been given in the early days of
Winter Hospital. The state of Kansas was willing to back the Menningers, but its funds were limited. The job was turned over to
Dr. Karl, and he went into the grounds that his father had helped

landscape more than fifty years before as he collected material for his paper, *The Insanity of Hamlet.*

Topeka State was just about as backward as a hospital could be. Its greatest source of pride was that it supplied each patient with a rocking chair and rug, and woe betide anyone who didn't appreciate them or who moved them so much as a foot from their allotted space. The men's recreation room in one section was a table and four chairs in a tunnel. Eighteen hundred patients were cared for by three doctors, one registered nurse, and 116 untrained and underpaid attendants. The staff could not or did not give enough attention to their charges to tell when a patient got well by himself, and one patient who spoke only Danish is said to have been held for seventeen years when it was doubtful that he had ever been psychotic. Patients who were psychotic had been allowed to recede into bedfast torpor and consequently they were filthy and covered with bedsores.

In order to better direct the job that faced him, Dr. Karl moved to Topeka State Hospital as clinical director. Nine doctors, mostly graduates of the Menninger School of Psychiatry, moved in as section chiefs. With them came nine resident psychiatrists and a few resident psychologists. Because of the training program, the state was getting nine first-class physicians for less than some registered nurses' wages. Registered nurses were also hired in a number sufficient to supervise each ward. At Winter Hospital a group of attendants had tried to start a sort of graduate school for psychiatric aides. It was to give attendants a year's intensive education in psychiatry and psychiatric techniques. The Rockefeller Foundation had given these attendants a grant of $70,000 for their school. Because of V.A. red tape and, sadly enough, resistance from the registered nurses' organizations, the school could not be started at Winter, but now it could be opened at Topeka State Hospital. It set the tone for the training of the general attendants. When segregation was abandoned a much better caliber of attendants was available, for quite often Negroes with college degrees took jobs at Winter and at State.

Perhaps what took place at Topeka State Hospital can be told best through the story of what one Menninger-trained doctor, James M. Mott, Jr., did with three women's wards of 185 chronic patients. A lanky, redheaded, seemingly easygoing Kansan, Dr.

Mott set about showing what could be done in a state hospital without any great expenditure of money for modern equipment. The first thing he did was to get his nurses and attendants together and tell them that from that day on they were all therapists. "Our job is to get people well," he said, "and recoveries don't attach themselves to medical degrees. Find patients you can work with and give them all you've got. We'll have daily conferences and you can discuss your treatment problems and I'll discuss mine. The first thing we do is get these people out of bed and get them cleaned up."

Seventy per cent of the patients were bedfast. Within a very short time they were out of bed, their sores were healed, and they had learned to walk again. The patients in this section were all women, and Dr. Mott appealed to their housekeeping instincts. Personal belongings that had been taken from them were returned to them, and he scouted around and found an iron or two and some ironing boards, as well as an old sewing machine. Since the average age of his patients was fifty-three, and they had been institutionalized for an average of sixteen years, their families had long ago lost interest in them. He wrote to the families, and when a few came he suggested that they supply a couple of cooking ranges, some radios, and other equipment the women needed. He did not want castoff clothing for them; he wanted material with which they could make their own clothing. The stoves would enable them to bake cakes and cookies for ward parties and for their visitors. It was difficult to convince relatives that the patients could recover or even begin to act like human beings, but he went on trying. Most of his patients were farm wives and he knew the things that would mean most to them. They were not basket weavers or interested in arts and crafts.

Dr. Mott chose as his own patients those women who seemed most hopeless. By word and manner he conveyed to them that he would come to them any time they called for him, even if it was four in the morning, and from the beginning he demonstrated that he would do this. Maybe he would just sit and hold some distraught woman's hand, but even the calmness of his movements seemed to convey an eternal sort of patience to his wards. Women who had been mute for years had to find words with which to thank him; when they found those words they could talk to him and therapy was initiated. When he made ward rounds he had time for everyone. The nurses and the attendants found themselves emulating Dr. Mott, and when a resident was assigned to his section for training he, too, adopted Dr. Mott's method. At the daily ward conferences the attendants discussed their patients and made plans for them. Very early in the program it was decided that the nurses and attendants would wear street clothes and not the traditional white which brought fear to all state hospital patients. Some attendants came back at night to see their patients and soon all three shifts were acting as therapists.

Women who had never been allowed the privilege of the grounds were allowed to go out. Eventually, some of them were allowed to go shopping downtown. The wards had stoves now, and cakes and pies for the hospital canteen were baked there. The money earned from this went into buying supplies for the ward. Some of the other women operated a laundry and the wards were rehabilitated by the women's own efforts. One woman who had been a patient for twenty-seven years, and who was extremely ill when Mott took over, had been a secretary and took a refresher course in shorthand and typing. While she was still in the hospital she got a job downtown and within a few months she was private secretary to her employer. More and more women were discharged as they recovered and improved. Since the hospital had been their home for so long, they were allowed to come back and spend a few nights there if they became frightened or homesick. Many more women could have been discharged if their families had been willing to take them back. Sadly enough, many families did not want the relatives who had been gone so long from the world.

In the first eighteen months in which Dr. Mott was chief of the most hopelessly chronic wards in the hospital 25 per cent of the patients were discharged, 50 per cent could go to town on shopping trips, and 85 per cent had ground privileges. There had been no shock or lobotomy, no excessive use of chemicals. "If we can love . . ." Dr. Karl says, "then we can live."

Dr. Mott had demonstrated that a state hospital does not need expensive buildings and equipment. The extra staff that was needed to bring about this seeming miracle cost less than a dollar a day per patient. What was accomplished could not have been accomplished by a politically subservient man; however, he had to have a freedom of action that is too rare in state hospitals. In no other hospital could he have allowed the aides to wear street clothes or patients to come back for a visit; few states would have allowed him to put pressure on reluctant families. At the same time that Dr. Mott was working with these women he was also teaching other doctors and was on the faculty of the School for Psychiatric Aides. People he helped to train can go out into other institutions and do as he has done. After all, he himself had just completed training at Winter. When he went into private practice in another state, he at once contributed teaching time to a nearby state hospital. This is typical of Menninger graduates.

Before the Menningers took over at Topeka State two out of three patients who were admitted were there for life. Now 80 per cent can expect to make social recoveries. Training in thirteen specialties is now available and includes a psychiatric training program for state hospital chaplains. Citizens of Topeka take pride in Topeka State now, and the Christmas tree is a big event each year. Carloads of gifts are piled beneath a big tree Dr. C.F. planted on the grounds sixty years ago. Five psychiatrists who completed their training at Topeka State went to other Kansas institutions to carry on the good work and soon these other institutions will be an active part of the Menninger training program.

The state hospital situation was not so hopeless after all. Many states have enacted the kind of program initiated by the Menningers, often under the supervision of Menninger-trained doctors. It is becoming increasingly difficult to explain away state hospital scandals.

How like the ideals of the Menninger home are the ideals that have influenced American institutional psychiatry so greatly.

CHAPTER NINETEEN

i

IN 1952, Dr. C. F. Menninger was in his ninetieth year. Unlike many aging men he was still tall and erect, and had never lost his air of quiet authority. His eyes showed a penetrating concern for every person he met. It was impossible to cater to his age, for any regard you might show for his years was lost in his greater concern for you. Almost three quarters of a century of listening to troubled people had not even begun to try his patience. That he had become more interested in teaching than in healing was beside the point. His concern now centered on the possibility that some area of ignorance in natural history might be holding you back from a delight that could be yours. For him, science was a route that led to God. The more thorough you were as a scientist the greater the final mystery of God's ways would be, for surely you would arrive at a mystery that could be explained only by the existence of God. He never gave the impression that he was trying to convert anyone, but he always gave the impression of being a man who had much to share.

If anyone sought to interview him in those days he would have to be at his house at seven o'clock on the mornings when the doctor was not at the clinic. If you were early—and he liked it if you were—you would find him with one of Pearl's aprons on as he dried the breakfast dishes. There was something youthful and yet dignified about Pearl and the doctor, a sort of freshness. They could have been starting a long life together and conserving each other's energy for what was to come. There was no sense of debility. And certainly they did not have to explain why they could not afford a maid. You always felt that they had been laughing about something before you arrived.

As the doctor met you at the door he would take your hand for a moment and look into your eyes to see if all was well with you. He somehow made it impossible to ask him how he was; to do so would have been an effrontery. As he led you to the study of their small but comfortable house he might pause for a moment to explain to you the principle upon which the new air conditioner worked. Certainly you would have to stop before a specimen case and see some new shell or mineral that had been added to his collection. If a new book had engaged him, he would hold it lovingly and show it to you. The study was small but lined with other book- and specimen cases and before the latter you would be stopped again as he told you a little of the work he had before him. He was subtly letting you know that beyond a certain point you would be keeping him from something to which he looked forward very much.

On his desk would be piles of the great variety of magazines about which Dr. Karl had once complained, and usually there would be neat packets of Foundation checks he had signed the night before. You had to be comfortably seated before he would take his chair and then, if you smoked, he would offer one of his cigarettes. The package would have been neatly opened and then closed again with a rubber band. You lost the aroma, he said, if you exposed the cigarettes to air. He enjoyed his after-breakfast cigarette, luxuriating for a moment in a wreath of smoke.

Getting him to talk about the past was difficult. He had to be convinced that what you wanted to know had some definite relationship to the present. It was not enough to tell him that he was a remarkable man and that everything he had done was of interest. He would tell you that all men were remarkable and that he was less remarkable than most. Nor did it do any good to point to all that he had accomplished. He would give most of the credit to his sons and their mother.

"All that I've done is the product of day-by-day living—living in which you don't much concern yourself with the past and future," he would say. "No one day is more spectacular than another if you live that way. On the day someone recovers, someone else you thought you had well may get sick again. It's more important that you question your failure than that you congratulate yourself on your success. Failures have a way of coming back to plague you; your daily problem is trying to get rid of them."

When you asked him which was the greatest day of his life he would answer, "Today." Of any other day, no matter how special it might seem, he would say, "That was a good day, too," and then recite:

> ". . . For yesterday is but a dream,
> "And tomorrow is only a vision.
> "But today well lived makes
> "Every yesterday a dream of happiness,
> "And every tomorrow a vision of hope.
> "Look well, therefore, to this day!
> "Such is the salutation of the dawn."

At one time he agreed to try to remember some of the high points of his childhood and youth. He said he would talk with his family and devote some time to bringing up recollections. When the day came upon which he was supposed to relate these memories he seemed to be a little more tired than usual, and he made a special point of displaying the amount of work he had to do with his studies and specimens. Then, talking very slowly and clearly, he said:

"Last night Karl and Jean were here for dinner. I told them some stories of my boyhood and early medical practice and they seemed to enjoy them. They were a good audience, and Pearl always is. I can't say that I didn't enjoy myself for a while. But when they'd left and I'd gone to bed, I couldn't sleep as I usually can. I was back in the past, lost in a bog of recollections. I couldn't be sure whether I'd see some room of the past or the room of the present if I switched on the light. In recalling useless memories, I'd lost my contact with the present and I saw how it was that some men of my age become senile without organic cause. For that reason I'm grateful for the experience. I saw how the things I'm doing could become of little consequence; how the work that awaits each awakening and makes it joyous could become unimportant. My sanity, my health, my happiness, my productiveness, rest in the *here* and *now* of things. I will never again go into the past for you unless something that happened or something I did has a definite relationship to the *here* and the *now*."

Such a man as Dr. C.F. was not dramatic in the ordinary sense. He had a skill in anticipating the dramatic use that might be made of things that he did—and flattening the drama. Ask him about the co-operative town of his childhood and he would make it clear that it had nothing to do with the co-operative practice of medicine. Play with the thesis that he must have gone into medicine because of the needless deaths from typhoid in his family and you would be quickly assured that he went into medicine because he had always felt physicians to be the most cultivated and most respected men of the town. He could even be quite tricky when you tried to fix upon the cause of his success, or find the key to it. In *The Insanity of Hamlet* he had said, "A series of external events in concurrence with steadily operating conditions within —but not a single event—an accident, a sorrow, or need, or adversity—can all be regarded as adequate cause for insanity."

After he had this read to him he said, "You can substitute sanity and success for insanity. There is always 'a steadily operating condition within.' That is why we should never pray to God to be given any one thing, no matter how much we may covet it and no matter what good use we may make of it. Our best prayer will always be that we may have the faith to accept supreme guidance. Faith should be the most steadfast condition in man."

One day a man in his mid-sixties came to see Dr. C.F. When he had introduced himself, Dr. C.F. recognized the family name.

"I'd hoped you would," said the man. "We left Topeka when I was young. As soon as I finished school I went into business and made good. I've had a good life and raised a family and left the business to them. Now I'm retired and they are happy and successful. I owe all of this to you. I had meningitis when I was a boy. All hope for me had been given up. And then you were called. You came about noon and you stayed all afternoon and night with me and you didn't leave until I was on the road to recovery."

"I must have been trying to make a reputation," Dr. C.F. said wryly.

"One of my dreams has always been that when I had retired I would make a special trip just to thank you," said the man.

"And then what are you going to do?" Dr. C.F. was all physician as he asked this. His manner conveyed concern, but his approach had become almost impersonal.

"Why, go to California and take it easy, I guess," the man said, looking puzzled. Then slowly you could see that a once lost boy had come back to his doctor again.

There was very little chance of having an unproductive relationship with the doctor, and no chance simply to thank him for something or just pass the time of day. Pearl protected him from relationships that might tire him or take too much time from his own work. When either spoke of Flo they did so reverently. In the doctor's mind she deserved the credit for all that had been accomplished. So far as he was concerned the rest of the credit went to his sons. He was sure no man had ever been blessed with better sons than Karl, Ed, and Will. "I had enough sense to tag along with them and their mother," he would say.

When he was asked to speak on his ninetieth birthday, as he laid the cornerstone for a new, million-and-a-half dollar hospital that was to bear his name, he replied to the many eulogies simply by asking that all present join him in prayer. In that prayer he rededicated the hospital to God. He was not ungracious, but he was plainly vexed that so much time should be spent in honoring him. On this occasion, as on all others, he planted a tree. If events had to be commemorated he felt that the least man could do was to plant a monument to beauty. As for the institution he had founded, unless something was wrong he did not want to hear about it. He would, however, join you for an hour or more if you wished to admire the great trees on the grounds. Somehow trees mean more in Kansas than in any other state, and Dr. C.F. had chosen his trees well.

ii

In the early fall of 1953 Dr. C.F., as Board chairman, presided over the annual meeting of the governors of the Menninger Foundation. Among these governors were some of the outstanding men of the nation—physicians, educators, public officials, industrialists, and representatives of other great institutions. Many Topeka friends were present. David Neiswanger, one of the earliest investors in the sanitarium corporation, was now president of the Foundation, and W. Laird Dean was the vice president and treasurer. There was Robert P. Knight, M.D., who had come to Menningers' as a resident and stayed on to become almost like one of the Menninger brothers. He was now the medical director of the Austen Riggs Foundation in Massachusetts. Dr. Paul R. Hawley, now director of the American College of Surgeons, was also a governor. John Stone was not there; cancer had claimed him four years before, but the meeting was held in the John Stone Memorial Room.

The doctor had fresh batteries in his hearing aid and he listened intently to the reports. If he had been a man who mixed memories with the business of the present, he could have conjured up some startling comparisons: for example, the contrast between this conference room and the reception room where the family washing had dried on weekends.

As the financial report was made he could easily have recalled Flo's anxiety over the number of appointments in the little black book. The total revenue of the Foundation was $2,837,998. Of this, $1,635,889 had come from clinical services and consultants' fees. Most of the other money consisted of contributions for the hospital that was to honor him. The doctor looked at Dr. Will as this was discussed. His son had practically lived in planes, trains, and hotels as he raised this and other money. But whether he had got money or not, he had left everyone he talked to with a better concept of mental-health problems. As a missionary for the social application of psychiatry, he had talked on this subject wherever he went. His work in the Army and his book, *Psychiatry in a Troubled World,* were indications of the healthy zeal that went into his cause. Dr. C.F. shared his son's quiet indignation over the fact that, although over a billion dollars a year was spent in hospitalizing people with emotional problems, only a fraction of 1 per cent of this went for research and education. Dr. Will was tired and the work he wanted to do was only barely begun.

Dr. C.F. felt a great pride in his profession as the report made it clear that the people who were giving the most were physicians, the physicians of his own institution. They had little money to give, though each gave what he could, nor could their contribution be measured by the things they had given up, such as lucrative income from private practice. When people said, "I'll give you a percentage of my income," they were making a tangible sacrifice. But when the Foundation doctors worked two or four hours a day overtime they were saying in effect, "I pledge a sixth of my active life." It was their extra hours that made most of the research possible and kept the Department of Education from going in the red. Dr. C.F. thought that perhaps Dr. Karl's example in this was a bit too strenuous, but he wondered if he himself would have done less in his active years.

One particular research project demanded extra hours from almost every doctor; this was the Psychotherapy Research Project, which was attempting to find out which methods were the most effective and produced the best results in the minimum of time. For every dollar given for this research each Menninger physician was giving at least an hour of his time. The value of this project could not be measured until it was completed, but in terms of bringing psychiatry to a greater number of patients it was second in importance only to education. Certainly it was the finest example of doctors working together; many men were to see their prized theories exploded.

Another project, a study of the development of healthy infants, had punctured many personal balloons as it indicated that most textbooks on the care of babies in their first year were obsolete, and that indeed there could be no standard procedure other than a deeply felt and directly conveyed love. Ignorant mothers were often more successful than their intellectual sisters. Non-vocal communication between mother and child was an important factor and no two babies used the same means of communicating their needs. Developments in personality that were thought to come much later in life were discovered to exist in the first weeks. Trauma blamed on the schools was often a trauma that had stemmed from the cradle. Most of the things mothers had to learn could not be taught on an intellectual level as many Menninger doctors had thought they could be. If he had wished, Dr. C.F. could have recalled the many sick babies he had seen communicating a need for comfort and reassurance and getting in return terror and despair. The best he had been able to do then was re-establish the parents' love and hope, and this had worked more often than not.

In the reports of the Department of Education, Dr. C.F. could have remembered all the training he had wanted and never had, except as he sought it out by reading and travel. Never were any two things to be found in one place. And as he heard the statistics on the number of doctors who had left their practices and traveled to Menningers' to lecture, he must have given some thought to the competitiveness of his early days of practice. Physicians were making greater sacrifices in order to share their knowledge. By association with these men he had found how right he had been when he judged physicians to be the greatest gentlemen and scholars. Very few men, for example, were Karl's equals in culture and scholarship. Had there been one book like Dr. Karl's *A Manual for Psychiatric Case Study*, how much more productive his practice would have been. Undoubtedly Karl had learned much from him, but by what a long and difficult route had Dr. C.F. arrived at his knowledge of case study.

He could not help finding some gratification in the knowledge that the school that bore his name was far greater than the school from which he got his first medical degree. His grandsons, now completing their interneships, could come home to continue training in almost any specialty they chose. There would be no jealous preceptors for them, no frustrating loneliness as they sought to repair their educational deficiencies. The school bearing their family name was the extension of one man's appetite for knowledge and he could only hope that his grandsons' appetites would be as large. It was not enough that the Menninger School was the largest of its kind in the world. It had to have about it a restlessness and hunger, an anxiety and impatience, and even an impetuousness like Dr. Karl's. There could be no rest; something had been started that could not be stopped. Each accomplishment created a new responsibility. This was a thought that would have tired most men, and yet it did not tire Dr. C.F. He had helped prepare a ten-year plan that was to be presented to the meeting.

Seventeen million dollars would be required for the work of the next decade. Physicians had to be freed from clinical demands for full-time research; free and low-cost treatment had to be subsidized; educational facilities had to be improved and extended; a team should be set up for industrial consultations; preventive psychiatry had to be pioneered. Seventeen million was really a

modest sum when one considered all there was to be done. A
half dozen foundations devoted to the research and treatment of
other diseases were able to raise that much every year, even
though the total incidence of these illnesses was less than that of
mental disease. The Foundation's plan would call for an uphill
fight, but that was as it should be, for men with a sense of mission
seemed to do well even though they were kept lean. It could be
that psychiatry was just entering its greatest period. The ideal
was that in some future day it would disappear as a specialty and
emerge as the most important factor in the general practice of
medicine. Medical historians would then understand why the
greatest psychiatric center of our time had been founded by a
general practitioner.

iii

In November of 1953 Dr. C.F. was stricken with a vascu-
lar lesion in the brain. He refused to enter the hospital, insisting
on being cared for at home. Even though it was difficult for him
to talk, he encouraged one of his nurses to become interested in
the study of sea shells and helped another with her Bible studies.
Although he was acutely ill it was difficult for the nurses to refer
to him as a patient.

Since his disease was neurological in nature, he used it as a
teaching device when neurological consultants were called, discussing the subjective symptoms and carefully noting all the manifestations of the disease process. Even when he was suffering
greatly he kept his clinical objectivity.

There was a period during which he became mentally disturbed.
When it had passed he said to Dr. Karl, "Do you know, I have
been out of my head? I've been crazy! Why, I have thought some
of the most absurd things. Now why didn't that happen to me
years ago, because it helps me understand patients better. It's a
terrible thing, that inability to distinguish reality from unreality."

With almost his last breath, he reassured his doctor that no man
could have done more for him, that he was a fine physician. The
last emotion he had shown was his concern for another man's distress. This was on November 28, 1953.

The art and science of healing has produced many more spectacular figures than Dr. Charles Frederick Menninger, but few have so dignified the virtues of the almost anonymous physicians who are the backbone of medical practice. He would have told you, and would have been partly right, that his greatest single discovery was not medical at all but human. Her name was Flo Knisely. The medical historian who looks for the clue to the Menninger success must find it in the Menninger home.

BIBLIOGRAPHY

THE GREAT MAJORITY of the material in this book was taken from transcriptions of recorded interviews with Dr. C. F. Menninger which took place in 1952 and 1953. These transcriptions are now the property of the library of the Menninger Foundation. I have also had access to and have studied the complete medical papers of the Menningers. These number well over one hundred, but unfortunately there is no complete bibliography of them available. In addition to these I have utilized material contained in all of the publications of the Menninger Foundation: *The Annual Reports of the Menninger Foundation, The Menninger Bulletin, The Menninger Quarterly*, and *T. P. R.* (published by employees of the Foundation).

While the above constitutes the primary source material of this book, the following publications have also been valuable and may be of interest for collateral reading.

A Mind That Found Itself. Clifford W. Beers. (Revised edition.) New York: Doubleday, 1950.

The Doctors Mayo. Helen Clapesattle. Minneapolis: University of Minnesota Press, 1941.

Behind the Doctor: The Romance of Medicine. Logan Clendening. New York: Knopf, 1933.

The Mentally Ill in America. Albert Deutsch. New York: Doubleday, Doran, 1938.

The Shame of the States. Albert Deutsch. New York: Harcourt Brace, 1948.

Medical Education in the United States and Canada. Abraham Flexner. New York: Carnegie Foundation, 1910.

Medical Education. Abraham Flexner. New York: Macmillan, 1925.

The Open Mind (Biography of Elmer Ernest Southard). Dr. Frederick P. Gay. Chicago: Normandie House, 1938.

Devils, Drugs, and Doctors. Howard Haggard, M.D. New York: Harper, 1929.

Medical Essays. Oliver Wendell Holmes, M.D.

Days of My Life. Flo V. Menninger. New York: Smith, 1940.

The Human Mind. Karl A. Menninger, M.D. New York: Knopf, 1930.

Man against Himself. Karl A. Menninger, M.D. New York: Harcourt Brace, 1938.

Love against Hate. Karl A. Menninger and Jeannetta Lyle Menninger. New York: Harcourt Brace, 1942.

A *Manual for Psychiatric Case Study.* Karl A. Menninger, M.D. Menninger Foundation Monograph. New York: Grune & Stratton, 1952.

Juvenile Paresis. William C. Menninger, M.D. Baltimore: Wood, 1936.

Psychiatry in a Troubled World. William C. Menninger, M.D. New York: Macmillan, 1948.

Psychiatry: Its Evolution and Present Status. William C. Menninger, M.D. Ithaca: Cornell University Press, 1948.

You and Psychiatry. William C. Menninger and Munro Leaf. New York: Scribner's, 1948.

Psychobiology and Psychiatry. Wendell Muncie, M.D. St. Louis: Mosby, 1939.

History of Psychoanalysis in America. Clarence P. Oberndorf, M.D. New York: Grune & Stratton, 1953.

The Story of Medicine. Victor Robinson. New York: Boni, 1931.

Mental Health in Modern Society. T. A. C. Rennie and L. E. Woodward. New York: Commonwealth Fund, 1948.

Mind, Medicine, and Man. Gregory Zilboorg. New York: Harcourt Brace, 1943.

A *History of Medical Psychology.* Gregory Zilboorg and G. W. Henry. New York: Norton, 1941.

One Hundred Years of American Psychiatry. (Published for the American Psychiatric Association.) New York: Columbia University Press, 1944.

	DATE DUE		
NOV 1 5 2000